MATHEMATICS FOR TECHNICAL STUDENTS

By A. Geary, M.A., M.Sc., H. V. Lowry,
M.A., and H. A. Hayden, D.Sc., M.Sc.

MATHEMATICS FOR TECHNICAL
STUDENTS
in three parts with Diagrams

ADVANCED MATHEMATICS FOR
TECHNICAL STUDENTS
Part I, with Diagrams
Part II, in preparation

By H. V. Lowry, M.A., and H. A. Hayden,
D.Sc., M.Sc.

INTRODUCTORY MATHEMATICS

MATHEMATICS FOR TECHNICAL STUDENTS

BY

A. GEARY, M.A., M.Sc.
Head of the Mathematics Department, Northampton Polytechnic

H. V. LOWRY, M.A.
Head of the Mathematics Department, Woolwich Polytechnic

AND

H. A. HAYDEN, D.Sc., M.Sc.
Head of the Mathematics Department, Battersea Polytechnic

PART I

WITH DIAGRAMS

LONGMANS, GREEN AND CO.
LONDON ◆ NEW YORK ◆ TORONTO

LONGMANS, GREEN AND CO LTD
6 & 7 CLIFFORD STREET LONDON W I

ALSO AT MELBOURNE AND CAPE TOWN

LONGMANS, GREEN AND CO INC
55 FIFTH AVENUE NEW YORK 3

LONGMANS, GREEN AND CO
215 VICTORIA STREET TORONTO I

ORIENT LONGMANS LTD
BOMBAY CALCUTTA MADRAS

FIRST PUBLISHED 1938
NEW IMPRESSIONS . . . *January* 1941,
August 1941, *June* 1942, *January* 1943,
March 1944, *August* 1944, *May* 1945,
January 1946, *January* 1947, *December* 1947,
September 1949

PREFACE

THIS series is designed to provide the basic mathematical equipment for technical students. The range of work is that covered by national certificate courses in engineering, building and chemistry. Each of the three volumes will include one year's work, but the second and third will contain sufficient revision to allow for variations in the syllabuses of different technical institutions. It is hoped that the series may also prove useful in junior technical schools, central schools and secondary schools with a technical side.

Short historical notes are included as they may help to develop in the student a further interest in the subject.

A. G.
H. V. L.
H. A. H.

AUTHORS' FOREWORD TO PART I

THIS volume is divided into five sections—Arithmetic, Algebra, Geometry, Mensuration and Trigonometry, for convenience of reference, but it is not intended that they should necessarily be read in this order. An attempt has been made to give adequate reasons for the mathematical processes involved ; as a consequence the algebra section is concerned, perhaps rather more than usual, with the elementary processes since they are the fundamental basis of so much of the work that follows.

At the beginning of the geometry section an appeal is made to ideas derived from experience, drawing and intuition, but it is shown later that these require confirmation. Proofs are given of a number of theorems which the student is likely to meet in his engineering subjects and in applications of trigonometry. Teachers, whose time is too limited to allow of such an extended course, will find that the earlier questions in each set of exercises are designed to give the necessary information by deduction from drawing.

The trigonometry section has been carried as far as the graphs of the sine and cosine of an angle of any magnitude in order that the engineering student may be familiar with the periodic expressions which he will meet at an early stage in his study of oscillations.

There are more than twelve hundred exercises, many of which are chosen from practical applications.

The following shorter course is recommended for schools in which it is desired : Chapters I, II, III, IV, V, VII (pages 108-121), X, XI, XII, XVI.

A. G.

H. V. L.

CONTENTS

ARITHMETIC

CHAP.   PAGE
I. Decimals ; factors ; fractions ; square root ;
   ratio ; proportion ; percentage . . . 1

ALGEBRA

II. Symbols and formulæ ; simple equations . 28

III. Directed numbers ; algebraic processes . . 42

IV. Further equations ; transformation of for-
    mulæ ; simultaneous equations . . 59

V. Graphs of statistics and of algebraic expressions 74

VI. Graphs with directed numbers ; use of graphs
    to solve equations and to find maxima and
    minima 94

VII. Indices and logarithms ; slide rule . . 108

VIII. Further algebraic processes ; factors ; equa-
     tions with two roots 128

IX. Ratio ; proportion ; variation . . . 137

GEOMETRY

X. Fundamental ideas 146

XI. Symmetry ; congruence ; similarity . . 169

XII. Areas ; Pythagoras' theorem . . . 185

XIII. Loci 194

XIV. The circle 199

MENSURATION

Chap.   PAGE

XV. Approximations to areas of irregular figures ;
areas of surfaces ; volumes of solids . . 214

TRIGONOMETRY

XVI. Sine, cosine and tangent of angles ; solution of
right-angled triangles 228

XVII. Polar co-ordinates ; vectors ; ratios of 30°,
45°, 60° ; graphs of sine and cosine of acute
angles 259

XVIII. Ratios of angles of any magnitude ; graphs of
$a \sin p\theta$ and $a \cos p\theta$ 279

being written ·568; the former method insures that the decimal point is not overlooked.

Example.—Express as a fraction 0·207 and as a mixed number 23·23. (A mixed number is composed of a whole number and a fraction.)

$$0\cdot207 = \tfrac{2}{10} + \tfrac{0}{100} + \tfrac{7}{1000} = \tfrac{207}{1000}.$$
$$23\cdot23 = 23 + \tfrac{2}{10} + \tfrac{3}{100} = 23\tfrac{23}{100}.$$

The Metric System

In 1790 the French Government invited a number of scientists to recommend a system of measures and a unit of length. They decided that the latter, which was called a *metre*, should be one ten-millionth part of the distance on the earth's surface from the North Pole to the Equator. The length was based on measurements made between Barcelona and Dunkerque, which have since been found to be inaccurate and the metre is now defined as a marked length on a bar of platinum kept in Paris. This length is approximately equal to 39·3708 inches.

Multiples and submultiples of the metre are named as follows :

1 kilometre (Km.)	= 1000 metres.
1 hectometre (Hm.)	= 100 metres.
1 decametre (Dm.)	= 10 metres.
1 metre (m.).	
1 decimetre (dm.)	$= \tfrac{1}{10}$ or 0·1 metre.
1 centimetre (cm.)	$= \tfrac{1}{100}$ or 0·01 metre.
1 millimetre (mm.)	$= \tfrac{1}{1000}$ or 0·001 metre.

Kilo-, hecto-, deca- are Greek, and *deci-, centi-, milli-* are Latin prefixes.

Approximations often used are : 1 metre = 39·37 inches ; 2·54 cm. = 1 in. ; 1 Km. = $\tfrac{5}{8}$ mile.

The unit of area is the *square metre.*

1 are	= 100 square metres.
1 hectare	= 100 ares.
1 are	= 119·6 sq. yd. approx.
1 hectare	= 2·47 acres approx.

ARITHMETIC

CHAPTER I

DECIMALS

The earliest discussion of a decimal system is contained in a work by the Arabian mathematician Bhaskara, who lived during the twelfth century, though there is reason to believe that some form of decimal system was known five centuries earlier. Towards the end of the sixteenth century a Dutchman, Stevinus, made use of decimals in stating results, though with an unsatisfactory notation, and it is to the Scotsman John Napier that our present notation is due. Early in the seventeenth century Napier wrote 25·379 for the number which Stevinus had written 25⊚3①7②9③. In the opinion of the late W. Rouse Ball, the credit for the introduction of the decimal notation into arithmetic is due to Briggs, who died in 1630, thirteen years after Napier, though it was not until a century later that the decimal point came into general use.

The student knows that when he writes the number 234, the figure 2 represents 2 hundreds, the 3 represents 3 tens and the 4 represents 4 units. If we continue the same idea, we can say that when we write 234·568,

> the 5 represents 5 tenths,
> the 6 represents 6 hundredths and
> the 8 represents 8 thousandths.

Such a number as 0·568 is known as a decimal fraction and the positions occupied by the figures to the right of a decimal point are known as decimal places. Thus there are three decimal places in the number 0·568.

Sometimes the 0 before the decimal point is omitted, 0·568

1   1

The unit of volume or capacity is the *litre*.

1 litre = 1000 cu. cm.

Multiples and submultiples are formed as in the case of the metre.

1 litre = 1·76 pints approx.

1 gallon = 4·546 litres approx.

The unit of mass is the *gramme*, which is the mass of 1 cu. cm. of water under specified conditions. Multiples and submultiples are formed as in other cases.

1000 Kg. = 1 tonne.

1 lb. = 453·6 gr. approx.

1 Kg. = 2·2 lb. approx.

Addition and Subtraction of Decimals

Example.—Add together 3 Dm. 4 m. 5 dm. ; 2 m. 4 cm. ; 4 Dm. 3 dm. 2 cm. ; 8 m. 6 dm. 7 cm. Give the result in metres.

3 Dm. 4 m. 5 dm.	=	34·5 m.
2 m. 4 cm.	=	2·04 m.
4 Dm. 3 dm. 2 cm.	=	40·32 m.
8 m. 6 dm. 7 cm.	=	8·67 m.
		85·53 m.

Each length is first expressed in metres. Numbers are written with the decimal points underneath each other as above. The numbers are then added in the usual way and a decimal point inserted in the result in line with the other decimal points.

In practice it is usual to express lengths in terms of one unit. 2 Km. 3 Hm. 5 m. would be expressed as 2·305 Km. or 2305 m.

Numbers are also subtracted in the usual way when written with the decimal points in line.

Example.—In a tensile test of a piece of steel, the initial area of cross-section was 1·045 sq. in. and the final area 0·658 sq. in. Find the contraction in area.

$$\text{Initial area} = 1\cdot045 \text{ sq. in.}$$
$$\text{Final area} = 0\cdot658 \text{ sq. in.}$$
$$\text{Contraction} = 0\cdot387 \text{ sq. in.}$$

Decimal Places and Significant Figures

If a circle of 2 inches radius be drawn, its area will be found to be approximately 12·5 square inches. Calculation will show its area to be more accurately 12·5664 square inches. If therefore the area be required *correct to one place of decimals*, the answer will be 12·6 square inches, as this is nearer than 12·5 square inches to the correct result; similarly, the result *correct to two decimal places* is 12·57 square inches.

The correct result is between 12 sq. in. and 13 sq. in. If the result be required *correct to two significant figures*, the answer will be 13 sq. in., as this answer contains two figures and is nearer than 12 sq. in. to the correct result.

Correct to three significant figures 419·8 is 420.

In the case of a number less than unity with noughts immediately after the decimal point, these noughts do not count as significant figures. Thus 0·02006 correct to three significant figures is 0·0201; correct to two significant figures the result is 0·020.

It will be seen that significant figures are those which must be retained for any position of the decimal point, e.g.—

$$0\cdot0203 \text{ metre} = 2\cdot03 \text{ centimetres.}$$

If we say that the diameter of a sphere is 7·3 cm. correct to two significant figures, we mean that it lies between 7·3 ± 0·05 cm. (i.e. between 7·3 − 0·05 cm. and 7·3 + 0·05 cm.) or between 7·25 cm. and 7·35 cm.

In accurate practical work the error permitted is called the *tolerance*. If it be necessary to turn a solid cylinder to have a diameter of 1·5 in. with a possible error of 0·005 in., the diameter must lie between 1·495 in. and 1·505 in. In this case it may be said that the diameter of the cylinder is 1·500 in. correct to four significant figures.

Example.—Express correct to three significant figures (i) 10256, (ii) 1·0256, (iii) 0·010256, (iv) 500·2, (v) 0·02065.

The results will be (i) 10300, (ii) 1·03, (iii) 0·0103, (iv) 500, (v) 0·0206 or 0·0207.

In (iv) it should be noted that the 0's in 500 are significant figures. In (v) the results 0·0206 and 0·0207 are equally correct as they differ from 0·02065 by the same amount ; two answers are possible, as in this case, when one further figure after the last significant figure is given and this is a 5. 0·020651 correct to three significant figures is 0·0207.

Exercise I

1. Express as fractions or mixed numbers, fractions to be in their lowest terms : 0·034, ·5, ·25, ·75, ·125, ·375, ·0625, 2·05, 20·025, 3·0205, 5·0045.

2. Express (i) correct to two significant figures and (ii) correct to three significant figures : 10·87, 108·7, 0·0364, 0·02045.

3. Express correct to two places of decimals : 1·087, 0·087, 4·599, ·0098.

Add the following :

4. 15·27, 11·86, 45·32, 17·89.

5. 3·47, 28·05, ·304, 15·006.

6. 1·897, ·456, 0·028, ·555.

Add the following lengths :

7. 3 Dm. 4 m. 5 dm., 5 Dm. 3 m. 2 dm., 4 m. 5 dm. 9 cm., 7 dm. 8 cm. ; give the answer in cm.

8. 8 Hm. 7 dm., 5 Km. 3 Dm. 5 m., 7 Dm. 8 m. 5 dm., 10 Km. 6 m. ; give the answer in Km.

9. 15 Km. 3 m., 5 Hm. 2 dm., 4 Km. 3 Dm. 7 dm., 8 Hm. 3 m. 8 dm. ; give the answer in cm.

10. In using a spherometer it was necessary to subtract 0·13 mm. from the experimental reading. What was the correct result when the reading was 4·01 mm. ?

11. What is the difference in level between two columns of a U-tube, if the heights of the columns above a fixed level are 8·57 cm. and 26·44 cm. respectively ?

12. To find the height of a point B above a point A, a surveyor makes observations which he records in two columns, all results being expressed in feet.

8·05	
5·32	5·08
1·18	4·44
5·32	2·36
4·27	3·48
	4·89

Find the height required if it is obtained by subtracting the sum of the second column from the sum of the first.

MULTIPLICATION AND DIVISION OF DECIMALS

Multiplication

As in the case of whole numbers, if a decimal be multiplied by 10, the digits forming the decimal remain but their place value is altered, e.g. $2·34 \times 10 = 23·4$; conversely, $23·4 \div 10 = 2·34$. Similarly $35·67 \times 100 = 3567$; $3567 \div 100 = 35·67$.

Consider the product $27·43 \times 15·8$.

Rough check : $25 \times 16 = 400$.

We shall obtain a whole number if we multiply 27·43 by 100 and also if we multiply 15·8 by 10. If, therefore, we evaluate 2743×158 instead of $27·43 \times 15·8$ we shall obtain an answer which is 1000 times too great and it will be necessary to divide our result by 1000.

$$
\begin{array}{r}
2743 \\
158 \\
\hline
2743 \\
13715 \\
21944 \\
\hline
433394 \\
\end{array}
$$

Dividing 433394 by 1000 gives the result 433·394.

It will be noted that the number of decimal places in the result is the sum of the number of decimal places in the original numbers. The decimal point in the answer may always be placed by making use of this rule, e.g. $0·04 \times 0·007$ $= 0·00028$; $0·03 \times 0·03 \times 0·03 = 0·000027$.

The practice of making rough checks is strongly recommended : it will tend to insure accuracy of thought and computation.

Division

Example.—Divide 173·3 by 27·8, giving the result correct to two places of decimals.

The method recommended is often known as the " standard form " method. The divisor is multiplied or divided repeatedly by 10 until it is a number with only a units digit before the decimal point—in effect, the decimal point is moved ; the dividend must then be multiplied or divided by the same number as the divisor, i.e. the decimal point in the two cases is moved the same number of places in the same direction, so that the quotient is unaltered.

$$\frac{173·3}{27·8} = \frac{17·33}{2·78} \simeq \frac{17}{3} \simeq 6$$

(The symbol $\simeq$ or $\fallingdotseq$ means " is approximately equal to ".)

```
              6·233
       2·78)17·33000
             16·68
             ─────
               650
               556
               ───
               940
               834
               ───
              1060
```

6·23 Answer.

It will be noted that in writing down a decimal, the addition of further 0's will not affect its value. In the case above, three 0's have been added to the dividend in order to obtain the result to the required degree of accuracy.

Averages

If the sum of a set of numbers is divided by the number of them, the result is called the *average* or *mean value* of the given numbers.

Example.—In an experiment on friction, the following values were obtained for the coefficient of friction between two wood surfaces : find the average value.

$$0\cdot397,\ 0\cdot399,\ 0\cdot386,\ 0\cdot389,\ 0\cdot377,\ 0\cdot378.$$

Sum of values $= 2\cdot326$.

Average $= \dfrac{2\cdot326}{6} = 0\cdot388$ correct to three places of decimals.

By inspection the average of a set of numbers can be determined approximately and the average can then be found more accurately as follows :

In the example given, several of the numbers are a little greater than $0\cdot39$ and the others a little less than $0\cdot39$. The average is therefore approximately $0\cdot39$. We now make a table of the differences from $0\cdot39$.

Number	Above 0·39	Below 0·39
0·397	0·007	
0·399	0·009	
0·386		0·004
0·389		0·001
0·377		0·013
0·378		0·012
By addition	0·016	0·030

The total amount below is $0\cdot030 - 0\cdot016 = 0\cdot014$.

Since there are six numbers the average is below $0\cdot39$ by an amount $\dfrac{0\cdot014}{6} = 0\cdot002$ to three decimal places.

The average is therefore $0\cdot39 - 0\cdot002$, i.e. $0\cdot388$.

It should be noted that the average of a set of values is only useful when it indicates a probable result. There would be little point, for example, in calculating the average age of ten persons whose names appear in a telephone directory.

In practical cases it is clearly impossible to depend on measurements beyond a certain degree of accuracy, and it is most important that a result should not suggest a higher degree of accuracy than the data warrant.

Suppose a rectangle has sides measured as 9·87 m. and 4·71 m. respectively, correct to three significant figures. The area is obtained by multiplying the length by the breadth ; in this case it is 46·4877 sq. m. As the lengths are only correct to three significant figures, we are only justified in stating that the area lies between 9·865 × 4·705 sq. m. and 9·875 × 4·715 sq. m., i.e. between 46·414825 sq. m. and 46·560625 sq. m. Correct to three significant figures the calculated area is 46·5 sq. m., whereas to this degree of accuracy we are only justified in saying that it lies between 46·4 sq. m. and 46·6 sq. m. We have above an example illustrating the fact that if each of two numbers is given correct to three significant figures, the accuracy of the product cannot be relied upon beyond the second significant figure ; there are exceptional cases where there is a small error even in the second significant figure.

Corresponding results are true in the case of division : the quotient of two numbers each of which is correct to three significant figures cannot be relied upon to more than two significant figures.

In all practical cases, where the data are approximate, the number of significant figures given in a calculated result must not exceed the number in the data ; e.g. in the product of two numbers which are not given to the same degree of accuracy, the result must only be stated to the same number of significant figures as in the less accurate of the given numbers.

Contracted Methods

When a result is required to a certain degree of accuracy

1*

only, it is clearly desirable that unnecessary work should be omitted from the calculation.

Example.—Multiply 35·7462 by 0·235776 correct to two places of decimals.

Rough check : $36 \times 0·2 = 7·2$.

As the product is required to two places of decimals, the answer will therefore contain three significant figures. To obtain this accuracy we retain five significant figures in our calculations and tabulate the work as below.

35746	
23578	
71492	Retaining five figures in each of the numbers
10724	to be multiplied, we draw a line to indicate that
1787	any figures which would appear to the right of
250	this line in the complete multiplication are un-
28	necessary.
84281	

In the second step of the multiplication, before multiplying by 3, we cross off the 6 in the first line ; but we carry 2 since $6 \times 3 = 18$ and 18 is nearer to 20 than to 10. Before multiplying by 5 we cross off the 4 in the first line but carry 2 since $4 \times 5 = 20$.

The rough check shows that the decimal point comes after the figure 8.

8·43 Answer.

Example.—Divide 872·146 by 23·4576 correct to one decimal place.

Rough check $\frac{900}{25} = 36$.

There will therefore be three significant figures in the answer.

Reducing to standard form :

$$\frac{872·146}{23·4576} = \frac{87·2146}{2·34576}$$

or retaining five significant figures since the result is required correct to three : $\dfrac{87 \cdot 215}{2 \cdot 3458}$.

$$
\begin{array}{r}
37 \cdot 17 \\
2 \cdot 3458)\overline{87 \cdot 215} \\
70 \cdot 374 \\
\hline
16 \cdot 841 \\
16 \cdot 421 \\
\hline
420 \\
235 \\
\hline
185 \\
164 \\
\hline
\end{array}
$$

In the second step of the division, instead of adding a 0, we cross off the 8 of the divisor ; on multiplying by the corresponding 7 of the quotient we carry 6, since $8 \times 7 = 56$ and 56 is nearer to 60 than to 50 ; this process is continued throughout.

37·2 Answer.

Exercise II

1. The diameter of a wire was measured in inches at different points along its length with the following results : 0·0287, 0·0275, 0·0278, 0·0294, 0·0288, 0·0268, 0·0272. Find the average diameter.

2. The following results were obtained when an experiment was repeated a number of times to find the strain in a wire : ·000356, ·000361, ·000363, ·000366, ·000360, ·000358. Find the average of these results.

3. In a pendulum experiment the time in seconds of ten oscillations was recorded six times, the results being : 22·2, 22·4, 22, 22·6, 22·4, 22·6. Find the average time of one oscillation.

4. A cricketer makes the following scores in seven completed innings : 85, 130, 6, 26, 95, 56, 99. What is his average ?

If his average after the next innings is 73, find his score (i) if he is out, and (ii) if he is not out.

5. The expenses of a business for five successive years were £38,513, £40,219, £37,385, £39,428, £42.531. What were the

average expenses ? If the average expenses including a further year were £40,215, find the expenses for this sixth year.

6. If 1 horse-power = 0·746 kilowatt, express 18·7 H.P. in kilowatts.

7. Making use of the data of the previous question, find the H.P. equivalent to 37·6 kilowatts.

8. The pressure of the atmosphere is 14·7 lb. per sq. in. Find the pressure in Kg. per sq. cm. if 1 lb. per sq. in. = 70·31 gm. per sq. cm.

9. During each second the velocity of a falling body increases by 981 cm. per sec. Express this increase in ft. per sec., given that 1 ft. = 30·48 cm.

1 metre = 3·280843 feet.

10. Express 1 yard as a decimal of a metre correct to three places of decimals.

11. Express 1 in. in cm. correct to three significant figures.

12. Find the number of square feet in a square metre correct to two places of decimals.

13. Find the number of cu. in. in a litre correct to the nearest integer.

14. The diameter of a circle may be found by dividing the circumference by 3·14159265. What should be the diameter to the nearest inch of a quarter-mile circular running track ?

15. In an experiment to find Young's modulus for steel, the following result was obtained :

$$\text{Young's modulus} = \frac{3 \cdot 225 \times 6 \cdot 97 \times 10,000}{7 \cdot 55 \times 2 \cdot 224} \text{ tons per sq. in.}$$

Evaluate this result correct to two significant figures.

FACTORS AND FRACTIONS

There is in the British Museum an Egyptian papyrus forming part of the Rhind collection, written by a priest named Ahmes somewhere about 1700 B.C. It is an early treatise on arithmetic in which appear some simple fractions such as $\frac{1}{2}$, $\frac{1}{3}$, $\frac{1}{4}$, $\frac{2}{3}$, $\frac{1}{26}$, $\frac{1}{78}$, etc., the practice of the Egyptians being to express a fraction as the sum of a number of fractions, each having unity for numerator. The methods of Ahmes were still in use some two thousand years later, and it was not until about A.D. 1000 that general methods of dealing with fractions were discovered.

Prime Factors

If a number is divisible by a second number without remainder, the second number is said to be a *factor* of the first and the first number to be a *multiple* of the second.

2 is a factor of 6 ; 6 is a multiple of 2.

If the only factors of a number are itself and unity, the number is said to be a *prime number* : 2, 3, 5, 7, 11, etc., are prime numbers.

A prime number which is a factor of a second number is said to be a *prime factor*, e.g. 7 is a prime factor of 42.

If a number be multiplied by itself and the product again by the same number, and this process be repeated several times, the result is said to be a *power* of the number.

$5 \times 5 \times 5 \times 5$ is a power of 5 and is written 5^4 : this is read as " 5 to the power 4 " or often more shortly as " 5 to the fourth." The number 4, which indicates how many 5's are multiplied together, is said to be an *index* (plural *indices*).

5^2 is read as " 5 squared " and 5^3 as " 5 cubed."

If any number be multiplied by itself, the result is said to be the square of the number. The *square root* of a number is the number whose square is the given number.

$13^2 = 169$; hence 13 is the square root of 169. $7^3 = 7 \times 7 \times 7 = 343$; hence 343 is the cube of 7 and 7 is the *cube root* of 343.

The symbol $\sqrt{}$ is used for square root and $\sqrt[3]{}$ for cube root.

$\sqrt{169} = 13$; $\sqrt[3]{343} = 7$.

Example.—Express in prime factors 1176.

$$1176 = 2 \times 588 = 2 \times 2 \times 294 = 2 \times 2 \times 2 \times 147$$
$$= 2 \times 2 \times 2 \times 3 \times 49 = 2 \times 2 \times 2 \times 3 \times 7 \times 7$$
$$= 2^3 \times 3 \times 7^2.$$

The method is to divide by the prime factors in turn, beginning with 2, division by each number to be repeated until that number is no longer a factor.

Example.—Express 3969 in prime factors and hence find its square root.

$$
\begin{array}{r|r}
3 & 3969 \\
3 & 1323 \\
3 & 441 \\
3 & 147 \\
7 & 49 \\
\hline
& 7
\end{array}
$$

$3969 = 3^4 \times 7^2$.

The square root is $3^2 \times 7$ or 63, since $3^2 \times 7 \times 3^2 \times 7 = 3 \times 3 \times 7 \times 3 \times 3 \times 7 = 3^4 \times 7^2$.

Example.—Express 1728 in prime factors and hence find its cube root.

$1728 = 2^6 \times 3^3$.

Cube root $= 2^2 \times 3 = 12$, since $2^2 \times 3 \times 2^2 \times 3 \times 2^2 \times 3 = 2^6 \times 3^3$.

H.C.F. and L.C.M.

The *Highest Common Factor* (usually abbreviated as H.C.F.) of two or more numbers is the greatest number which is a factor of each of them : 12 is the H.C.F. of 36, 48, 84.

The *Lowest Common Multiple* (L.C.M.) of two or more numbers is the smallest number which is a multiple of each of them : the L.C.M. of 36 and 48 is 144.

The H.C.F. and L.C.M. of several numbers can be found by expressing each of them in its prime factors.

Example.—Find the H.C.F. and L.C.M. of 1764, 2100, 2940.

$1764 = 2^2 \times 3^2 \times 7^2$.

$2100 = 2^2 \times 3 \times 5^2 \times 7$.

$2940 = 2^2 \times 3 \times 5 \times 7^2$.

Selecting factors common to each of the numbers, H.C.F. $= 2^2 \times 3 \times 7 = 84$.

To find the L.C.M. the highest power of each prime factor must be included, since the L.C.M. is to be a multiple of each number.

$$\text{L.C.M.} = 2^2 \times 3^2 \times 5^2 \times 7^2 = 44,100.$$

Example.—Two cogwheels working together have 30 and 40 cogs respectively. How many revolutions will each wheel make from the time when two particular cogs are together until the time when they are again in this position ?

$$30 = 2 \times 3 \times 5 \; ; \; 40 = 2^3 \times 5.$$
$$\text{L.C.M.} = 2^3 \times 3 \times 5 = 120.$$

When 120 cogs of the first wheel have passed a certain point, it will have made $\frac{120}{30}$, i.e. 4 complete revolutions. During the same time the second wheel will have made $\frac{120}{40}$, i.e. 3 complete revolutions.

∴4 revolutions of the first wheel and 3 revolutions of the second will bring two particular cogs together again.

FRACTIONS

A proper fraction is one in which the denominator is greater than the numerator, an improper fraction one in which the numerator is greater than the denominator. The student is reminded of the following facts.

When some parts of an expression are separated by + or − signs and others by × or ÷ signs, it is agreed that the operations of multiplication and division shall be performed before those of addition and subtraction.

When a part of an expression is enclosed within brackets, it is to be treated as a single number and should therefore be simplified first.

Multiplication by a Fraction

To multiply a number by a fraction, e.g. $\frac{4}{5}$, we multiply by the numerator 4 and divide by the denominator 5, since multiplication by $\frac{4}{5}$ is defined as meaning four-fifths of the number.

Division by a Fraction

To divide a number by $\frac{1}{7}$ we have to find how many sevenths there are in it. Since there are 7 sevenths in 1, we must multiply the number by 7.

If we wish to divide the number by 3 times $\frac{1}{7}$, i.e. by $\frac{3}{7}$, we must divide the previous answer by 3. Division by $\frac{3}{7}$ is therefore equivalent to multiplication by 7 and division by 3.

Example.—Divide $\frac{4}{5}$ by $\frac{3}{7}$.

$$\frac{\frac{4}{5}}{\frac{3}{7}} = \frac{4}{5} \times \frac{7}{3} = \frac{28}{15}. \quad \text{Answer.}$$

In effect, to divide by a fraction, we invert the fraction and multiply.

Example.—Simplify : $\dfrac{4 - (4\frac{1}{3} - 1\frac{2}{5})}{4 + 5\frac{1}{2} \times 1\frac{3}{5}}$.

$$\frac{4 - (4\frac{1}{3} - 1\frac{2}{5})}{4 + 5\frac{1}{2} \times 1\frac{3}{5}} = \frac{4 - (4\frac{5}{15} - 1\frac{6}{15})}{4 + \frac{11}{2} \times \frac{8}{5}}$$

$$= \frac{4 - (3\frac{20}{15} - 1\frac{6}{15})}{4 + \frac{44}{5}} = \frac{4 - 2\frac{14}{15}}{\frac{20}{5} + \frac{44}{5}}$$

$$= \frac{1\frac{1}{15}}{\frac{64}{5}} = \frac{16}{15} \times \frac{5}{64}$$

$$= \frac{1}{12}. \quad \text{Answer.}$$

The following points should be noted.

Mixed numbers should not be reduced to improper fractions in simple addition or subtraction.

When simplifying a fraction by " cancelling," a number should not be crossed out by drawing a separate line through each digit, though this is frequently done in text-books owing to the difficulties of printing.

Example.—Simplify $\dfrac{3\frac{1}{2} + 4\frac{3}{5} - 5\frac{9}{10}}{7\frac{2}{3} - 4\frac{2}{15} - \frac{1}{5}}$.

Considering numerator of expression, L.C.M. of 2, 5 and 10 is 10 ; considering denominator, L.C.M. of 3, 15 and 5 is 15.

$$\frac{3\frac{1}{2}+4\frac{3}{5}-5\frac{9}{10}}{7\frac{2}{3}-4\frac{2}{15}-\frac{1}{5}}=\frac{3\frac{5}{10}+4\frac{6}{10}-5\frac{9}{10}}{7\frac{10}{15}-4\frac{2}{15}-\frac{3}{15}}=\frac{2\frac{5+6-9}{10}}{3\frac{10-2-3}{15}}$$

$$=\frac{2\frac{2}{10}}{3\frac{5}{15}}=\frac{2\frac{1}{5}}{3\frac{1}{3}}=\frac{\frac{11}{5}}{\frac{10}{3}}$$

$$=\frac{11}{5}\times\frac{3}{10}=\frac{33}{50}. \quad \text{Answer.}$$

Vulgar and Decimal Fractions

To express a vulgar fraction, e.g. $\frac{3}{8}$, in decimal form, we divide 3 by 8, adding 0's to the former and inserting the decimal point as in division by decimals. The division is continued until the decimal terminates or the required number of decimal places has been obtained. $\frac{3}{8}=0\cdot375$.

If $\frac{4}{27}$ be expressed as a decimal, it will be found that $\frac{4}{27}=0\cdot148148---$, the figures 148 recurring continuously.

Here we have a *recurring decimal* which is written $0\cdot14\dot{8}$.

Any fraction in its lowest terms which has 3 or any prime factor greater than 5 as a factor of its denominator, will give rise to a recurring decimal.

Reciprocal of a Number

The reciprocal of a number is 1 divided by the number. Thus the reciprocal of 16 is $\frac{1}{16}$ which, expressed as a decimal, is $0\cdot0625$.

Mathematical tables are published which usually contain a table of reciprocals of numbers expressed as decimals. Further reference is made to these tables in connection with square roots and with logarithms, and every student should have a copy.

Exercise III

Express the following sets of numbers in prime factors and hence find the H.C.F. and L.C.M. in each case : give the L.C.M. in prime factors :

1. 315, 1323.

2. 40, 100, 30.

3. 693, 297, 1287.

4. 572, 2860, 3146.

5. 3528, 756, 1008, 12348.

Express in prime factors and hence find the square root of :

6. 1225.   **7.** 2304.   **8.** 24,336.   **9.** 680,625.

By expressing each number in prime factors, find the cube root of :

10. 42,875.   **11.** 13,824.   **12.** 91,125.

13. Two gear wheels have 18 and 24 teeth respectively. If they start revolving with two particular teeth in contact, what is the smallest number of revolutions each wheel will make before the same two teeth are again in contact ?

14. Three bells are tolling at intervals of 30, 36 and 48 seconds respectively. If they toll together, find how long it will be before they again toll together.

15. For a sports meeting, it is necessary to measure exactly 100 yards, a furlong, and a quarter-mile. What is the longest measure which could be used ?

Simplify the following expressions :

16. $8\frac{2}{3} - 3\frac{1}{4} \times 2\frac{1}{3}$.

17. $\dfrac{\frac{1}{3} + \frac{1}{5} - \frac{1}{7}}{\frac{1}{7} + \frac{1}{5} - \frac{1}{3}}$.

18. $6\frac{2}{3} \times (8\frac{2}{5} - 3\frac{3}{4})$.

19. $10\frac{3}{22} + \frac{7}{8} \div 2\frac{3}{4} - 4\frac{8}{11}$.

20. $\dfrac{(4\frac{1}{8} - 2\frac{2}{3}) \times (\frac{3}{7} + \frac{3}{5})}{2\frac{1}{6} - \frac{2}{5}}$.

21. $\dfrac{3\frac{6}{7} + 2\frac{1}{4}}{3\frac{1}{10} - 2\frac{1}{5}} \div \dfrac{10 - 1\frac{6}{7}}{\frac{2}{3} + 2\frac{3}{5}}$.

Express in decimal form :

22. $\frac{1}{64}$.   **23.** $\frac{1}{125}$.   **24.** $\frac{1}{8^3}$.   **25.** $\frac{1}{107}$.   **26.** $5\frac{8}{11}$.   **27.** $\frac{8}{7}$.

Evaluate correct to three significant figures :

28. $\dfrac{\frac{1}{3} + \frac{1}{5}}{0 \cdot 288}$.

29. $\frac{1}{5} + \frac{1}{5^2} + \frac{1}{5^3} + \frac{1}{5^4} + \frac{1}{5^5} + \frac{1}{5^6}$.

30. The length and breadth of a room are 16 feet and 15 feet respectively. A second room has the same area but is $1\frac{2}{3}$ feet narrower. Find its length.

31. If three wires of resistances 3, 4 and 5 ohms respectively are joined in parallel, the combined resistance is $\dfrac{1}{\frac{1}{3} + \frac{1}{4} + \frac{1}{5}}$ ohms : evaluate this resistance.

32. A petrol tank can be filled from one pipe in 10 minutes and from a second pipe in 15 minutes. If both pipes are turned on, find what fraction of the tank will be filled in 1 minute and hence the time required to fill the tank.

33. One pipe can fill a cistern in 8 minutes and a second in 12 minutes : a third pipe can empty it in 16 minutes. The first and second pipes are opened together for 4 minutes and the third pipe is then opened also. After how long will the cistern be full ?

34. $\frac{1}{2}$ of the goods in a warehouse belonged to one man, $\frac{3}{8}$ of the goods to a second man and the remainder to a third. After a fire it was found that $\frac{3}{4}$ of the first man's goods, $\frac{5}{8}$ of the second man's, and the whole of the third man's had been destroyed. If £5000 insurance money was received, what should be each man's share to the nearest penny ?

SQUARE ROOT

In many calculations it is necessary to find the square root of a number to a required degree of accuracy when the square root is not an integer (i.e. a whole number) and use cannot be made of prime factors. The method is illustrated below.

Example.—Find the square root of 532·703 correct to one place of decimals.

```
          2 3 · 0 8
   2  |  5'32 · 70'30
      |  4
  43  |  132
      |  129
4608  |  37030
```

As the square root is required correct to one decimal place, it must be found to two decimal places. The calculation is as follows.

The figures are marked off in pairs to the left and to the right of the decimal point. When the answer is required to two decimal places, two pairs of figures must be written after the decimal point, by adding 0's if necessary ; in the example one 0 has been added.

The highest whole number whose square is less than 5, viz. 2, is the first divisor. This is divided into 5 giving a quotient 2 and a remainder 1. The next pair of figures is then brought down, giving 132 as the next dividend. The answer obtained to this stage, viz. 2, is doubled, giving 4 as the first figure of the next divisor. This divisor is completed by a further figure, this being the highest whole number which can also be the quotient, in this case 3. After carrying out this division the decimal point is reached which is now inserted in the answer. The next pair of figures, 70, is now brought down, giving a dividend of 370. The answer obtained to this stage is doubled, giving 46 as the first two figures of the next divisor. This divisor is completed by a further figure, the highest whole number which can also be the quotient; in this case 0. The next pair of figures, 30, is now brought down, giving 37030 as the dividend. The figures of the answer obtained to this stage, 230, are doubled, giving 460 as the first three figures of the next divisor. The divisor is completed by a further figure, the highest whole number which can also be the quotient, viz. 8.

The square root of 532·703 correct to one decimal place is 23·1.

Tables of squares and square roots are usually included in the books of tables to which reference has been made previously in connection with reciprocals.

Exercise IV

Find the square root of :

1. 5329.   3. 1524·1216.   5. 101·8081.   7. 0·00066049.
2. 2766·76.   4. 221·1169.   6. 0·034596.   8. 0·829921

Find correct to three significant figures, the square root of :

9. 277.   12. 7·592.   15. 0·093547.   18. 0·000999.
10. 5374·32.   13. 235·08.   16. 0·0083.   19. 0·00144.
11. 312·8.   14. 11·007.   17. 1·0048.   20. 0·00049.

21. A square template has an area of 41·3 sq. cm. Find the length of a side correct to the nearest mm.

22. A square field has an area of 3¼ acres. If a 5-wire fence is put round it, find the length of wire required to the nearest 10 yards.

23. The compressive stress in a certain boiler plate is $7396 - 327 \times \sqrt{57}$ lb. per sq. in. Calculate the stress to the nearest lb. per sq. in.

24. The resistance of a certain wire carrying a current of 385 amp. is $\dfrac{40 \times \sqrt{3}}{3 \times 385}$ ohms. Calculate the resistance in ohms correct to two places of decimals.

25. The nominal diameter of a cotton rope running at 1900 ft. per min. and transmitting 6·1 horse-power is $\sqrt{\dfrac{6 \cdot 1 \times 240}{1900}}$ in. Calculate the diameter in inches correct to two places of decimals.

26. The time of a beat of a pendulum 2 ft. 9 in. long is approximately $2 \times 3 \cdot 14 \times \sqrt{\dfrac{2 \cdot 75}{32}}$ seconds. Calculate the time correct to two significant figures.

27. The diameter of a steel cylinder of height 7 cm, weighing 1970 gm. is $2 \times \sqrt{\dfrac{1070}{3 \cdot 14 \times 7 \times 7 \cdot 75}}$ cm. Find the diameter correct to the nearest mm.

28. To make a particular die it is calculated that the blank diameter of a circular shell is $2 \times \sqrt{2 \cdot 542 + 0 \cdot 351}$ in. Calculate the diameter in inches to two places of decimals.

29. A stay rope is $\sqrt{(21 \cdot 5)^2 + (6 \cdot 5)^2}$ ft. long. Find its length correct to the nearest $\frac{1}{4}$ ft.

30. The radius of gyration of the cross-section of a certain beam about a perpendicular axis through the centre of the section is $\sqrt{\dfrac{(4 \cdot 7)^2 + (3 \cdot 9)^2}{12}}$ ft. Calculate this radius correct to the nearest inch.

RATIO, PROPORTION, PERCENTAGE

Ratio and Proportion

If we wish to compare the sizes of two quantities of the same kind, we may do so in two different ways. We may say that one is so much smaller than the other or that one is so many times smaller than the other.

Suppose we had a model of an aeroplane. We might be

told that the wing span of the model was 48 feet less than that of the aeroplane. It would give a much better idea of the aeroplane if we were told that the wing span of the model was $\frac{1}{25}$ of that of the machine. Assuming the model to be correctly made, we should then know that any length in the model was $\frac{1}{25}$ of the corresponding length in the machine. In this second method of comparison, one quantity is expressed as a fraction of the other; this fraction is called the ratio of the two quantities.

A ratio, e.g. $\frac{2}{3}$, is sometimes written 2 : 3 (to be read as 2 to 3).

Two quantities are said to be proportional when they are so related that the ratio of any two values of the first quantity is equal to the ratio of the two corresponding values of the second quantity.

We know that if we hang a weight from a piece of elastic, the latter extends in length. Robert Hooke, a noted scientist of the seventeenth century, found that with certain precautions, the weight is proportional to the extension. If therefore we are told that a 50 gm. weight causes an extension of 3 cm., we know that a 100 gm. weight would cause an extension of 6 cm., since the ratio $\frac{50}{100}$ = the ratio $\frac{3}{6}$.

Example.—18 cwt. of copper and 7 cwt. of tin are used to form an alloy. What weight of tin must be used when the weight of copper is 24 cwt. ?

18 cwt. of copper are used with 7 cwt. of tin.

∴ 1 cwt. of copper is used with $\frac{7}{18}$ cwt. of tin.

∴ 24 cwt. of copper are used with $\frac{7}{18} \times 24$ cwt. of tin,

$= \frac{7 \times 4}{3} = \frac{28}{3} = 9\frac{1}{3}$ cwt.

(The symbol ∴ means " therefore ")

The above is known as the " Unitary Method " of solution. If this method be used, the first sentence should be so worded that the quantity required comes last—in the above case, the weight of tin.

The question may also be answered by the " Ratio Method " as follows :

The weight of copper is increased in the ratio $\frac{24}{18}$.

$\therefore$ the weight of tin is increased in the ratio $\frac{24}{18}$ and is $\frac{24}{18} \times 7$ cwt. $= 9\frac{1}{3}$ cwt.

Example.—A man employing 60 men contracts to complete a piece of work in 50 days. After 32 days he finds that only three-fifths of the work is completed. How many additional men should he employ, assuming that the amount of work done each day is proportional to the number of men employed ?

As $\frac{3}{5}$ of the work is completed in 32 days, the remaining $\frac{2}{5}$ of the work must be completed in 18 days.

Since $\frac{2}{5}$ of work has still to be done and $\frac{3}{5}$ has been done, number of men could be reduced in the ratio $\frac{\frac{2}{5}}{\frac{3}{5}}$ or $\frac{2}{3}$; but since work has been done for 32 days and 18 days only remain, number of men must be increased in the ratio $\frac{32}{18}$.

$\therefore$ number of men to be employed $= 60 \times \dfrac{2}{3} \times \dfrac{32}{18} = \dfrac{640}{9}$, *i.e.*,

rather more than 71.

$\therefore$ 72 men must be employed.

$\therefore$ number of additional men necessary $= 12$.

The idea of ratio is not restricted to two quantities only ; we may speak of the ratios of any number of quantities of the same kind. If we say that three quantities are in the ratios $3 : 4 : 6$, we mean that the first quantity is $\dfrac{3}{3+4+6}$, *i.e.*, $\frac{3}{13}$ of the whole, the second quantity is $\frac{4}{13}$ of the whole and the third quantity is $\frac{6}{13}$ of the whole.

It should be noted, for example, that the ratios $12 : 20 : 28$ $= 3 : 5 : 7$ since $\dfrac{12}{12+20+28} = \dfrac{3}{3+5+7}$, and similarly with the other fractions. From this example we see that numbers expressing ratios may be divided by a common factor.

Example.—Three partners put £4000, £5000 and £6000 respectively into a business. If the profits are £1000, what is the share of each ?

Capital subscribed is in the ratios 4000 : 5000 : 6000, i.e., in the ratios 4 : 5 : 6.

Hence first man's share of profits $= \frac{4}{15}$ of £1000 $= £\frac{4}{3} \times 200$ $= £\frac{800}{3} = £266$ 13s. 4d.

Second man's share $= \frac{5}{15} \times £1000 = £\frac{1000}{3} = £333$ 6s. 8d.

Third man's share $= \frac{6}{15} \times £1000 = £\frac{2}{5} \times 1000 = £400$ 0s. 0d.

Check : £266 13s. 4d. + £333 6s. 8d. + £400 = £1000.

Percentage

We shall define 5 per cent. of a quantity as meaning 5 hundredths of the quantity. 5 per cent. is usually written 5%.

A quantity is increased by 5% by adding $\frac{5}{100}$ of its value to it ; the result is the same if the quantity be multiplied by $\frac{105}{100}$.

Example.—An electric sweeper is listed at ten guineas. Owing to decreased costs, the manufacturers reduce the price by 10% and a purchaser is then allowed 5% discount for cash How much is paid for the sweeper ?

	£	s.	d.
List price	= 10	10	0
Reduction of 10% $= \frac{1}{10}$ of £10 10s. 0d.	= 1	1	0
∴ revised price	= 9	9	0
5% discount $= \frac{5}{100} \times £9$ 9s.		9	5
∴ price paid	= £8	19	7

The following solution might be given.

New price $= \frac{90}{100}$ of old price $= \frac{90}{100} \times £10$ 10s. 0d.

Price paid $= \frac{95}{100}$ of new price.

$$= \frac{\overset{9}{\cancel{90}}}{\underset{10}{\cancel{100}}} \times \frac{\overset{19}{\cancel{95}}}{\underset{20}{\cancel{100}}} \times £10 \ 10s. \ 0d.$$

$$= \frac{9}{10} \times £9 \ 19s. \ 6d.$$

$$= \frac{£89 \ 15s. \ 6d.}{10} = £8 \ 19s. \ 7d.$$

When we say that 40% by weight of a certain alloy is zinc, we mean that the weight of zinc is $\frac{40}{100}$ of the total weight, or in 100 gm. of alloy there are 40 gm. of zinc.

Example.—In 12 lb. of a certain bronze there were 11 lb. of copper, 0·925 lb. of tin, and 0·075 lb. of phosphorus. Find the percentage composition (i.e. express the weight of each metal as a percentage of the total weight).

This question may be solved by finding the weight of each metal in 100 lb. of bronze.

More shortly :

Percentage of copper $= \dfrac{11}{12} \times 100 \fallingdotseq 91\cdot7.$

Percentage of tin $= \dfrac{0\cdot925}{12} \times 100 \fallingdotseq 7\cdot7.$

Percentage of phosphorus $= \dfrac{0\cdot075}{12} \times 100 \fallingdotseq 0\cdot6.$

Check : $91\cdot7 + 7\cdot7 + 0\cdot6 = 100.$

Example.—In an experiment to find the length of a pendulum which would beat seconds, the result was 39 inches. If the correct result is 38·9 inches, find the percentage error.

The percentage error in a magnitude is the error expressed as a percentage of the true value.

Error $= 0\cdot1$ inch.

$$\frac{0\cdot1}{38\cdot9} \times 100\%$$

$$= \frac{10}{38\cdot9}\%$$

$$\fallingdotseq 0\cdot26\%.$$

$$\begin{array}{r} 0\cdot26 \\ 3\cdot89)\overline{1\cdot000} \\ 778 \\ \overline{2220} \end{array}$$

Exercise V

1. A wheel revolves 40 times in 100 yards. How many times does it revolve in a quarter of a mile ? How far does it move when it makes 500 revolutions ?

2. A piece of copper wire 10 yards long has a resistance of

0·26 ohms. Assuming the resistance to be proportional to the length, find what length of wire will have a resistance of 0·33 ohms.

3. When petrol was 1*s.* 3*d.* a gallon, a motorist travelled 400 miles a week. If petrol was reduced to 1*s.* 1*d.* a gallon, how many more miles a week could he travel without increasing his petrol costs ?

4. If £1 = 138 francs and 1 dollar = 4*s.* 3*d.*, find the number of francs to a dollar.

5. If it costs £58 10*s.* 0*d.* for a family of 6 persons for 13 weeks, find the cost for 7 persons for 8 weeks at the same rate.

6. In a certain brass, which is an alloy of copper and zinc, the ratio of the weight of copper to the weight of zinc is 13 : 7. How much copper should be mixed with 50 lb. of zinc ? What weight of each is contained in 60 lb. of brass ? What is the percentage composition of brass by weight ?

7. Three papers were set in an examination and marks awarded for them in the ratios 1 : 2 : 2. If a candidate obtained 50% on the first paper, 60% on the second and 65% on the third, what percentage did he obtain of the possible total of marks ?

8. On a map drawn to a scale of half an inch to a mile, the area of a district was shown as 1¼ sq. in. What is the true area in acres ?

9. When petrol was 1*s.* 2*d.* a gallon a man used a car with a petrol consumption of 35 miles to the gallon and travelled 390 miles in a week. Petrol was reduced in price and he bought a larger car, which would only travel 30 miles to the gallon. After travelling 450 miles in a week he found that his petrol costs were one and a quarter times their original amount. What was the reduced price of petrol ?

10. A contractor undertook to complete a piece of work in 14 days. After 8 days he decided that a further 8 days would be necessary to complete the work unless the men worked overtime. If the normal working day was 8 hours, how many hours a day overtime were worked in order to complete the contract ?

11. Two men put £1000 each into a business ; three months later a third partner put in £2000, and after a further three months a fourth partner put in £2000. If the profits at the end of the year were £300, how much should each partner receive, assuming the profit on capital to be proportional to the time it is invested in the business ?

12. A man employing 80 men contracted to do a piece of work in 26 weeks. After 21 weeks he finds that only three-quarters of the work has been completed. How many additional men must he employ to complete his contract, assuming the amount of work done per week to be proportional to the number of men employed ?

13. The weights of equal volumes of sea water and fresh water are in the ratio 65 : 64. By how much per cent. is sea water heavier than fresh water ?

14. Each year a machine depreciates by 10% of its value at the beginning of the year. By what percentage has its value depreciated at the end of four years ?

15. A motor cycle is marked for sale at 30% above cost price but 5% discount is allowed for cash. What is the true percentage profit ? If the amount paid for the machine is £24 14s. 0d., find the sale price and the cost price.

16. A surveyor found his chain to be 3 inches short. What was the percentage error in any measured distance ? If he measured a distance as 400 yards, what was the correct distance to the nearest inch ?

17. If 1 m. = 39·37 in. find the percentage error in stating that 3 m. = 10 ft.

18. The length and breadth of a rectangular piece of gold leaf are 2·5 cm. and 1·8 cm. respectively, correct to two significant figures. Find the greatest possible percentage error in the area.

19. A boy is asked to find the area of a rectangle of length 3·54 m. and breadth 2·67 m. By mistake he copies down the length as 3·45 m. and the breadth as 2·76 m. What is the percentage error in his calculated area assuming he multiplies correctly ?

20. Two men, A and B, work similar machines in a factory. A does 10% more work than B in an hour, but B works 12 hours a day while A only works 10½ hours a day. Will A or B do the greater amount of work per day and by how much per cent. ? If B's wages are £4 a week, what should be A's wages ?

21. Three partners, A, B and C, subscribe £3000, £4000 and £5000 respectively as capital for a business. A receives 15% of the profits as manager and B 10% as assistant manager, after which the remaining profits are divided in proportion to the capital subscribed. Find the shares of B and C in a year when A receives £540.

ALGEBRA

CHAPTER II

Progress in arithmetic was dependent on the development of a suitable symbolism. In algebra the need was still greater and progress correspondingly slow. A collection of questions was made by the Greek Metrodorus at an uncertain date but believed to be not earlier than the fourth century. Rouse Ball in his *History of Mathematics* gives as an example of these : " Make a crown of gold, copper, tin and iron weighing 60 minæ ; gold and copper shall be two-thirds of it, gold and tin three-fourths of it, and gold and iron three-fifths of it ; find the weights of the gold, copper, tin and iron which are required." It is now generally believed that such questions were solved by reasoning in words without the use of symbols. As early as the third century B.C. Euclid used lines to represent magnitudes and in 600 years little progress seems to have been made.

The mathematician who may be said to have created algebra is Diophantus. Very little is known about his life. He lived in Alexandria, probably in the fourth century, but quite likely was not Greek. He introduced symbols for the frequently occurring operations and for the unknown in equations ; the latter arose from the problems he considered, mostly of the " find a number " type. Little interest was taken in his work, which was forgotten for centuries. The first edition of his Arithmetic to be published in Europe was a Latin translation by Xylander near the end of the sixteenth century.

The work of Diophantus was known to Arab mathematicians, but apparently not until after they themselves had established algebra independently. The greatest of these was

Alkarismi, who lived in the ninth century and wrote *Al-gebr we' l mukabala* ; the first word of the title is the origin of the word " algebra." The solution of the quadratic equation in various forms is given and the existence of two roots recognized, though only real positive roots are considered. This work became known in Europe during the twelfth century.

Symbolism was still not satisfactory, and little further real progress was made in algebra until after the invention of printing in the fifteenth century. This greatly facilitated the spread of knowledge and algebra was notably advanced during the sixteenth century by Tartaglia, Cardan, and Vieta, to mention but three of the more illustrious names. By this time a compact symbolism was evolved ; equations of the third and fourth degree were solved and negative and imaginary roots admitted. It may be said that the discovery of logarithms by Napier in the early part, and of the binomial theorem by Newton in the latter half of the seventeenth century, completed the algebraic equipment of the technical student.

SYMBOLS AMD FORMULÆ

The symbols below have the meanings indicated :

Symbol	Meaning
$\neq$	is not equal to.
$\simeq$ or $\risingdotseq$	is approximately equal to.
$>$	is greater than.
$<$	is less than.
$\therefore$	therefore.

The area of a rectangle in square feet can be found by multiplying the number of feet in its length by the number of feet in its breadth. The statement is equally true if we substitute other units, e.g. centimetres for feet, and is often stated shortly as follows :

Area of rectangle = length × breadth.

Suppose now we call the area A square feet, the length

l feet and the breadth b feet ; we may write the result still more simply as :

$$A = l \times b.$$

This relation is called a *formula*, and letters used in this way are called *symbols*.

We see that this formula expresses a general result, giving the area of any rectangle in terms of its length and breadth ; in arithmetic we give the area of each individual rectangle. *In this generalization of results lies the essential difference between arithmetic and algebra.* It leads to a great saving of labour and to the solution of many problems which would be difficult if not impossible by the methods of arithmetic.

The multiplication sign in such a formula is usually omitted, it being understood that when two symbols are written next to each other they are to be multiplied, e.g. $rs = r \times s$; $xy = x \times y$.

In arithmetic $4 \times 7 = 7 \times 4$; similarly $xy = yx$.

This is also true in the case of a number and a symbol, the number being written first : $4a = 4 \times a$; $c \times 6 = 6c$; $2a \times 3b = 6ab$.

In the case of two numbers the multiplication sign must be used ; 2×3 cannot be written 23, as this represents twenty-three.

We know in the case of a rectangular box that the volume (in cu. ft.) = length (in ft.) × breadth (in ft.) × height (in ft.).

This may be more simply expressed as :

$$V = l \times b \times h \text{ or } V = lbh.$$

It should be emphasized that letters are used to represent numbers and not quantities.

We do not speak of the length of a room as l, but as l feet or l yards ; we say that a lathe costs x pounds, a wheel makes n revolutions.

Example.—The wheel of a car makes n revolutions when the car travels s yards. Find the circumference of the wheel in feet.

As n and s represent numbers, the method is exactly similar to that of a corresponding question in arithmetic.

When the wheel revolves once, the distance the car moves is equal to the circumference of the wheel.

$\therefore$ n times the circumference $= s$ yards

$\qquad\qquad\qquad\qquad\qquad = 3s$ feet.

$\therefore$ the circumference $= \dfrac{3s}{n}$ feet.

Example.—The stress s lb. per sq. in. in a boiler plate is given by the formula $s = \dfrac{6pd}{t}$, where p lb. per sq. in. is the pressure, d ft. is the diameter of the boiler, and t in. is the thickness of the plate. Find the stress when the pressure is 150 lb. per sq. in., the diameter 9 ft. and the thickness $\frac{3}{4}$ in.

$$s = \frac{6 \times 150 \times \overset{2}{9}}{\frac{3}{4}} = \frac{\overset{2}{6} \times 150 \times 9 \times 4}{\overset{}{3}} = 10{,}800.$$

Stress $= 10{,}800$ lb. per sq. in.

Exercise VI

1. Find the area of each of the following rectangles :
   (a) length $= x$ feet, breadth $= y$ feet ;
   (b) length $= a$ yards, breadth $= b$ feet ;
   (c) length $= 2a$ feet, breadth $= 3c$ feet ;
   (d) length $= p$ cm., breadth $= q$ mm.

2. If screws cost threepence a dozen, find the cost of n dozens.

3. If screws cost x pence per dozen, find in shillings, the cost of (i) 4 dozens, (ii) d dozens.

4. A train travels s feet in 10 minutes. Find the distance travelled in an hour. Express the speed in (i) feet per minute, (ii) feet per second.

5. If a train travels s feet in t seconds, in how long will it travel (i) $3s$ feet, (ii) 300 feet ? Express its speed in (i) feet per second, (ii) miles per hour.

6. There are n turns of wire round a cylinder of circumference c inches. What is the length of the wire in (i) inches, (ii) feet ?

7. Two cars travel in opposite directions from the same town, one at 20 m.p.h. and the other at 25 m.p.h. How far apart will they be after t hours ?

8. The power W kilowatts supplied by a current of C ampères at V volts is given by $W = \dfrac{CV}{1000}$. Find the power when the current is 15 ampères and the voltage 220 volts.

9. If the difference in potential between the two ends of a wire of resistance R ohms is V volts, the current through it is I ampères, given by $I = \dfrac{V}{R}$. Find the current when the difference in potential is 3·4 volts and the resistance is 7·9 ohms.

10. If a cylinder weighs w gm., $w = \pi ahd$ where $\pi = 3·142$, a sq. cm. is the area of the cross-section, h cm. the height, and the material weighs d gm. per c.c. What is the weight of an iron cylinder of 11 sq. cm. cross-section, height 13·5 cm., if iron weighs 7·79 gm. per c.c. ? Give the answer correct to three significant figures.

11. If $f = \dfrac{g\text{P}}{\text{W}}$, find f when $g = 32$, $P = 73$ and $W = 17·3$, correct to the nearest integer.

12. Find H from the formula $H = \dfrac{1·73pe\text{IV}}{746}$ when $p = ·7$, $e = ·85$, $I = 30$, $V = 120$, correct to two significant figures.

If a petrol tank contains 10 gallons and 4 gallons are used we know that the number of gallons remaining is $10 - 4$. We can say equally that if n gallons are used, the number of gallons remaining is $10 - n$.

We can make our statement still more general by saying that if the tank contains c gallons and n gallons are used, the number of gallons remaining is $c - n$. In each case in which a letter is used it represents a number.

Example.—(i) A hanging spiral spring is 15 inches long. Each ounce weight hung from the end stretches the spring $\frac{1}{2}$ inch. What is the total length of the spring when 8 ounces are hung from the end ? (ii) A hanging spiral spring is a inches long. Each ounce weight hung from the end stretches the spring b inches. What is the total length of the spring when w ounces are hung from the end ?

(i) 1 ounce stretches the spring $\frac{1}{2}$ inch.

∴ 8 ounces stretch the spring $\frac{1}{2} \times 8$ inches = 4 inches.

Total length of spring = 15 inches + 4 inches

$$= (15 + 4) \text{ inches}$$

$$= 19 \text{ inches.}$$

(ii) 1 ounce stretches the spring b inches.

∴ w ounces stretch the spring $b \times w$ inches = bw inches

Total length of spring = a inches + bw inches.

$$= (a + bw) \text{ inches.}$$

It will be seen from the above example that the methods of arithmetic and algebra are identical. Brackets are used in each case to indicate that the contents are to be treated as a single number. It is not possible to write $a + bw$ in any simpler form until we know more about the numbers which a, b and w represent.

Example.—A man's ordinary rate of pay is a shillings an hour but b shillings an hour for overtime. How much should he receive after working 11 hours, including 2 hours overtime ?

He works 9 hours at the ordinary rate and 2 hours overtime.

For 9 hours work he should receive $9a$ shillings.

For 2 hours overtime he should receive $2b$ shillings.

∴ total amount = $9a$ shillings + $2b$ shillings

$$= (9a + 2b) \text{ shillings}$$

$$= \frac{9a + 2b}{20} \text{ pounds.}$$

As in arithmetic, the straight line separating numerator and denominator acts as a bracket. It binds together the numbers $9a$ and $2b$ and indicates that their sum is to be divided by 20.

Example.—The weekly expenses in a factory may be calculated as £a with an addition of £b for each man employed. If n men are employed when the weekly expenses are £E

2

express E in terms of a, b and n. Find the weekly expenses when $a = 1000$, $b = 2\frac{1}{2}$ and $n = 50$.

Cost for 1 man $= \pounds b$.

∴ cost for n men $= \pounds bn$.

Total weekly cost $= \pounds a + \pounds bn$.

∴ $\pounds E = \pounds a + \pounds bn$.

i.e. $E = a + bn$.

When $a = 1000$, $b = 2\frac{1}{2}$ and $n = 50$.

$$E = 1000 + 2\frac{1}{2} \times 50$$
$$= 1000 + 125 = 1125.$$

Weekly expenses $= \pounds 1125$.

Exercise VII

1. A carpenter's bag weighs 2 lb. and his tools p lb. What is the total weight ?

2. If a retailer buys valves at p shillings each and sells them at q shillings each, what is (i) his profit in £'s per dozen, (ii) his percentage profit ?

3. One lap of a running track is l yards in length. If a man has b yards start in a six-lap race, how far has he run on completing the course ? $(6l - b) \, yds$

4. A motorist pays x shillings for repairs and y pence a gallon for 4 gallons of petrol. What is the total amount in shillings ?

5. A car's petrol consumption averages 25 miles to the gallon. If the motorist starts with k gallons of petrol, how many gallons should remain after he has travelled (i) 100 miles, (ii) n miles ? What is the greatest distance he can travel before needing more petrol ? $K - 4, \quad K - \frac{n}{25}, \quad 25K \, miles$

6. A light spiral spring is hanging with a weight of W gm. attached to its lower end, the length of the spring being l cm. What is the unstretched length of the spring if it is known that each 20 gm. weight attached to its lower end stretches it x cm. ?

7. A workman is paid a shillings an hour for ordinary time and b shillings an hour for overtime. What should he receive after working p hours ordinary time and q hours overtime ? $(pa + qb) \, shill.$

8. If a speed boat does a miles per hour over a measured mile in one direction and b miles per hour in the opposite direction, what is the time taken to cover the two miles ? $\left(\frac{1}{a} + \frac{1}{b}\right) \, hour$

9. Photographs cost a shillings each for the first six copies and s shillings for each additional copy. If £C is the cost of n copies (when *n* is greater than 6), express C in terms of *a*, *n* and *s*. Find C when $a = 3$, $s = 2$ and $n = 24$.

10. A car travelling at 10 m.p.h. increases its speed by 5 m.p.h. every minute until the maximum speed is reached. If *s* miles per hour is the speed after *t* minutes, express *s* in terms of *t*, assuming that *s* miles per hour is less than the maximum speed. $s = 10 + 5t$

11. The postage rate for letters in England is $1\frac{1}{2}d$. for the first 2 oz. and $\frac{1}{2}d$. for each additional 2 oz. Find the cost in pence of a letter weighing *m* oz. if *m* is an even number greater than 2.

12. An empty box weighs *x* lb. and when full of bolts the total weight is *y* lb. Find the weight of the bolts and the total weight when the box is half full. If there are *n* bolts in the full box, what is the weight of a bolt ? $(y - x) lb., \frac{x+y}{2} lb. \frac{y-x}{n} lb.$

13. The cost of a telephone is £1 6*s*. 0*d*. a quarter with the addition of a penny per call. How much is the bill in a quarter in which there are *n* calls ?

If the bill is C shillings in a quarter in which there are *x* calls, express C in terms of *x*.

14. The cost of a weekly season ticket between two stations on the London Underground Railway is *x* shillings and the cost for a single journey is *p* pence. How much does a man save per week by buying a season ticket if he does the return journey twice each day from Monday to Friday and once on Saturday ?

Like and Unlike Terms

Suppose a wagon to be loaded with 12 bags each holding *n* lb. Then the total weight is 12*n* lb. If two further bags be added, the number of bags is 14 and the total weight is 14*n* lb. But the weight is 12*n* lb. + 2*n* lb.

∴ $12n + 2n = 14n$ in the same way as, for example, 12 thousand + 2 thousand = 14 thousand.

Suppose 6 bags are now removed. A weight of 6*n* lb. is removed and the number of bags remaining is 8.

∴ $14n - 6n = 8n$.

An expression of the type $7a - 3a + 5a$ is said to consist of *like terms*, as its three parts or *terms* are numerical multiples of the same number *a*. 7 is said to be the *coefficient* of the term 7*a*.

Any expression consisting of like terms can be reduced to a single term ; when simplifying, work from the left as below.

unless brackets or × or ÷ signs show, as in arithmetic, that operations are to be performed in a particular order.

Thus $7a - 3a + 5a = 4a + 5a = 9a$.

$$8x^2 - 5x^2 - 2x^2 = 3x^2 - 2x^2 = x^2.$$

NOTE.—xx is written shortly as x^2 and xxx as x^3.

Expressions of the type $5a + 3b$, $7x - y$, $5p^2 + 2p - 4$ are said to consist of unlike terms and no further simplification is possible.

Example.—Simplify $7b - 5b + 4b + 6b - 8b$.

$$7b - 5b + 4b + 6b - 8b$$
$$= 2b + 4b + 6b - 8b$$
$$= 6b + 6b - 8b$$
$$= 12b - 8b$$
$$= 4b.$$

Expressions consisting of terms involving the same symbol and numerical terms may be partly simplified.

Example.—Simplify $8d + 13 - 5d - 7 + 4d - 2$.

$$8d + 13 - 5d - 7 + 4d - 2$$
$$= 8d + 4d - 5d + 13 - 7 - 2$$
$$= 12d - 5d + 6 - 2$$
$$= 7d + 4.$$

As in arithmetic, the order in which additions and subtractions are carried out is immaterial.

Example.—A man travels x miles at 4 miles an hour and returns at 3 miles an hour. Find the total time taken.

Time for outward journey $= \dfrac{x}{4}$ hours;

time for return journey $= \dfrac{x}{3}$ hours.

$\therefore$ total time $= \left(\dfrac{x}{4} + \dfrac{x}{3}\right)$ hours

$$= \left(\dfrac{3x}{12} + \dfrac{4x}{12}\right) \text{ hours}$$

$$= \dfrac{7x}{12} \text{ hours}.$$

Exercise VIII

Simplify :

1. $11a + 5a - 13a$.
2. $7p - 6p + 4p$.
3. $8f + 13f - 15f - 2f$.
4. $10b^2 - 8b^2 + 3b^2$.
5. $14xy - 3xy - 7xy + 2xy$.
6. $5x + 13x - 11$.
7. $25y + 14y + 5 - 7y$.
8. $18c + 6 + 5c - 4$.
9. $20 + 10k^2 - 7 + 3k^2 - 13k^2$.
10. $22yz - 15yz + 12 - 4yz - 7$.
11. $\dfrac{p}{4} + \dfrac{p}{8}$.
12. $\dfrac{2c}{5} - \dfrac{c}{3}$.
13. $\dfrac{3l}{8} + 2l - \dfrac{l}{2}$.
14. $5cd - \dfrac{2cd}{7} + \dfrac{cd}{14}$.

15. A rectangular piece of sheet metal is $10a$ in. long and $8b$ in. wide. 4 equal holes are punched in it each $2a$ in. long and b in. wide. What is the remaining surface area ?

16. The weekly wages of a man are £$3a$, of a woman £$2a$ and of a boy £a. Find the wage bill for a week in a factory employing 50 men, 75 women and 25 boys.

17. From a square of side $2a$ cm. a square of side $\dfrac{a}{2}$ cm. is removed and a second square of side $\dfrac{a}{5}$ cm. What is the remaining area ?

18. Find the cost of a gross of screws at s shillings a gross, half a gross at $\dfrac{3s}{4}$ shillings a gross and a quarter of a gross at $\dfrac{s}{2}$ shillings a gross.

SIMPLE EQUATIONS

Example.—A man completed a journey of 42 miles by bus, train, and car. The distance travelled by train was three times that by bus and by car twice that by bus. What was the distance travelled by each method ?

Let x be the number of miles travelled by bus. Then $3x$ miles is the number of miles travelled by train and $2x$ miles is the number of miles travelled by car. The total number of miles travelled is therefore $x + 3x + 2x$; but we are told that the number of miles travelled is 42.

$$\therefore x + 3x + 2x = 42.$$
$$\therefore 6x = 42.$$

$6x$ and 42 are therefore equal numbers and if we divide each by 6, the results will still be equal.

$$\therefore x = 7.$$

Distance travelled by bus is therefore 7 miles.

Distance by train $= 3x$ miles $= 21$ miles.

Distance by car $= 2x$ miles $= 14$ miles.

The various steps of the work will be understood if it is remembered that x is simply a number.

A statement of the form $x + 3x + 2x = 42$ expressing that two numbers are equal is called an *equation*, in which x is the *unknown*. The process of finding the unknown is called *solving the equation* and the value of the unknown when found is the *root* of the equation.

Example.—A man wishing to exchange an old wireless set for a new was told that he would be allowed one third the cost of the new set for the old. If he paid £8 in cash, what was the cost of the new set ?

Let £n be allowed for the old set.

Then £$3n$ was the cost of the new.

Number of pounds paid was therefore $3n - n$.

$$\therefore 3n - n = 8.$$
$$\therefore 2n = 8.$$

Dividing each side by 2, $n = 4$.

Cost of new set $= 3n$ pounds $= £12$.

In questions of this type it is usually simpler to let the unknown be the smallest number concerned. Any letter may be used for the unknown, though x is most frequently employed.

Since an equation merely expresses that two numbers are equal :

(i) *equal numbers may be added to each side;*

(ii) *equal numbers may be subtracted from each side ;*
(iii) *each side may be multiplied by the same number ;*
(iv) *each side may be divided by the same number.*

Example.—Solve the equation $3x - 15 = 24$.

Add 15 to each side.
$$3x - 15 + 15 = 24 + 15.$$
$$\therefore 3x = 39.$$

Divide each side by 3.
$$x = 13.$$

Example.—Solve $6x - 13 = 2x + 19$.

Add 13 to each side.
$$6x - 13 + 13 = 2x + 19 + 13.$$
$$\therefore 6x = 2x + 32.$$

Subtract $2x$ from each side.
$$\therefore 6x - 2x = 2x - 2x + 32.$$
$$\therefore 4x = 32.$$

Divide each side by 4.
$$x = 8.$$

Example.—Solve $\dfrac{x}{3} + 11 = \dfrac{3x}{4} + 6$.

Subtract 6 from each side.
$$\therefore \frac{x}{3} + 5 = \frac{3x}{4}.$$

As the L.C.M. of the denominators is 12, multiply each side by 12.
$$12 \times \frac{x}{3} + 12 \times 5 = 12 \times \frac{3x}{4}.$$
$$\therefore 4x + 60 = 9x.$$

Subtract $4x$ from each side.
$$\therefore 60 = 5x.$$

Divide each side by 5.
$$12 = x.$$
$$\text{i.e. } x = 12.$$

It is advisable to check your answer by substituting your result in each side of the given equation separately.

Check :

Left side $= \dfrac{x}{3} + 11 = \dfrac{12}{3} + 11 = 4 + 11 = 15.$

Right side $= \dfrac{3}{4}x + 6 = \dfrac{3}{4} \times 12 + 6 = 9 + 6 = 15.$

$\therefore$ Left side $=$ right side when $x = 12.$

It should be remembered that the symbol $=$ means " is equal to " and care should be taken not to use the symbol incorrectly.

Exercise IX

Solve the equations :

1. $9x - 5x + 3x = 28.$

2. $5t - 8 = 7.$

3. $14 - 3z = 4z.$

4. $6s - 13 = 4s - 8.$

5. $7\frac{1}{2} + 3y = 2y + 9\frac{1}{4}.$

6. $13p - 5 - 7p = 3p - 1.$

7. $6l + 11 = 25 - l.$

8. $3a - 23 = 8a - 68.$

9. $\dfrac{r}{2} - \dfrac{r}{3} = 1.$

10. $0 \cdot 75d. = 13 \cdot 2.$

11. $\frac{4}{5}h - \frac{2}{3}h = 3.$

12. $\dfrac{x}{3} + \dfrac{x}{4} - \dfrac{x}{6} = \dfrac{1}{12}.$

13. $3 \cdot 2y - 2 \cdot 1 = 5 \cdot 6 + 1 \cdot 4y.$

14. $\dfrac{q}{2} + \dfrac{q}{3} + 2 = 2 + \dfrac{q}{6}.$

15. $3k + \frac{5}{3} = 4 + \frac{2}{3}k.$

16. A foreman and three men earn £15. If the foreman earns £1 more than each man, find how much each earns.

17. The longest side of a triangle is 5 inches longer than the shortest side and 3 inches longer than the other side. If the sum of the lengths of the three sides is 37 inches, find the length of each side.

18. A motorist decided to buy a new car of the same make as his old one after prices had fallen by £25. For his old car he was allowed one quarter of its original cost and had to pay £200 in addition. What was the price of the new car ?

19. A car moving at a certain speed increases its speed each minute by 10 m.p.h. up to its maximum. If its speed after four

minutes is twice its speed after one minute, at what rate was it moving when it began to accelerate ? What was its speed after three minutes ?

20. The average speed of the " Coronation " train is ten miles an hour greater than that of the " Flying Scotsman." Find the average speed of each if, when travelling in opposite directions, they are forty miles apart twenty minutes after passing.

21. The potential difference between the two ends of a wire carrying a current is equal to the product of the current and the resistance. If the current is increased by 10% and the resistance by 10%, what is the percentage increase in the potential difference ?

22. When a gas is compressed without change of temperature, the product of the pressure and the volume is constant. A volume of 375 c.c. under a pressure of 30 in. of mercury is compressed to 325 c.c. What is the new pressure in inches of mercury ?

23. If a Fahrenheit temperature of F° corresponds to a Centigrade temperature of C°, $F = \frac{9}{5}C + 32$. If the freezing and boiling-points of water are 0° and 100° respectively on the Centigrade scale, find the corresponding Fahrenheit temperatures. What Fahrenheit temperature corresponds to 55° Centigrade and what Centigrade temperature corresponds to 59° Fahrenheit ?

24. The radius of curvature R cm. of a lens is determined by a spherometer from the formula $R - \frac{h}{2} = \frac{d^2}{6h}$. Find R when $d = 4.5$ and $h = 0.24$.

25. Huyghen's formula for the length l in. of a circular arc is $l = \frac{8h - c}{3}$, where c in. is the chord of the arc and h in. is the chord of half the arc. Find h when $l = 3.49$ and $c = 3.42$.

26. When n cells are connected in series, the current is determined from the formula $C = \frac{nE}{R + nr}$. Find E when $C = 1.4$, $R = 4.5$, $n = 6$ and $r = 1.2$.

27. If a stone be thrown upwards with a velocity of u ft. per sec. it will reach a height of s ft. in t sec., where $s = ut - 16t^2$. Find the velocity with which a stone was thrown, upwards which was at a height of 24 ft. after $1\frac{1}{4}$ sec.

2*

CHAPTER III

DIRECTED NUMBERS

Previously the signs + and − have been taken to mean simply " add " and " subtract." 9 − 4 means "from 9 subtract 4 ", and for many of our calculations nothing more is necessary. When other ideas are involved it simplifies our work to attach further meanings to the symbols + and − when this can be done without leaving any doubt as to their meaning.

On the Centigrade scale of temperatures, freezing point is 0 degrees. A temperature of 7 degrees below freezing is − 7 degrees ; a temperature of 58 degrees above freezing is + 58 degrees. The symbols + and − here indicate above and below a certain zero.

NOTE.—Read + as " plus " and − as " minus."

Suppose a man bought and sold five cars with the following results :

	1st	2nd	3rd	4th	5th
Profit	£50	£0			£35
Loss		£0	£10	£15	

This can be written shortly :

	1st	2nd	3rd	4th	5th
Profit	£(+ 50)	£0	£(− 10)	£(− 15)	£(+ 35)

The symbols + and − here are a short way of indicating that the man either gained or lost. Brackets are used to show that the + and − are not simply instructions to add or subtract.

If a gunner attempted to hit a certain target and his range was 200 yards too great, the distance the shot fell beyond the target could be expressed as (+ 200) yards ; if the range was 50 yards short, this would then be expressed as (− 50) yards.

We have here a notation which indicates a rise and fall or a backwards and forwards movement with reference to a certain zero. Numbers such as (+ 200) or (− 50) are called directed numbers. The symbols + and − are the signs of the numbers; (+ 200) is a positive number and (− 50) is a negative number.

As in the case of temperatures, scales are often used to indicate positive and negative numbers. If the scale is drawn up and down the page, positive numbers are usually marked above and negative numbers below the fixed zero; if the scale is drawn from left to right, positive numbers are to the right and negative numbers to the left of the zero.

Consider the case of a man who buys and sells two cars, on the first of which he gains £40 and on the second loses £30. We know that the effect of adding the two results is a gain of £10. Hence £(+ 40) + £(− 30) = £(+ 10).

Let a scale now be drawn from left to right with + numbers marked to the right and − numbers to the left of zero.

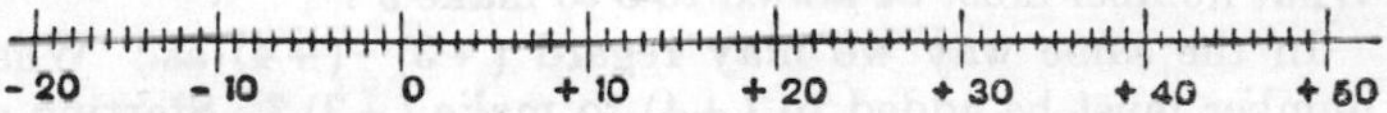

FIG. 1.

Starting from zero, to reach (+ 40) we must move 40 divisions to the right. To reach (+ 10) from this position we must move 30 divisions to the left. We know above that this is the result of adding (− 30) to (+ 40). Hence we see that adding a positive number will mean moving to the right and adding a negative number moving to the left.

Addition and Subtraction

Suppose we have a horizontal scale with divisions to the right of a zero point marked by + numbers and divisions to the left by − numbers

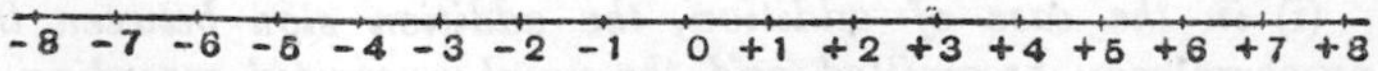

FIG. 2.

(+ 3) + (+ 4) will mean starting at + 3 on the line and moving 4 divisions to the right which brings us to + 7.

We say therefore that $(+3)+(+4)=(+7)$.

$(-3)+(+4)$ will mean starting at -3 on the line and moving 4 divisions to the right, which brings us to $+1$.

$\therefore$ $(-3)+(+4)=(+1)$.

$(+3)+(-4)$ will mean starting at $+3$ on the scale and moving 4 divisions to the left, which brings us to -1.

$\therefore$ $(+3)+(-4)=(-1)$.

Similarly $(-3)+(-4)=(-7)$.

We may tabulate these results as follows :

$$(+3)+(+4)=(+7).$$
$$(-3)+(+4)=(+1).$$
$$(+3)+(-4)=(-1).$$
$$(-3)+(-4)=(-7).$$

Any question in subtraction may be converted into a question in addition. We may regard $9-5$ as the question : What number must be added to 5 to make 9 ?

In the same way we may regard $(+3)-(+4)$ as : What number must be added to $(+4)$ to make $(+3)$? Starting at $+4$ on our line, we find what move it is necessary to make to reach $+3$. To do this we must move 1 division to the left.

$\therefore$ $(+3)-(+4)=(-1)$.

In the same way $(-3)-(+4)$ will mean starting at $+4$ and moving 7 divisions to the left to reach -3.

$\therefore$ $(-3)-(+4)=(-7)$.

Treating other cases similarly and tabulating our results :

$$(+3)-(+4)=(-1).$$
$$(-3)-(+4)=(-7).$$
$$(+3)-(-4)=(+7).$$
$$(-3)-(-4)=(+1).$$

From the above examples we see that :

(i) *in the case of addition, the addition sign between the numbers may be omitted and the numbers treated according to their own signs ;*

(ii) *the subtraction of a number is equivalent to changing its sign and adding the resulting numbers.*

In practice, positive signs and brackets are omitted when directed numbers are written alone. ($+5$) is written as 5, (-5) is written -5.

Example.—Add 4 and -7.

Starting at 4 on the line and moving 7 divisions to the left, the result is -3.

Hence $4 - 7 = -3$.

We may condense our deductions into the following three rules :

In addition of numbers with like signs, add the numbers and prefix the common sign ;

In addition of numbers with unlike signs, find the difference of the numbers and prefix the sign of the greater ;

In subtraction, change the sign of the number to be subtracted and treat the question as one in addition.

$$-3 - 15 = -18.$$
$$3 - 15 = -12.$$
$$-3 - (-15) = -3 + 15 = 12.$$

Similarly $-3x - 15x = -18x.$
$$3y - 15y = -12y.$$
$$-3z - (-15z) = -3z + 15z = 12z.$$

Exercise X

Find the value of :

1. $-8 - 7.$ 2. $-9 - 6.$ 3. $-10 - 5.$
4. $-13 - 18.$ 5. $-4 + 10.$ 6. $-6 + 12.$
7. $5 - 13.$ 8. $7 - 27.$ 9. $8 - (-4).$
10. $10 - (-6).$ 11. $-10 - (-6).$ 12. $-7 - (-8).$

Simplify :

13. $-8x - 7x.$ 14. $-9x - 6x.$ 15. $-5x - 13x.$
16. $-7x - 10x.$ 17. $-4x + 10x.$ 18. $-6x + 12x.$
19. $7a - 15a.$ 20. $6a - 12a.$ 21. $8x - (-4x).$
22. $10y - (-6y).$ 23. $-8z - (-17z).$ 24. $-5c - (-2c).$

Add :

25. $-13a$ and $4a$.	26. $13y$ and $-4y$.
27. $-8t$ and $5t$.	28. $7a$ and $-10a$.
29. $-10z$ and $3z$.	30. $-10z$ and $-3z$.
31. $-4s$ and $-6s$.	32. $-20s$ and $2s$.

Subtract :

33. 5 from 3.	34. -5 from -10.	35. 5 from -5.
36. -5 from 0.	37. $6x$ from $9x$.	38. $9x$ from $6x$.
39. $-2x$ from $-7x$.	40. $4x$ from 0.	

What must be added to :

41. 8 to make 6 ?	42. -8 to make 6 ?
43. 8 to make -6 ?	44. -8 to make -6 ?
45. $4x$ to make $7x$?	46. $4y$ to make $-7y$?
47. $-4t$ to make $7t$?	48. $-4t$ to make $-7t$?

49. The Centigrade temperature in Kingsway at 6 p.m. one evening was 5 degrees. By 2 a.m. the temperature had fallen 8 degrees. What was the temperature at 2 a.m. ?

50. The last trains from Charing Cross to certain suburbs leave at the times stated : Earl's Court 12.36 a.m., South Harrow 11.47 p.m., Uxbridge 11.30 p.m., Richmond 12.6 a.m. Express these times by use of directed numbers, taking midnight as the zero time.

51. A stone is thrown upwards with a velocity of 64 feet per second. Explain what is meant by the following table which gives the velocity at intervals of 1 second :

Time in sec.	..	..	0	1	2	3	4
Velocity in ft. per sec.	..	64	32	0	-32	-64	

52. A man's salary increases by £15 a year. If his present salary is £300 a year, find an expression which will give his salary in n years. Make use of this expression to find his salary 5 years ago.

53. If a stone is thrown upwards with a velocity of 50 feet per second, its velocity after t seconds is $50-32t$ feet per second. Find the velocity after 1 second and after 2 seconds. Explain the meaning of your results.

54. The profits from a boarding house are $50n-400$ pounds a year, where n is the number of people in residence. Calculate the profits when $n=20$ and when $n=6$, and explain your results.

55. The heights of three towns, A, B and C, above sea-level are given as +200 ft., −80 ft. and −120 ft. respectively. How much higher is A than C and how many feet is B below C ?

56. The time of high tide at London Bridge is the time at Putney −30 min. and at Hammersmith it is the time at Putney +10 min. Find the time of high tide at Hammersmith when it is 11.53 a.m. at London Bridge, and the time at Putney when it is 12.5 p.m. at Hammersmith.

Multiplication and Division

Let us suppose that a train runs at 30 m.p.h. We shall use directed numbers to express that the velocity of the train when running north is +30 m.p.h. and when running south is −30 m.p.h. Let us select Leeds as a centre and consider the case of a train running north and due at Leeds at noon. Making further use of directed numbers, 60 miles south of Leeds will be −60 miles and 60 miles north of Leeds will be +60 miles ; 2 hours before noon will be −2 hours and 2 hours after noon will be +2 hours.

We know that if a train travels at 30 m.p.h. for 2 hours, the distance travelled is 60 miles and in fact that : velocity × time =distance.

At 2 p.m. the velocity is +30 m.p.h., the time +2 hours, and the distance +60 miles.

$$\therefore \ (+30) \times (+2) = (+60).$$

The distance from Leeds at t o'clock will be $(+30) \times t$ miles. At 10 a.m. $t = -2$ and distance $= -60$ miles.

$$\therefore \ (+30) \times (-2) = (-60).$$

Let us consider now the case of a train travelling south and due at Leeds at noon. Velocity is −30 m.p.h. and distance from Leeds at t o'clock is $(-30) \times t$ miles. At 2 p.m. $t = 2$ and distance $= -60$ miles.

$$\therefore \ (-30) \times (+2) = (-60).$$

At 10 a.m. $t = -2$ and distance is +60 miles since train is 60 miles north of Leeds.

$$\therefore \ (-30) \times (-2) = (+60).$$

Tabulating these results :

$$(+30) \times (+2) = (+60) \quad \text{(i).}$$
$$(+30) \times (-2) = (-60) \quad \text{(ii).}$$
$$(-30) \times (+2) = (-60) \quad \text{(iii).}$$
$$(-30) \times (-2) = (+60) \quad \text{(iv).}$$

From which we see that *when two directed numbers are multiplied together, like signs give a positive number and unlike signs a negative number.*

Dividing each side of (i) by (+30) :

$$(+2) = \frac{(+60)}{(+30)}.$$

Similarly from (ii), (iii) and (iv) :

$$(-2) = \frac{(-60)}{(+30)},$$

$$(+2) = \frac{(-60)}{(-30)} \quad \text{and}$$

$$(-2) = \frac{(+60)}{(-30)}.$$

Hence also *in the division of one directed number by another, like signs give a positive number and unlike signs a negative number.*

As in the case of addition and subtraction, brackets are often omitted when this can be done without ambiguity.

As $(-2) \times (-3) = 6$ so also $(-a) \times (-b) = ab.$

NOTE.—The $\times$ sign between two pairs of brackets is usually omitted : $(-a) \times (-b)$ is written $(-a) (-b).$

$$(-2a)(-3b)(-4c) = (6ab)(-4c) = -24abc.$$
$$(-12a) \div (-4) = \frac{-12a}{-4} = 3a.$$

Exercise XI

Simplify

1. $(+8) \times (-7)$. 2. $(-8) \times (+7)$.

3. $(+8) \times (+7)$. 4. $(-8) \times (-7)$.

5. $(-9) \times (-\frac{1}{3})$. 6. $(+10) \times (-\frac{1}{4})$.

7. $(-3) \times (-4) \times (-5)$. 8. $(+5) \times (-6) \times (-2) \times (+4)$.

9. $(+6) \div (-2)$. 10. $(-10) \div (+5)$.

11. $(-10) \div (-5)$. 12. $(+10) \div (+5)$.

13. $(-3) \div (-1)$. 14. $(-1) \div (+3)$.

15. $(-1) \div (-1)$.

16. $\dfrac{(-8) \times (-4)}{(-2)}$. 17. $\dfrac{(-10)}{(-5) \times (-2)}$.

18. $\dfrac{(-4) \times (-5) \times (-3)}{(+2) \times (-15)}$.

19. $(+x) \times (-y)$. 20. $(-a) \times (+ab)$.

21. $(-7) \times (-3s)$. 22. $(-4p) \times (+3t)$.

23. $(-a) \times (-2b) \times (-3c)$. 24. $(-2a^2)(+4b)$.

25. $(-5m)(-3n)\left(\dfrac{p}{2}\right)$.

26. $(-10x) \div (-5)$. 27. $(-4a)(3b) \div (-6)$.

28. $(12p)(3q) \div (-9r)$. 29. $8ab \div (-4c)$.

30. $(-l)(-m)(-n) \div (-4)$.

Brackets

In addition to their use in connection with directed numbers, brackets are also used as in arithmetic, to show that the expression within the brackets is to be treated as a single number.

We know that $2(7-3)$ means $2 \times (7-3)$.

$2 \times (7-3) = 2 \times 4 = 8$.

$2(7-3)$ might have been evaluated as $2 \times 7 - 2 \times 3$ and $2 \times 7 - 2 \times 3 = 14 - 6 = 8$.

We can say therefore that :

$2(7-3) = 2 \times 7 - 2 \times 3$, illustrating the rule that *when an expression within brackets is multiplied by a number, each term within the brackets is multiplied by the number when the brackets are removed.*

Corresponding examples will show that *when an expression within brackets is divided by a number, each term within the brackets is divided by the number when the brackets are removed.*

NOTE.—In evaluating $2 \times 7 - 2 \times 3$ we have made use of the accepted convention that, when the signs $\times$, $\div$, $+$, $-$ occur without indication of the order in which operations are to be carried out, multiplication and division take precedence over addition and subtraction.

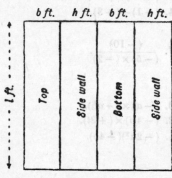

FIG. 3.

Let the figure represent the top, bottom and side walls of a rectangular subway of length l feet, width b feet and height h feet.

Total area
$$= l(b + h + b + h) \text{ sq. ft.}$$
$$= l(2b + 2h) \text{ sq. ft.}$$

Considering each of the smaller rectangles separately, total area $= lb + lh + lb + lh$ sq. ft.

$$= 2lb + 2lh \text{ sq. ft.}$$

$\therefore l(2b + 2h) = 2lb + 2lh$, showing that when the brackets are removed from the expression $l(2b + 2h)$, each number within the bracket is multiplied by l.

If a £1 note is offered to pay for two articles, one of which costs 9s. and the other 7s., the change will be $20 - (9 + 7)$ shillings.

If the articles are paid for separately, the amount remaining will be $20 - 9 - 7$ shillings.

It appears then that $20 - (9 + 7) = 20 - 9 - 7$ and *the effect of the $-$ sign before the brackets is to change the signs within when the brackets are removed.*

Types of brackets in common use are :

$10 - (5 + 3)$, $10 - \overline{5 + 3}$, $10 - \{5 + 3\}$. $10 - [5 + 3]$, the result in each case being $10 - 5 - 3$, or 2.

Example.—Simplify :

(i) $-3(4a - 3b)$ and verify the result when $a = 2$ and $b = -1$.

(ii) $-3p(5p - 4q - 3)$ and verify the result when $p = -3$ and $q = 0$.

(i) $-3(4a - 3b) = -12a + 9b$.

$a = 2$, $b = -1$.

Left side $= -3(8 + 3) = -3 \times 11 = -33$.

Right side $= -24 - 9 = -33$.

∴ result is verified when $a = 2$, $b = -1$.

(ii) $-3p(5p - 4q - 3) = -15p^2 + 12pq + 9p$.

$p = -3$ and $q = 0$.

Left side $= 9(-15 - 0 - 3) = 9(-18) = -162$.

Right side $= -15(-3)^2 + 0 - 27 = -15(9) - 27 = -135 - 27$
$= -162$.

∴ result is verified when $p = -3$ and $q = 0$.

Example.—A rectangular piece of sheet metal is *a* inches long and *b* inches wide ; a piece is to be punched out leaving a frame of width *t* inches. What is the area punched out and what area remains ?

Evaluate the latter when $a = 10$, $b = 8$, $t = 1\frac{1}{2}$.

Sides of hole are $a - 2t$ inches and $b - 2t$ inches.

Area punched out $= (a - 2t)(b - 2t)$ sq. in.

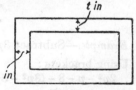

FIG. 4.

Total area $= ab$ sq. in.

∴ area remaining $= ab - (a - 2t)(b - 2t)$ sq. in.

When $a = 10$, $b = 8$, $t = 1\frac{1}{2}$:

area remaining $= 80 - (10 - 3)(8 - 3)$ sq. in. $= 80 - (7)(5)$ sq. in.
$= 80 - 35$ sq. in. $= 45$ sq. in.

Like and Unlike Terms

Many expressions consist partly of like terms and partly of unlike terms and may be simplified.

Example.—Simplify $3x + 5y - 5 - 4x - 7y - x$.

In this expression $3x - 4x - x$ are like terms and also $5y - 7y$.

$$\text{Expression} = 3x - 4x - x + 5y - 7y - 5$$
$$= -2x - 2y - 5.$$

which cannot be further simplified.

Example.—Add $-3xy + 4x - 7$ and $2xy - 8x + 4$.

$$\text{Sum} = -3xy + 4x - 7 + 2xy - 8x + 4$$
$$= -3xy + 2xy + 4x - 8x - 7 + 4$$
$$= -xy - 4x - 3.$$

The expression may be written down as in arithmetic with like terms in columns.

$$-3xy + 4x - 7$$
$$\underline{2xy - 8x + 4}$$
$$-xy - 4x - 3$$

Example.—Simplify $3a - 5b + c - (-4a + 3b - c)$.

Removing the brackets :

$$\text{expression} = 3a - 5b + c + 4a - 3b + c$$
$$= 3a + 4a - 5b - 3b + c + c$$
$$= 7a - 8b + 2c.$$

Example.—Subtract $3p^2 - 5p - 2$ from $2p^2 - p - 8$.

Using brackets :

$$2p^2 - p - 8 - (3p^2 - 5p - 2) = 2p^2 - p - 8 - 3p^2 + 5p + 2$$
$$= -p^2 + 4p - 6.$$

In subtraction the expressions may be written down as in arithmetic :

$$2p^2 - \ p - 8$$
$$\underline{3p^2 - 5p - 2}$$
$$-p^2 + 4p - 6$$

The result shows that we may subtract by changing (mentally) the sign of each term in the lower line and adding. This method is commonly used but a great deal of practice is necessary if mistakes are to be avoided.

When pairs of brackets are used within each other, the inner brackets are removed first.

Example.—Simplify $-2a - \{5a - 8b - (3a - 2b)\}$.

$$\text{Expression} = -2a - \{5a - 8b - 3a + 2b\}$$
$$= -2a - \{2a - 6b\}$$
$$= -2a - 2a + 6b$$
$$= -4a + 6b.$$

Exercise XII

Simplify :

1. $3a - 5a + 8a - 2a$.   2. $-t - 2t - 3t - 4t$.

3. $5p^2 - 8p^2 - 7p^2 + p^2$.   4. $7xy + xy - 5xy$.

5. $a^2b - 2a^2b + 3a^2b$.   6. $abc - 3abc - 6abc$.

7. $-2pq - 5pq + 6pq - 8pq$.   8. $-4k^3 + k^3 + 4k^3 - k^3$.

Simplify :

9. $a - 2b + 3a - b$.

10. $3a + 4b - 2c - 5a - 7b - 6c$.

11. $8ab + 7bc - 6ab - 6bc$.

12. $p^2 + 7p + 6 - 5p^2 - 9p - 11$.

13. $-a - b - c - 2a - 3b - 4c$.

14. $x^3 - 3x^2y + 3xy^2 - y^3 + x^3 + 3x^2y + 3xy^2 + y^3$.

15. $-a - ab - abc + 10abc - 9ab - 8a$.

16. $z^3 - 5z + 8 + 4z^3 + z^2 - 5 + 3z^2 - 4z^2 + 9$.

Simplify :

17. $(3a - 5a) + (8a - 2a)$.

18. $(a - 2b) - (3a - b)$.

19. $5p^2 - 8p^2 - (7p^2 - p^2)$.

20. $-t^2 - 2t - (-7t^2 + 4t)$.

21. $3a + 4b - 2c + (-5a + 7b + 6c)$.

22. $-(-4p^2+8p+4)-(4p^2-8p-4)$.

23. $xy+x+y-(3xy-5x-2y)$.

24. $x^3+x+1-(2x^3+3x+4)$.

25. $-\{2m+2n-(5m+3n)\}$.

26. $3p-\{6q-5r+(2p+3q-5r)\}$.

27. $a-[2b-\{3c-(4a-\overline{5b-6c})\}]$.

28. $p-[p-\{p-(p-2p)\}]$.

Simplify the following expressions and verify the result in each case for the numbers given :

29. $-a(a-b-2)$; $a=3$, $b=-3$.

30. $-2x(x-3y)-3x(4x+2y)$; $x=-2$, $y=-5$.

31. $-a(b-c)-b(c-a)-c(a-b)$; $a=1$, $b=2$, $c=3$.

32. $-3p(p+q^2-1)+q(3pq-q-2)$; $p=0$, $q=-3$.

33. $l(l-2m+3n)-2m(-l+m+n)-3n(l+m-2n)$; $l=-1$. $m=-2$, $n=0$.

34. $-bc(b-c)-ca(c-a)-ab(a-b)$; $a=-4$, $b=3$, $c=3$.

Add :

35. $3x^2-5x+7$ and $-5x^2+5x-9$.

36. $-2p^2-3pq-q^2$ and $-4p^2-2pq-3q^2$.

37. x^3-4x-3, $-2x^2+5x-7$ and $3x^2-11x+8$.

38. $-4x^2+5x-1$, $-x^2-8$ and $-3x-4$.

39. $-2(a^2-3a+2b)$, $4(-2a^2+2a-b)$ and $-3(a^2-a-3b)$.

40. $-3(yz-2zx+xy)$, $-2(-2yz+3zx+xy)$ and $-(yz-2zx-5xy)$.

41. $2a(a-4b-3c)$, $-3a(-a-3b+c)$ and $-(a^2-ab-2ac)$.

42. $k^2(3k-m-2n)$, $-2k^2(4k-3m-4n)$ and $5k^2(k-5m-n)$.

Subtract :

43. $a+3b-2c$ from $4a+5b-6c$.

44. p^2-7p+8 from $-p^2+2p+6$.

45. $a^2+b^2+c^2$ from $a^2-b^2-c^2$.

46. $-(a-b+c)$ from $-a+b+c$.

47. $-(2p+3q-5r)$ from $-(3p+4q-6r)$.

48. $x-\{3x^2-(x-2)\}$ from $2x^2+4x+8$.

49. $yz+zx+xy$ from $-\{2y^2-(3zx-4xy)\}$.

50. $a - \{b - (c - d\overline{-e})\}$ from $-a + \{b - (c + d\overline{-e})\}$.

51. What must be subtracted from $2a(a - b) - b^2$ to give $-a^2 - ab - b^2$?

52. By how much does $3l(l + m) - 4l^2$ exceed $5l^2 - 2l(3l - 2m)$?

In the following examples, assume, where necessary, that the area of a circle of radius r feet is πr^2 sq. ft., where $\pi = \frac{22}{7}$.

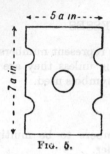

FIG. 5.

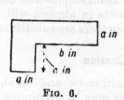

FIG. 6.

53. What is the area of the plate shown in Fig. 5 if each semicircle is of radius a in. and the circular hole is of radius a in. ? Evaluate the result when $a = 2\frac{1}{2}$.

54. Find the area of the section shown in Fig. 6.

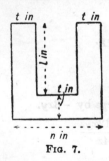

FIG. 7.

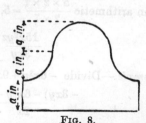

FIG. 8.

55. Find the area of the section shown in Fig. 7 and evaluate in sq. ft. when $n = 11$, $l = 9$ and $t = 1\frac{1}{2}$.

56. Find the area of the section of the moulding shown in Fig. 8, the curves being quarter-circles and a semicircle.

57. The total surface area of a cylinder of height h ft. and radius r ft. is $2\pi r(r+h)$ sq. ft. What is the total surface area of a cylinder of height 15 cm. and radius 11 cm. ?

58. $\pi(r_1+r_2)(r_1-r_2)$ sq. ft. is the area of a circular ring cut from sheet metal, r_1 feet and r_2 feet being the external and internal radii respectively. What is the area of a ring of external radius $7\frac{1}{4}$ in. and of width $\frac{3}{4}$ in. ?

ALGEBRAIC PROCESSES

It is again emphasized that symbols represent numbers and statements in algebra will not be true unless they are true when numbers are substituted for the symbols used.

Multiplication

In arithmetic and in algebra, numbers to be multiplied together may be multiplied in any order.

$$ac \times bd = abcd.$$
$$bc \times b = b \times bc = b^2c.$$
$$pq(ap - bq) = ap^2q - bpq^2.$$

Division

As in arithmetic $\dfrac{5 \times \cancel{2} \times \cancel{7}}{\cancel{2} \times \cancel{7}} = 5$, so $\dfrac{p\cancel{q}\cancel{z}}{\cancel{q}\cancel{z}} = p.$

$$\frac{15x^2yz}{3xy} = 5xz.$$

Example.—Divide $-6x^2y + 9xy^2 - 12xyz$ by $-3xy$.

$$-3xy) \underline{\;-6x^2y + 9xy^2 - 12xyz\;}$$
$$\qquad\quad 2x \quad -3y \quad +4z$$

Highest Common Factor and Lowest Common Multiple

The methods for finding H.C.F. and L.C.M. in algebra are the same as those used in arithmetic when the numbers are expressed in prime factors.

Consider the numbers $10ab^2c$, $5abc^2$, $15abcd$.

$10ab^2c = 2 \times 5 \times a \times b \times b \times c.$
$5abc^2 \ = 5 \times a \times b \times c \times c.$
$15abcd = 3 \times 5 \times a \times b \times c \times d.$
H.C.F. $= 5 \times a \times b \times c = 5abc.$
L.C.M. $= 2 \times 3 \times 5 \times a \times b^2 \times c^2 \times d = 30ab^2c^2d.$

Fractions

Corresponding examples in arithmetic and algebra are shown side by side.

$$\frac{2}{5} + \frac{1}{3}$$

$$= \frac{2 \times 3 + 5}{15}$$

$$= \frac{11}{15}.$$

$$\frac{2}{a} + \frac{1}{b}$$

$$= \frac{2b + a}{ab}.$$ This expression cannot be further simplified, but it would generally be written $\frac{a + 2b}{ab}$, as it is usual to write the symbols in alphabetical order.

$$\frac{5}{12} - \frac{1}{21} + \frac{2}{28}$$

$$= \frac{5 \times 7 - 4 + 2 \times 3}{3 \times 4 \times 7}$$

$$= \frac{37}{84}$$

$$\frac{p}{bc} - \frac{q}{ca} + \frac{r}{ab}$$

$$= \frac{pa - qb + rc}{abc}$$

or $\frac{ap - bq + cr}{abc}$,

which cannot be further simplified.

Exercise XIII

Simplify the following expressions :

1. $xy \times xz.$

2. $4ac \times 5bcd.$

3. $6a^2 \times 7ab^3.$

4. $9p^3q \times \dfrac{pq^2}{6}.$

5. $lm \times 2mn \times 3nl.$

6. $\dfrac{r^2s}{5} \times 20rst \times \dfrac{t}{2}.$

7. $lm(-2al+3bm)$.   **8.** $-4xy(3xy-2x+4y)$.

9. $2ab(a^2-2ab+b^2)-a(3a^2b-4ab^2)$.

10. $10abc \div 5ab$.   **11.** $10a^3 \div 5a^2$.   **12.** $21p^2q \div 14p$.

13. $16r^2s^2t \div 12r^2s$.   **14.** $3e^2f \div \dfrac{ef}{5}$.

15. $\dfrac{8xy \times 5yz}{20xyz}$.   **16.** $\dfrac{3a^2b \times 4abc \times 14bcd}{6ab \times 7cd}$.

Divide :

17. $3p^2-6pq$ by $-3p$.   **18.** $4a^2-10ab-6ac$ by $-2a$.

19. $8x^3-16x^2-12x$ by $-4x$.

20. $-25x^2y-20xy^2+5xy$ by $5xy$.

21. $-32a^2b+16ab^2-24abc$ by $-8ab$.

22. $-6l^2m+lm^2$ by $-3lm$.   **23.** $2f^3-3f^2g-7f^2h$ by $-7f^2$.

24. $-6x(2x^2-5xy+3xz)$ by $-4x^2$.

Find the H.C.F. and L.C.M. of :

25. $2ab, 5a$.   **26.** $5p^2q, 15pq$.   **27.** $12x^2yz, 18xz$.

28. $4a^2bc, 15ab^2c, 20abc^2$.   **29.** $12, 6x, 4xy, 6xy^2$.

30. $10pq, -5p, -10p^2$.   **31.** $-14r^2, -6rs, -2s^2$.

32. $-3a^2bc, 9ab^2c, -6abcd, 3bcd^2$.

Simplify :

33. $\dfrac{a}{3} - \dfrac{a}{4} + \dfrac{a}{5}$.   **34.** $\dfrac{2p}{q} - \dfrac{3p}{q}$.   **35.** $\dfrac{3}{x} - \dfrac{4}{x} - \dfrac{7}{2x}$.

36. $\dfrac{2}{y} - \dfrac{3}{4y}$.   **37.** $\dfrac{4}{3u} - \dfrac{2}{5v}$.   **38.** $\dfrac{3a}{2b} - \dfrac{5b}{6a}$.

39. $\dfrac{2a}{5b} - \dfrac{3a}{10b} - \dfrac{4}{15}$.   **40.** $2a - \dfrac{3b}{5c}$.   **41.** $-2p - \dfrac{q}{12} + \dfrac{5}{18}$.

42. $\dfrac{2a}{bc} - \dfrac{3b}{ca} - \dfrac{4c}{ab}$.   **43.** $-\dfrac{2x}{3yz} - \dfrac{y}{6zx} + \dfrac{5z}{9xy}$.

44. $\dfrac{x-1}{4} + \dfrac{2}{3}$.   **45.** $\dfrac{2p-3}{5} - \dfrac{p}{10}$.   **46.** $\dfrac{p-q}{3p} - \dfrac{p}{6q}$.

47. $\dfrac{x-1}{4} + \dfrac{x-2}{3}$.   **48.** $\dfrac{2x-3}{10} + \dfrac{3x-1}{15}$.   **49.** $\dfrac{x-2}{4} + \dfrac{5}{6x}$.

50. $\dfrac{x-1}{2} - \dfrac{x-2}{?}$.   **51.** $\dfrac{2x-1}{8} - \dfrac{x-1}{12}$.   **52.** $\dfrac{3x-2}{10} - \dfrac{4x+3}{15}$.

53. $-\dfrac{2x+5}{12}+\dfrac{3x-1}{18}$. **54.** $-\dfrac{x-2}{14}-\dfrac{x-3}{21}$.

55. $-\dfrac{2x-1}{15}-\dfrac{3x+2}{20}$.

56. A motorist travels 100 miles at an average speed of $4p$ miles an hour and the return journey at an average speed of $5p$ miles an hour. What is the total time taken ?

57. If a motorist averages a miles an hour over a journey and b miles an hour over the return journey, what is his average speed for the whole distance ?

58. A tank holding 50 gallons is filled by two pipes, one of which delivers $2x$ gallons in 3 minutes and the other $3x$ gallons in 4 minutes. How many gallons are delivered per minute and how long will it take to fill the tank ?

59. A tank holding a gallons is filled by two pipes, one delivering 1 gallon in x seconds and the other 3 gallons in $2x$ seconds. How many gallons are delivered per second and how long will it take to fill the tank ?

60. A wireless dealer sells sets at £p and £q each, the cost prices being £a and £b respectively. What percentage profit on the cost price has he made after selling 2 sets at £p and 4 sets at £q ? Evaluate your result when $a = 8$, $b = 10$, $p = 10\frac{1}{2}$, $q = 13\frac{1}{2}$.

61. In turning a cylinder a fraction $\dfrac{1}{g}$ of the metal is removed and then $\dfrac{1}{r}$ of the remainder. What fraction of the original metal now remains ?

62. In estimating for a job, a firm charges a man's time as n hours at a shillings an hour, £c for materials and then adds on 10%. What is the total cost and what percentage of this total cost is for labour ?

CHAPTER IV

FURTHER EQUATIONS

Example.—Find the Fahrenheit temperature in a refrigerator with a temperature of $-6°$ Centigrade, given that C° Centigrade corresponds to F° Fahrenheit, where $C = \frac{5}{9}(F - 32)$.

Substituting -6 for C, we have the equation:
$$-6 = \tfrac{5}{9}(F - 32).$$

Multiply each side by 9.

$$-54 = 5(F - 32).$$
Removing brackets $\quad -54 = 5F - 160.$
Add 54 to each side. $\qquad 0 = 5F - 106.$

Subtract 5F from each side.

$$-5F = -106.$$

Multiply each side by -1.

$$5F = 106.$$

Divide each side by 5.

$$F = \tfrac{106}{5} = 21 \cdot 2.$$

$\therefore$ temperature is $21 \cdot 2°$ Fahrenheit.

Check:

Left side of equation $= -6$.
When $F = 21 \cdot 2$:
Right side $= \tfrac{5}{9}(21 \cdot 2 - 32) = \tfrac{5}{9}(-10 \cdot 8) = -\tfrac{54}{9} = -6.$
Since each side $= -6$, solution is verified.

It will be found that with practice, some of the intermediate steps in the solution may be omitted. We have illustrated above a rule commonly used in solving equations, viz. a term may be taken from one side of an equation to the other *provided that the sign of the term is changed*.

Consider the equation $a = b - x$.

Adding x to each side we obtain $a + x = b$. The $-x$ on the right-hand side of the original equation has become $+x$ on the left-hand side of the new equation.

Consider also the equation $a = b + x$.

Subtracting x from each side, $a - x = b$. The $+x$ on the right-hand side of the original equation has become $-x$ on the left-hand side of the new equation.

In the equation $a = b - x$, multiply each side by -1 and we have $-a = -b + x$, which is equivalent to changing all the signs in the original equation. When this is done care must be taken to see that *all* the signs are changed.

Example.—Solve $3(x-5)-2(x+7)=4(x-2)$.

Removing brackets,

$$3x-15-2x-14=4x-8$$

Adding $15+14$ to each side and subtracting $4x$ from each side,

$$3x-2x-4x=-8+15+14$$
$$\therefore 3x-6x=-8+29$$
$$\therefore -3x=21$$

Dividing each side by -3,

$$x=-7.$$

Check. When $x=-7$:

Left side $=3(-7-5)-2(-7+7)$
$$=3(-12)-2(0)=-36.$$

Right side $=4(-7-2)=4(-9)=-36.$

$\therefore$ when $x=-7$, left side $=$ right side.

Example.—Solve $5-\dfrac{3x-1}{4}=\dfrac{7-x}{3}-\dfrac{7x-5}{8}.$

The L.C.M. of the denominators 4, 3, 8 is 24.
Multiply each side of the equation by 24 :

$$120-6(3x-1)=8(7-x)-3(7x-5).$$

Removing brackets,

$$120-18x+6=56-8x-21x+15$$
$$\therefore -18x+8x+21x=56+15-120-6$$
$$-18x+29x=71-126$$
$$11x=-55$$
$$\therefore x=-5.$$

Check. When $x=-5$:

Left side $=5-\dfrac{-15-1}{4}=5-\dfrac{-16}{4}=5+4=9.$

Right side

$$= \frac{7+5}{3} - \frac{7(-5)-5}{8} = \frac{12}{3} - \frac{-35-5}{8} = 4 - \frac{-40}{8} = 4+5 = 9.$$

∴ when $x = -5$, left side = right side.

Example.—The pressure p gm. per sq. cm. and the volume v c.c. of a certain quantity of a gas are connected with the temperature $t°$ C. by the formula $\frac{pv}{273+t} = 12\cdot4$. Find the temperature when $p = 65$ and $v = 62$.

Substituting in the formula, we obtain the equation for t,

$$\frac{65 \times 62}{273+t} = 12\cdot4$$

i.e. $\frac{4030}{273+t} = 12\cdot4$.

Multiplying each side by $273 + t$,

$$4030 = 12\cdot4(273+t)$$

Dividing each side by $12\cdot4$,

$$325 = 273 + t$$
$$\therefore 325 - 273 = t$$
$$\therefore 52 = t.$$

∴ Temperature is $52°$ C.

NOTE.—The answer asked should always be given and not merely the value of the unknown in the equation when found.

Exercise XIV

Solve the following equations and check your solutions in each case :

1. $3(x+4) - 5(x-1) = 19$.   2. $5(2y-7) - 4(3y+1) = -45$.

3. $3(r-7) - 4(2r+11) - 5(5r-13) = 0$.

4. $0 = 7p + 4 - 4(2p-1) - 3(3p+11)$.

5. $4(1-2a) - 3(4-3a) + 5a - 14 = 0$.

6. $\frac{1}{2}(x-1) + \frac{1}{3}(2x-3) = 1$.

7. $\frac{1}{2}(3t-1) - \frac{1}{5}(4t-2) = t.$

8. $\frac{3s-5}{5} - \frac{s-3}{4} - \frac{2s+4}{3} = 0.$

9. $\frac{3a-1}{4} - \frac{a+1}{6} = 1 + \frac{a}{2}.$

10. $\frac{2b+1}{5} - \frac{3b+4}{10} = 2 - \frac{1}{4}(1-3b).$

11. $\frac{1}{4x} - \frac{1}{5x} = \frac{3}{20}.$

12. $\frac{4}{7k} - \frac{3}{5k} - 2 = 0.$

13. $\frac{5}{3r} - \frac{1}{4} = \frac{2}{5r} - \frac{7}{12}.$

14. $2k(k-1) - 3(2k-7) = k(2k-5).$

15. $\frac{10l-3}{5} = \frac{4l^2-7}{2l}.$

16. $5\left(\frac{c}{3}-2\right) - 2\left(\frac{c}{4}-3\right) = \frac{c}{2}+4.$

17. $0.3(2d-3) + 0.7(6d+5) = 0.$

18. $\frac{2f+1}{\cdot 3} - \frac{\cdot 5f-1}{\cdot 2} + 1 = 0.$

19. The following equation occurs in connection with gear ratios on a gun lathe, $\frac{R}{H} = \frac{A}{2\cdot25-A}$, where R = number of teeth in rack gear, H = number of teeth in helical gear and A in. = movement of support. Find the movement when $\frac{R}{H} = 3$.

20. In the case of haulage of one vehicle by a second, $C = \frac{M_1 V}{M_1 + M_2}$, where C ft. per sec. is the common speed after motion begins, V ft. per sec. is the speed of one vehicle before the rope becomes taut, and the vehicles weigh M_2 tons and M_1 tons respectively. Find M_2 when $C = \cdot06$, $V = \cdot15$ and $M_1 = 7$.

21. The equation $\frac{I}{M} = \frac{r-c}{r(c-1)}$ occurs in connection with gear trains for changeable speed ratios, r being the ratio of the speeds of two shafts. Calculate r when $I = 21$, $M = 12$, $c = 1\cdot24$.

22. When n cells are connected in series, the current C ampères is given by $C = \frac{nE}{R+nr}$, where E volts is the E.M.F. and r ohms the internal resistance of each cell and R ohms the external resistance. Find n when $C = 0\cdot9$, $E = 1\cdot7$, $R = 5\cdot5$ and $r = 1\cdot1$.

23. In the lens formula $\frac{k}{v} - \frac{1}{u} = \frac{k-1}{r}$, k is the refractive index of the glass. Find the refractive index if $v = 15$ when $u = 18$ and $r = 12$.

24. If $\dfrac{3x-11}{4} - \dfrac{2x-23}{5}$ and $\dfrac{5x+3}{6} - 3$ are equal, show that each expression is equal to 5.

25. 240 workpeople are employed in a factory, the men earning 11s. 6d. and the women 8s. 6d. a day each. If wages amount to £114 a day, find the number of men and of women employed.

26. A motorist covered half his journey at an average speed of 30 m.p.h., one third of the journey at an average speed of 25 m.p.h. and the remainder at an average speed of 15 m.p.h. If the total time taken was $9\frac{1}{4}$ hours, find the distance gone at an average speed of 25 m.p.h.

27. If I walk down a moving escalator, I can reach the bottom in 16 seconds if I take 28 steps, and in 24 seconds if I walk slowly taking 22 steps. How many steps must I take if the escalator is stationary and how long would it take me to reach the bottom when moving if I took 10 steps ?

28. A dealer sells dry batteries at 2s. each more than they cost him. He later receives a discount of 10% on the cost price and by selling at the same price as previously makes a profit of $33\frac{1}{3}\%$ of the new cost price. What is the selling price ?

29. If I walk to the station at 4 m.p.h. I shall be there 2 min. before the train is due, but if I walk at 3 m.p.h. I shall be $\frac{1}{2}$ min. late. How far is it to the station and how far must I walk at 3 m.p.h. to arrive there just on time ?

30. Brass is an alloy of copper and zinc. How many c.c. of each metal must be used in a total volume of 100 c.c. if there is a shrinkage of 3% in the process of making the alloy, given that sp. gr. of copper = 8·94, sp. gr. of zinc = 7·19, sp. gr. of brass = 8·49 ?

Transformation of formulæ

A formula is usually given in some standard form, but for the purposes of a particular problem it may be helpful to express it differently.

We know that the circumference of a circle C in. is given by the formula $C = 2\pi r$, where r in. is the radius of the circle. Suppose now we know the circumference and wish to find the radius.

$$C = 2\pi r.$$

Dividing each side by 2π,

$$\frac{C}{2\pi} = r \quad \text{or} \quad r = \frac{C}{2\pi},$$

and we have expressed r in terms of C.

The methods used in transforming a formula are those used in solving equations.

It should be emphasized that the letter required must appear isolated on one side in the final statement.

Example.—In a block and tackle, the power P lb. wt. and the load W lb. wt. are connected by the relation $P = aW + b$, where a and b are constants.

Express W in terms of P.

$$P = aW + b$$
$$\therefore -aW = b - P$$
$$\therefore aW = P - b$$
$$\therefore W = \frac{P - b}{a}.$$

In expressing W in terms of the other symbols, we are said to make W the " subject " of the formula.

Example.—In the relation $C = \frac{5}{9}(F - 32)$ connecting Centigrade and Fahrenheit temperatures, make F the subject of the formula.

$$C = \tfrac{5}{9}(F - 32).$$

Multiplying each side by 9,

$$9C = 5(F - 32).$$

Removing the brackets,

$$9C = 5F - 160$$
$$\therefore -5F = -9C - 160$$
$$\therefore 5F = 9C + 160$$
$$\therefore F = \tfrac{9}{5}C + 32.$$

Example.—From the formula $C = \frac{nE}{R + nr}$ giving the current

3

supplied by a number of cells connected in series, express n in terms of the other symbols.

$$C = \frac{nE}{R + nr}.$$

Multiplying each side by $R + nr$,

$$C(R + nr) = nE.$$

Removing the brackets,

$$CR + Cnr = nE.$$

Writing the terms containing n on one side of the equation,

$$Cnr - nE = -CR$$
$$\text{or } nE - nCr = CR$$
$$* \therefore n(E - Cr) = CR.$$

Dividing each side by $E - Cr$,

$$n = \frac{CR}{E - Cr}.$$

* NOTE.—When a number n is multiplied in succession by several different numbers, we can express the resulting numbers by which n is multiplied by using brackets. Thus :

$$na + nb = n(a + b).$$

Exercise XV

1. If l in. be the length and b in. the breadth of a rectangle of area 5 sq. in., $lb = 5$. Express b in terms of l.

2. If k kilometres $= m$ miles, $k = \frac{8}{5} m$. Express m in terms of k.

3. Make C the subject of the formula $F = 32 + \frac{9C}{5}$. Find C from the given formula when $F = 212$ and also from your new formula and hence check your result.

4. The formula $I = \frac{V}{R}$ refers to a current I amp. passing through a resistance R ohms with a potential difference V volts. Express (i) R in terms of I and V ; (ii) V in terms of I and R.

5. The resistances in a Wheatstone bridge are connected by the relation $\dfrac{R_1}{R_2} = \dfrac{R_3}{R_4}$. Make (i) R_3, (ii) R_4 the subject of the formula. Evaluate R_4 from the original formula and from your new formula when $R_1 = 15$, $R_2 = 10$, $R_3 = 27$.

6. From Huyghen's formula for the length of a circular arc $l = \dfrac{8h-c}{3}$, express h in terms of l and c.

7. The area s sq. cm. of the surface of a cylinder of radius r cm. and height h cm. is given by $s = 2\pi r(r+h)$. Find h when $s = 528$ and $r = 7$, assuming that $\pi = \frac{22}{7}$.

Express h in terms of s and r and again find h, using your new formula.

8. The efficiency of a differential pulley is given by $E = \dfrac{(a-b)W}{2aP}$. Express a in terms of the other symbols.

9. If a particle at the end of a string be describing complete vertical circles, the tension when the particle is at the highest point is given by $T = \dfrac{m}{r}(u^2 - 5gr)$. Express r in terms of the other symbols.

10. The velocity-ratio of a differential pulley is given by $n = \dfrac{2a}{a-b}$. Express (i) b, (ii) a as the subject of the formula.

11. In the formula $\dfrac{pv}{273+t} = k$ relating to the pressure, volume and temperature of a gas, make t the subject of the formula.

12. If r ohms and s ohms are two resistances connected in parallel, the equivalent resistance R ohms is given by $\dfrac{1}{R} = \dfrac{1}{r} + \dfrac{1}{s}$. Find s when $R = 3$ and $r = 5$.

Express s in terms of R and r and again find s.

13. In the girder formula $w = \dfrac{lrW}{kf - lr}$, make (i) k, (ii) r the subject of the formula.

14. From the gear train formula $\dfrac{I}{M} = \dfrac{r-e}{r(c-1)}$, calculate c when $I = 24$, $M = 18$, $r = 2{\cdot}4$.

Make c the subject of the formula and again calculate its value. Also make r the subject.

15. In the lens formula $\dfrac{k}{v} - \dfrac{1}{u} = \dfrac{k-1}{r}$ make (i) k, (ii) u, (iii) v, the subject of the formula.

Simultaneous equations

Two chromium-plate handles and 1 door plate costs $1s.\ 9d.$; for 3 handles and 2 plates the cost is $3s.\ 0d.$ What is the cost for a handle and a plate ?

Let x pence be the cost for 1 handle and y pence the cost for 1 plate.

Then 2 handles and 1 plate cost $2x + y$ pence and since $1s.\ 9d.$ $= 21$ pence,

$$\therefore\ 2x + y = 21.$$

In this equation, if we substitute a value for x, we can find a corresponding value for y; e.g. if we substitute 2 for x :

$$4 + y = 21,\ \therefore\ y = 17.$$

In this way we can draw up a table of corresponding values of x and y :

x	2	4	6	8	10
y	17	13	9	5	1

But we also know that for 3 handles and 2 plates the cost is $3s.\ 0d.$

$$\therefore\ 3x + 2y = 36.$$

A table for corresponding values of x and y in this case will be :

x	2	4	6	8	10
y	15	12	9	6	3

From the two tables, the only common solution is $x = 6$, $y = 9$.

We now say that the equations $2x + y = 21$, $3x + 2y = 36$ are simultaneously (i.e. at the same time) true when $x = 6$, $y = 9$.

The cost for a handle is therefore $6d.$ and for a plate $9d.$

It is not necessary to draw up tables when we wish to solve

a pair of simultaneous equations, in fact, this method would be difficult when the solutions are not integers.

Two methods, either of which may be used, are shown below.

Example.—Solve $4x + 2y = 2$;
$$7x + 3y = 5.$$

Solution by elimination.
$$4x + 2y = 2 ; \quad (1)$$
$$7x + 3y = 5. \quad (2)$$

In dealing with several equations we number them on the right as shown.

We form an equation in x only, i.e. we eliminate y, as follows.

Multiply each side of (1) by 3, i.e. by the coefficient of y in (2) :
$$12x + 6y = 6.$$

Multiply each side of (2) by 2, i.e. by the coefficient of y in (1) :
$$14x + 6y = 10.$$

By subtraction,
$$-2x = -4$$
$$\therefore x = 2.$$

Substituting in (2),
$$14 + 3y = 5$$
$$\therefore 3y = -9$$
$$\therefore y = -3.$$
$$x = 2, \ y = -3. \quad \textbf{Answer.}$$

We should have obtained the same results if we had first found y by eliminating x.

Check : Substituting the values found in (1),
$$4x + 2y = 8 - 6 = 2.$$

NOTE.—Since we used (2) to find y, we must check by substituting in (1) *not* (2).

Solution by substitution.

$$4x + 2y = 2; \quad \textbf{(1)}$$
$$7x + 3y = 5. \quad \textbf{(2)}$$

From (1):

$$2y = 2 - 4x$$
$$\therefore y = 1 - 2x. \quad \textbf{(3)}$$

Substituting this value of y in (2),

$$7x + 3(1 - 2x) = 5.$$

Removing brackets,

$$7x + 3 - 6x = 5$$
$$\therefore x = 5 - 3 = 2.$$

Substituting in (3),

$$y = 1 - 4 = -3.$$
$$x = 2, \quad y = -3. \quad \textbf{Answer.}$$

The same results would have been obtained if the value of x in terms of y from (1), viz. $x = \dfrac{1}{2} - \dfrac{y}{2}$, had been substituted in (2); in this case y would have been found first.

Example.—Solve :

$$3x - 5y = 8; \quad \textbf{(1)}$$
$$5x + 7y = -25. \quad \textbf{(2)}$$

Multiply each side of (1) by 7 :

$$21x - 35y = 56.$$

Multiply each side of (2) by 5 :

$$25x + 35y = -125.$$

By addition,

$$46x = -69$$
$$\therefore x = -\frac{69}{46} = -\frac{3}{2}.$$

Substituting in (2),

$$\frac{-15}{2} + 7y = -25.$$

$$7y = -25 + \frac{15}{2} = -\frac{35}{2}.$$

$$\therefore y = -\frac{5}{2}.$$

Solution $x = -1\frac{1}{2}$, $y = -2\frac{1}{2}$.

Example.—In a machine the load W lb. and the effort P lb. are connected by the relation $W = a + bP$, where a and b are constants. If $P = 3$ when $W = 16$ and $P = 6$ when $W = 29\cdot5$, find the load when the effort is 10 lb.

Substituting $P = 3$ and $W = 16$ in the given relation:

$$16 = a + 3b. \quad (1)$$

Substituting $P = 6$ and $W = 29\cdot5$:

$$29\cdot5 = a + 6b. \quad (2)$$

By subtraction,

$$-13\cdot5 = -3b$$
$$\therefore 3b = 13\cdot5$$
$$\therefore b = 4\cdot5.$$

Substituting in (1),

$$16 = a + 13\cdot5$$
$$\therefore a = 2\cdot5.$$

The law of the machine is therefore:

$$W = 2\cdot5 + 4\cdot5P.$$

When $P = 10$, $W = 2\cdot5 + 4\cdot5 \times 10 = 47\cdot5$.
$\therefore$ the required load is 47·5 lb.

Exercise XVI

Solve the following pairs of simultaneous equations and check your solution in each case :

1. $3x + 4y = 11.$
   $2x + 5y = 12.$

2. $5a + 2b = 16.$
   $7a - 2b = 32.$

3. $-8p + 3q = 17.$
$\quad 2p - 5q = 0.$

4. $7r + 11s = -16\frac{1}{2}.$
$\quad 4r - 5s = 7\frac{1}{2}.$

5. $l + 7m = -30.$
$\quad l - 18m = 1\frac{1}{4}.$

6. $3c + 2d = -1.$
$\quad 4d = 19 + c.$

7. $p = \frac{3}{4}q - 11.$
$\quad p = \dfrac{5q}{2} - 25.$

8. $3x - 7y = 5x - 3y + 1 = 18.$

9. $4y + 7z - 2 = 2y - 5z = 3y.$

10. $\dfrac{p}{3} + \dfrac{2q}{5} = 1.$
$\quad \dfrac{p}{6} - \dfrac{q}{10} = 2.$

11. $\dfrac{1}{x} + \dfrac{1}{y} = \dfrac{3}{4}.$
$\quad \dfrac{2}{x} + \dfrac{3}{y} = \dfrac{7}{4}.$

12. $\dfrac{3}{a} - \dfrac{2}{b} = -2.$
$\quad \dfrac{9}{a} + \dfrac{4}{b} = 14.$

$\left[\text{NOTE.—Solve first for } \dfrac{1}{x} \text{ and } \dfrac{1}{y}.\right]$

13. When a wire of length l inches is stretched by a weight of W lb., $l = c + k\text{W}$, where c and k are constants. When the weight is 2 lb. the length is 19·5 in. and when the weight is 8 lb. the length is 19·8 in. Find c and k and the length when the weight is 11 lb. ; find also the weight when the length is 20 in.

14. The Reaumur temperature R° and the Fahrenheit temperature F° are connected by a relation of the form $\text{R} = c\text{F} + h$. On the Reaumur scale the freezing and boiling points of water are 0° and 80° respectively ; on the Fahrenheit scale they are 32° and 212°. Find the Fahrenheit temperature corresponding to 60° R.

15. The weight of oil W lb. used in an oil engine test and the brake horse-power H were connected by the relation $\text{W} = m\text{H} + c$. When H was 2·1, W was 2·06, and when H was 4·7, W was 4·40. Find the value of W when H was 4·2 and the value of H when W was 4·90.

16. When a car is accelerating, the distance s miles travelled in t hours is given by $s = at + bt^2$. If $s = 1$ when $t = \frac{1}{30}$ and $s = 1\frac{3}{4}$ when $t = \frac{1}{20}$, find a and b.
What is the distance travelled in 4 minutes ?

17. The resistance R ohms of a wire at $t°$ C. is given by $\text{R} = \text{R}_0(1 + at)$, where R_0 ohms is the resistance at 0° C. The resistance is 19·5 ohms at a temperature of 50° C. and 25·8 ohms at 120° C. Find R_0 and a. Hence determine the temperature when the resistance is 22·2 ohms.

18. In a canteen there were a number of packets of cigarettes at 1s. a packet and a number of ounce packets of tobacco at 9d. an oz. The total number of packets was 84 and the total value was £3 15s. How many ounces of tobacco were there ?

19. There were 150 students in attendance at an evening technical school ; some attended two evenings a week for 3 hours an evening and the others three evenings a week for $2\frac{1}{2}$ hours an evening. If the total number of student-hours in a week was $1042\frac{1}{2}$, how many attended two evenings a week ?

[NOTE.—If 10 students attended 2 evenings for 3 hours the number of student-hours would be 60.]

20. At a shooting range you pay 2d. for a miss and receive 6d. for a hit. If you are poorer by 2s. 4d. after thirty shots, how many hits do you make ?

21. When wires are connected in series, the equivalent resistance is the sum of the resistances of the separate wires.

Three wires each of resistance x ohms and four each of resistance y ohms are connected in series and the equivalent resistance is 20·2 ohms ; when two of the former and five of the latter are connected in series, the equivalent resistance is 21·4 ohms. Find x and y.

22. When wires of resistances p, q, r ohms respectively are connected in parallel the equivalent resistance R ohms is given by

$$\frac{1}{R} = \frac{1}{p} + \frac{1}{q} + \frac{1}{r}.$$

Two wires each of resistance x ohms and three each of resistance y ohms are connected in parallel and the equivalent resistance is $\frac{1}{4}$ ohm ; when three of the former and two of the latter are connected in parallel the equivalent resistance is $\frac{6}{13}$ ohms. Find x and y.

23. The wages of a workman and his mate are in the ratio $2 : 1$; their weekly expenditures are in the ratio $13 : 6$. If each saves five shillings a week, find their weekly wages.

24. If a template be in the form of a trapezium with parallel sides of lengths a inches and b inches respectively at a distance h inches apart, its area is $\frac{1}{2}(a+b)h$ sq. in. and its centre of gravity divides the distance between them in the ratio $\dfrac{a+2b}{2a+b}$. In a particular case the area was 20 sq. in., the parallel sides were 4 in. apart and the centre of gravity divided the distance between them in the ratio $\frac{4}{7}$. What were the lengths of the parallel sides ?

3*

CHAPTER V

GRAPHS

The diagram shows the curve traced by a self-recording barometer during a week in July ; it shows the atmospheric pressure measured in inches of mercury at any time during the week.

Along the line across the page are marked times during the week ; along the vertical line are marked numbers which give the pressure in inches of mercury.

Suppose we take a point, e.g. A on the curve, vertically

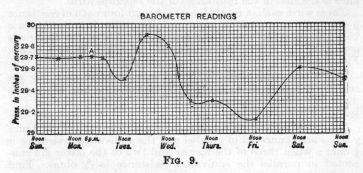

FIG. 9.

above Monday, 6 p.m., on the horizontal line. This point A is at the same horizontal level as the graduation 29·7 on the vertical scale. We are therefore able to say that at 6 p.m. on Monday the atmospheric pressure was 29·7 inches of mercury.

The curve shows us that the barometer was fairly "steady" (little change in atmospheric pressure) from noon on Sunday to midnight on Monday, that there was then a rapid fall until just before noon on Tuesday followed by a still more rapid rise until midnight ; after this there was a fall till noon on Friday excepting for a few hours on Thursday morning.

Assuming that a steady barometer means dependable weather, we may expect that there was little change in the weather from noon on Sunday to midnight on Monday, but afterwards it was changeable with probable rain between midnight on Tuesday and noon on Friday as rain is generally associated with a falling barometer.

Consider now the diagram below.

This diagram shows the numbers of therms of gas used in a house for heating purposes during each week in a quarter.

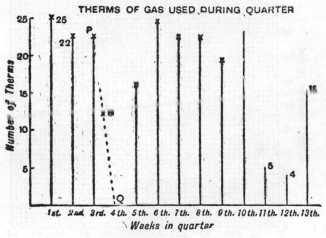

THERMS OF GAS USED DURING QUARTER

Fig. 10.

The uprights show that in the first week 25 therms were used, in the second 22 therms, and so on; in the eleventh week 5 therms, in the twelfth week 4, and in the last week of the quarter 15 therms. We might deduce that in the quarter of the year in question, the number of therms likely to be used in a normal week would be 22, that the house was probably closed during the fourth week, and that there was very likely a warm spell during the eleventh and twelfth weeks.

It will be noticed that in this case the ends of the uprights are not connected by a continuous curve. This is because such a curve would have little or no meaning. Suppose, for example, we connected the points P and Q and considered a point B on this line. If this point signified anything, it would signify that some therms were used during part of the fourth week, whereas we know that no therms were used during this week.

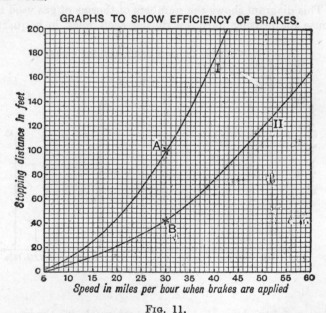

GRAPHS TO SHOW EFFICIENCY OF BRAKES.

Stopping distance in feet

Speed in miles per hour when brakes are applied

Fig. 11.

It will be seen that in diagrams such as we are considering much more information can be obtained when the points may be connected by a curve showing the *continuous* change of some quantity which has been measured. Such curves we call *graphs*. They are usually drawn on squared paper as this saves time in drawing and makes the reading of values easier.

The graphs above show the distances in which the same

car can be stopped by two different types of brakes applied at speeds up to 60 m.p.h.

A graph should have a definite heading, as in this case—" Graphs to show Efficiency of Brakes."

Every graph shows a relation between two sets of numbers. One set can be chosen in an experiment and the second set follows from observation. The values which can be chosen are always plotted from left to right across the page and the resulting observed values along the uprights.

Consider the graphs above. The speeds at which the brakes are applied can be chosen and these values are plotted from left to right. The distances in which the car stops are then observed and these values are plotted along the uprights.

The point A on the curve I is above the mark 30 on the horizontal line. This shows that the brakes were applied when the car was travelling at 30 m.p.h. A is in line with the mark 100 on the upright, which shows that the car travelled 100 feet before stopping.

The point B on curve II shows that in the second case, if the brakes are applied when the car is travelling at 30 m.p.h. it can be stopped in 42 feet.

Axes

The horizontal and vertical lines along which the numbers are marked are called *axes*. Each axis should be labelled—in this case " Speed in miles per hour when brakes are applied " and " Stopping distance in feet."

Scale

The number of units represented by unit length along an axis is the *scale*, e.g. 1 inch could represent 4 hours, or 1 cm. represent 10° Centigrade.

Scales should be chosen which will allow intermediate readings to be determined rapidly and scale divisions to represent 3 or 7 units should therefore be avoided.

The chosen scales should be as large as the paper will

permit, bearing in mind that all necessary points on the curve must be included. Scales on the two axes will often not be the same ; they will depend on the range of values it is necessary to represent on each axis.

The scale divisions must be clearly marked at convenient regular intervals along the axes.

Origin

The point where the axes intersect is called the *origin*. The origin is on both axes but it need not necessarily represent the same number on each ; this again will depend on the range of values included. In the case above, the origin is at 5 along the horizontal axis and at 0 along the vertical axis.

Example.—In an experiment on belt friction, the values of the end tension, T lb. wt., and the corresponding values of the angle of lap, *θ radians, are shown in the table, the initial tension in each case being 10 lb. wt. Draw a graph showing the relation between T and θ and hence find the tension when the angle of lap is 2·2 radians and the angle of lap when the tension is 49 lb. wt.

θ (radians) ..	0·5	1	1·5	2	2·5	3
T (lb. wt.) ..	13·5	18	24·5	33	45	60·5

[* NOTE.—θ is a Greek letter often used for an angle and read as " theta."]

Points plotted to draw a graph from given data should be marked, as in the example, Fig. 12, by small crosses, *not* dots.

The angle of lap is chosen in this experiment and its values plotted from left to right. The observed values of the tension are plotted along the uprights.

When symbols, in this case θ and T, are used, the corresponding axes are labelled at their ends.

Having chosen suitable scales we plot the points represented by the given data. To determine the first point we know that T = 13·5 when θ = 0·5. From the point, therefore, 0·5 on the

θ-axis we move along the upright until we reach A, where our vertical scale tells us that T is 13·5. The other points are determined in the same way. These are then joined by a smooth curve as the tension varies continuously with the angle.

GRAPH SHOWING RELATION BETWEEN TENSION
AND ANGLE OF LAP WITH BELT FRICTION.

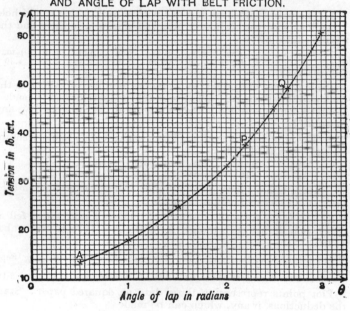

Fig. 12.

T when $\theta = 2·2$.

From the point 2·2 on the θ-axis we move along the upright until we reach the point P on the curve. From the vertical scale we see that at P, T = 37·5.

Hence the tension is 37·5 lb. wt. when the angle of lap is 2·2 radians.

θ when T = 49.

From the point 49 on the T-axis we move to the right until

we reach the curve at Q. Q is above the point 2·65 on the θ-axis.

Hence the angle of lap is 2·65 radians when the tension is 49 lb. wt.

Exercise XVII

1. The petrol indicator of a car with a tank which would hold 10 gallons was read at hourly intervals during a journey and the results shown below:

Time	a.m. 10.30	a.m. 11.30	p.m. 12.30	p.m. 1.30	p.m. 2.30	p.m. 3.30	p.m. 4.30
Gallons in tank	7	5	4	4	2	9	8

Draw a series of uprights showing the number of gallons in the tank at different times. What probable deductions can be made ? Would a continuous line joining the ends of the uprights have any meaning ?

2. The number of class B air licences granted to pilots is shown for the years 1930–1935 :

1930	1931	1932	1933	1934	1935
110	104	103	142	137	175

Draw uprights showing the number of licences granted in each year. Can any deductions be made ?

3. The table gives the number of inches of rain which fell at Greenwich during each month from October 1935 to September 1936 :

Month	Oct.	Nov.	Dec.	Jan.	Feb.	Mar.	Apr.	May	June	July	Aug.	Sept.
Inches of rain	2·55	3·58	2·45	3·54	1·47	0·80	1·70	0·40	3·36	2·93	0·56	3·16

Plot points representing these data on squared paper. State the deductions, if any, which can be made.

4. The speedometer of a car is read at $\frac{1}{2}$-minute intervals with the results shown in the table :

Time in min.	0	$\frac{1}{2}$	1	$1\frac{1}{2}$	2	$2\frac{1}{2}$	3	$3\frac{1}{2}$	4	$4\frac{1}{2}$	5
Speed in m.p.h.	20	24	33	40	45	52	54	51	45	37	30

Draw a graph showing the relation between the speed and time and make any deductions you can.

5. The following table gives the list prices per dozen of wrought iron butt hinges :

Length in inches	$1\frac{1}{2}$	$1\frac{3}{4}$	2	$2\frac{1}{2}$	3	$3\frac{1}{2}$	4
Price	3s. 3d.	3s. 9d.	4s. 3d.	5s. 6d.	7s. 3d.	9s. 6d.	12s. 0d.

Draw a graph showing the relation between length and price and hence find what you would expect the price of $2\frac{1}{4}$ in. butt hinges to be.

6. The pressure, p lb. per sq. in., of gas escaping through an orifice is measured after t minutes with the following results :

t	0	$\frac{1}{2}$	1	$1\frac{1}{2}$	2	$2\frac{1}{2}$	3	$3\frac{1}{2}$	4	$4\frac{1}{2}$
p	75	64	55	47	40	35	30	25	21	18

Draw a graph showing the relation between p and t and hence find the pressure after 2 min. 40 sec. and also after how long the pressure will be reduced to 27 lb. per sq. in.

7. Draw a graph from the following table which may be used for converting knots into miles per hour :

Knots	5	10	20
Ml. per hr.	5·76	11·52	23·03

Hence express a speed of 18 knots in m.p.h. and a speed of 12 m.p.h. in knots.

8. The necessary percentage increase of the centre distance of a pair of involute gears when the pressure angle is increased is given in the table :

Press. angle (degrees)	$14\frac{1}{2}$	16	18	20	22	24	26
Increase of centre distance (%)	0	0·7	1·8	3·0	4·4	6·0	7·9

Draw a graph and find the percentage increase in centre distance when the pressure angle is 19° and the pressure angle when the centre distance is increased by 6·5%.

9. The percentage efficiency and the horse-power of a single-phase alternating current motor are given :

Horse-power	5	10	15	20	25	30	40	50
Efficiency (%)	76	79	81	82·5	83·5	84	85	85·5

Draw a graph and find the percentage efficiency of a 14 horse-power motor.

10. The table of British standards for flexible cords shows the number of wires (each of 0·0076 in. diam.) and the standard resistance in ohms per 1000 yd. at 60° F. :

No. of wires	14	23	40	70	110	162
Resistance (ohms)	39·7	24·2	13·9	7·94	5·05	3·43

Draw a graph and hence determine the resistance for 30 wires.

11. The table shows the nominal bore in inches and the weight in lb. per foot of welded steel tubes for low-pressure steam :

Bore (in.)	2	3	4	5	6	7	8
Wt. per ft. (lb.)	2·80	4·61	6·70	9·13	11·89	14·99	17·04

Draw a graph and hence determine the weight of a foot of such a steel tube when the nominal bore is $3\frac{1}{2}$ in.

12. In calibrating an illumination photometer the following figures were obtained, where I foot-candles denotes the illumination and D degrees the reading of the instrument pointer :

I ..	4·0	3·5	3·0	2·5	2·0	1·5	1·0	0·75	0·5
D ..	224	215	203	187	166	139	105	85	60

Draw a calibration curve for the photometer and hence find the illumination when the reading is 156°.

13. The percentage efficiency of a mercury arc rectifier is shown for different D.C. voltages :

D.C. voltage ..	100	200	300	400	500	600	700
Efficiency (%) ..	78	86·2	90·1	92·3	93·7	94·5	95·0

Draw a graph and hence determine the efficiency for a 220 voltage and also the voltage when the efficiency is 93%.

14. The weights in lb. per foot length of cast iron pipes of different internal diameters when the metal is ½ in. thick, are shown in the table :

Internal diameter (in.)	1½	2	2½	3	3½	4	4½	5
Wt. (lb.)	9·82	12·27	14·72	17·18	19·64	22·10	24·54	26·99

Draw a graph and hence find the weight per foot of a cast iron pipe ½ in. thick with internal diameter 3¼ in. and also the diameter of such a pipe weighing 13 lb.

15. The sum to which an annuity of £1 would accumulate at 3½% compound interest in a number of years is shown in the table :

Number of years	3	6	8	12	15	18	23	25
Sum ..	£3 2s.	£6 11s.	£9 1s.	£14 12s.	£19 6s.	£24 10s	£34 9s.	£38 19s.

Find graphically the sum accumulated by such an annuity in 10 years.

16. The velocity of a leather belt in feet per minute and the corresponding horse-power are shown below :

Vel. (ft. per min.) ..	500	700	1000	1200	1400	1600	1800	2000
Horse-power	1·36	1·91	2·73	3·27	3·82	4·36	4·91	5·45

Find graphically the horse-power when the belt is moving at 1500 ft. per min.

17. The fusing current in ampères for copper wire of different diameters is shown :

Current (amp.) ..	232	198	166	132	107	81·5	69·9	48·0
Diameter (in.) ..	0·080	0·072	0·064	0·056	0·048	0·040	0·036	0·028

Draw a graph showing the relation between fusing current and diameter.
Find the fusing current for a wire of diameter 0·05 in.

18. The table shows the horse-power developed by an aircraft engine for different rates of revolution of the crankshaft :

Rev. per min...	1600	1700	1800	1900	2000	2100	2200	2300	2400
Horse-power ..	345	385	420	448	475	500	524	547	567

Draw a graph and determine the horse-power when the crankshaft is making 1850 rev. per min. and also the number of revolutions per minute the crankshaft must make to develop 465 horse-power.

19. The expectation of life of males and females of different ages is shown below :

Age (years)	5	10	20	25	30	40	50	60
Male expectation (years)	60·11	55·79	46·81	42·52	38·21	29·62	21·60	14·43
Female expectation (years)	63·24	58·87	49·88	45·55	41·22	32·55	24·18	16·50

With the same axes and to the same scales draw graphs showing the expectation of life of a male and of a female at different ages. Hence find how many years a woman of 35 may expect to live longer than a man of the same age.

Example.—A weight w oz. is hung from the end of a spiral spring and its length l in. is observed with the following results :

w (oz.) ..	4	8	12	16	20
l (in.) ..	18	20	22	24	26

Draw a graph showing the relation between l and w.

Suppose we were told that the length l in. of a spiral spring and the weight w oz. which it supported at its end were connected by the relation $l = \frac{1}{2}w + 16$. We could form a table giving the values of l corresponding to a set of values for w, e.g. when $w = 4$, $l = \frac{1}{2} \times 4 + 16 = 18$.

Let us choose values of w which increase by the same numbers, say 4. The corresponding values of l and w are shown in the table :

w	4	8	12	16	20
l	18	20	22	24	26

We notice that the values of l also increase successively by the same numbers in this case 2. This means that every time w increases by 4, l increases by 2 and the graph (drawn in Fig. 13) has the same slope throughout. It is therefore a straight line.

Whenever the graph showing the relation between two numbers y and x is a straight line, y and x will be connected by a relation of the form $y = ax + b$, for when the values of x

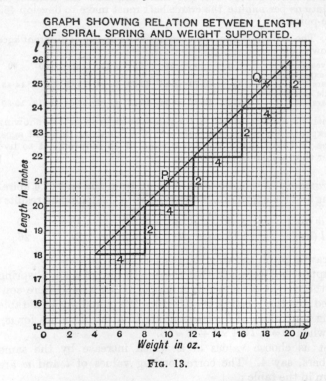

GRAPH SHOWING RELATION BETWEEN LENGTH OF SPIRAL SPRING AND WEIGHT SUPPORTED.

Fig. 13.

increase by equal amounts, the corresponding values of y will also increase by equal amounts.

When the straight line is drawn the constants a and b can easily be determined.

Two convenient points, as P and Q above, are taken on the graph. At P, $w = 10$ and $l = 21$; at Q, $w = 18$ and $l = 25$.

Substituting these corresponding values in the relation $l = aw + b$, we have :

$$21 = 10a + b \quad (1) \text{ and}$$
$$25 = 18a + b \quad (2)$$

which we solve as a pair of simultaneous equations.

By subtraction,

$$-4 = -8a$$
$$\therefore a = \tfrac{1}{2}.$$

Substituting in (1),

$$21 = 5 + b$$
$$\therefore b = 16.$$

The relation is therefore $l = \tfrac{1}{2}w + 16$.

When the data for drawing a graph are the results of experiment it is sometimes found that the points lie nearly on a straight line. In such a case it is generally assumed that there are small errors of observation. A straight line is then drawn lying as evenly as possible between the points, and this line is assumed to show the correct relation.

Quantities which are related by an equation of the form $y = ax + b$ are said to satisfy a straight-line law.

Example.—A motorist finds that, if he keeps his accelerator in the same position, the readings of his speedometer at intervals of 5 sec. for half a minute are as follows :

Time (t sec.)	0	5	10	15	20	25	30
Speed (v m.p.h.)	30	34·2	37	40·2	44·5	47·3	51

Plot a graph of v against t and show that the points lie nearly in a straight line. Draw the straight line, which lies as evenly as possible between the points. Find the relation between v and t by assuming that this straight line is its graph.

The graph, Fig. 14, shows that the points lie very nearly on a straight line, and AB is the straight line that appears to lie as evenly as possible between the points. Let this line be the graph of $v = at + b$, where a and b are constant numbers.

GRAPH OF THE SPEED OF A MOTOR CAR AGAINST THE TIME.

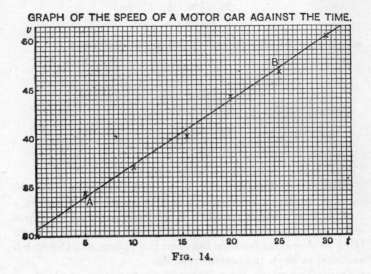

FIG. 14.

At the point A, $t = 5$, $v = 33\cdot75$;
$\qquad$ B, $t = 25$, $v = 47\cdot7$.

$\therefore 33\cdot75 = 5a + b$;
$\qquad 47\cdot7 = 25a + b$.

$\therefore 13\cdot95 = 20a$

$$\therefore a = \frac{13\cdot95}{20} = 0\cdot698.$$

$$\therefore b = 33\cdot75 - 5 \times 0\cdot698 = 33\cdot75 - 3\cdot49$$
$$= 30\cdot26.$$

Hence $v = 0\cdot698t + 30\cdot26$.

The fact that the graph is a straight line shows that v increased by equal amounts in equal time intervals, in other words, the velocity increased at a uniform rate.

Exercise XVIII

1. In an experiment on a screw-jack, the values of the load W lb. and the effort P lb. are given in the table :

P	..	..	10	16	25	28	34
W	..	..	50	100	175	200	250

Draw a graph and hence determine the relation between P and W in the form $P = aW + b$.

2. The values of the load W lb. and the effort P lb. in an experiment on a differential wheel and axle are as below :

P	..	..	10	13	17	18	20
W	..		40	100	180	200	240

Draw a graph and find the law of the machine, i.e. the relation between P and W.

3. Corresponding values of the load W gm. and the effort P gm. in a model of an Archimedes system of pulleys are given in the table :

P	..	..	30	38	47	55
W	..	..	25	90	160	225

Draw a graph and hence find the relation between P and W in the form $W = mP + c$, where m and c are constants.

4. t is the number of thousands of ampère-turns in a limb of a transformer producing a flux density of n kilo-lines per sq. cm. in another limb. Corresponding values are given in the table :

t	..	..	13·05	14·15	15·25	16·35
n	..	..	14·1	14·3	14·5	14·7

Draw a graph and hence determine the relation between n and t in the form $n = at + b$.

5. The table shows the maximum pitch p in. for a single riveted double butt joint in a plate of thickness t in. :

t	..	..	$\frac{1}{8}$	$\frac{1}{4}$	$\frac{3}{8}$	$\frac{1}{2}$	$\frac{3}{4}$	1
p	..	..	2·28	2·50	2·72	2·94	3·16	3·38

Draw a graph and hence find p in terms of t.

6. In the following table I amp. is the maximum current for rubber-covered wires exposed to ordinary temperatures, of cross section A sq. in. :

I	..	116	236	265	350	422	492	561	625	690
A	..	0·1	0·25	0·3	0·4	0·5	0·6	0·7	0·8	0·9

Draw a graph and hence express I in terms of A.

7. The table shows the speed N rev. per min. of a 5 h.p. motor under no load when the armature potential difference is V volts :

N ..	130	436	743	1048	1354	1661
V ..	20	60	100	140	180	220

Draw a graph and hence find the relation between N and V.

8. With a given difference of potential between the ends of a wire, the current I ampères and the resistance R ohms are given below :

R ..	..	2	2·5	4	7	9	10
I ..	..	5	4	2·5	1·4	1·1	1

Calculate $\dfrac{1}{R}$ for each value of I.

Draw a graph showing the relation between I and $\dfrac{1}{R}$ and hence determine I in terms of R.

9. The volume v cu. in. and the corresponding pressure p in. of mercury of a certain quantity of gas are as shown :

p ..	..	50	37·5	30	25	21·4	18·7
v ..	..	30	40	50	60	70	80

Plot p against $\dfrac{1}{v}$ and from the graph determine the relation between p and v.

10. The distance u cm. of the object and the corresponding distance v cm. of the image from a lens are given in the table :

u ..	..	15	20	30	40	50
v ..	..	60	30	20	17	15·8

Plot $\dfrac{1}{u}$ against $\dfrac{1}{v}$ and from your graph determine the relation between u and v.

11. The length l cm. and the tension T lb. wt. of steel wires having the same mass per unit length and the same frequency of vibration were measured ; the results are shown in the table :

T ..	20	18	16	14	12	10	8	6	4
l ..	50·25	48·1	45·5	42·6	39·4	36·4	32·6	28·1	23·6

Draw a graph showing the relation between l and the square root of T and hence express l in terms of $\sqrt{T}$.

Graph of an equation connecting two quantities

If $y = \sqrt{x}$ we can make a table of corresponding values of y and x:

x ..	0	1	2	3	4	5	6
y ..	0	1	1·414	1·732	2	2·236	2·449

From this table points can be plotted in the same way as if these numbers were the results of observations made in an

GRAPH OF THE EQUATION, $y = \sqrt{x}$

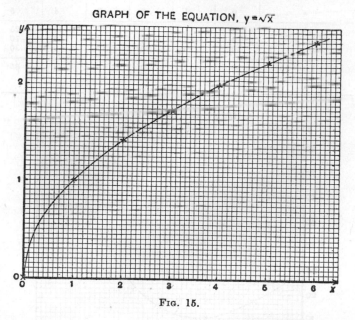

FIG. 15.

experiment. If a smooth curve is drawn through these points, it is reasonable to suppose that the values of x and y at intermediate points satisfy the relation $y = \sqrt{x}$ and so the curve can be used to find the approximate values of the square roots of numbers between 0 and 6. For example from the graph $y \simeq 1·87$ when $x = 3·5$; $\therefore \sqrt{3·5} \simeq 1·87$. The process of finding values of y for values of x between those given in the table is called *interpolation*.

To draw the graph of an equation like $y = x^3 - 14x + 30$, tables of the values of each of the terms x^3, $-14x$ and 30 should be made, as this makes the calculation of y easier and ensures greater accuracy. In making the table the sign of each term should be included. The value of y is then found by adding the values of the three terms.

x	0	1	2	3	4	5
x^3	0	1	8	27	64	125
$-14x$	0	-14	-28	-42	-56	-70
30	30	30	30	30	30	30
$x^3 - 14x + 30$ $(=y)$	30	17	10	15	38	85

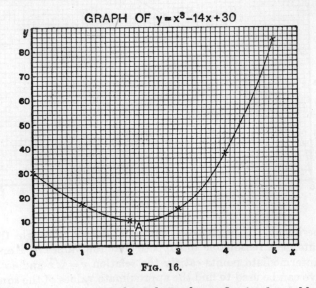

GRAPH OF $y = x^3 - 14x + 30$

Fig. 16.

The points given by the values of x and y in this table are plotted in Fig. 16 and joined by a smooth curve. This curve can be used to find the values of y for values of x not included in the table, that is to interpolate values of y between those in the tables. For instance, when $x = 4.2$ the graph shows that $y \simeq 45$.

The graph can also be used to find the least value of y for values of x between 0 and 5. This is the ordinate of the point A, which is approximately 10, and the corresponding value of x is approximately 2·1.

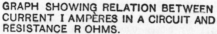

GRAPH SHOWING RELATION BETWEEN
CURRENT I AMPÈRES IN A CIRCUIT AND
RESISTANCE R OHMS.

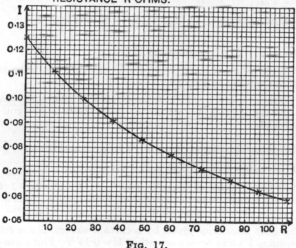

Fig. 17.

Example.—When 24 cells each of $\frac{1}{2}$ volt and internal resistance 4 ohms are connected in series with each other and with a resistance of R ohms, the current I ampères is given by

$$I = \frac{12}{96 + R}.$$

Draw a graph to show the variation of I as R increases from 0 to 100.

Owing to the fact that 12 divides exactly into 96 it is better here to divide numerator and denominator by 12 and take R at intervals of 12, rather than 10. Dividing numerator and denominator by 12 :

$$I = \frac{1}{\dfrac{96}{12} + \dfrac{R}{12}} = \frac{1}{8 + \dfrac{R}{12}}.$$

R	0	12	24	36	48	60	72	84	96	108
$\dfrac{R}{12}$	0	1	2	3	4	5	6	7	8	9
I	$\frac{1}{8}$	$\frac{1}{9}$	$\frac{1}{10}$	$\frac{1}{11}$	$\frac{1}{12}$	$\frac{1}{13}$	$\frac{1}{14}$	$\frac{1}{15}$	$\frac{1}{16}$	$\frac{1}{17}$
I	0·1250	0·1111	0·1	0·0909	0·0833	0·0769	0·0714	0·0667	0·0625	0·0588

The graph drawn from this table is shown in Fig. 17.

Exercise XIX

1. Plot the graph of $y = x^2$ from $x = 0$ to $x = 3$. From the graph read off the squares of 1·24 and 2·16.

2. Plot the graph of $y = x^3$ from $x = 0$ to $x = 1$, using the following values of x : 0, $\frac{1}{4}$, $\frac{1}{2}$, $\frac{3}{4}$, 1. From the graph read off the cubes of 0·65 and 0·82.

3. Plot the graph of $y = \dfrac{1}{x}$ from $x = 1$ to $x = 5$ and from the graph read off the reciprocals of 2·45 and 4·12.

4. Plot the graphs of $y = x^2$, $y = x^2 + 2$, $y = x^2 - 2x + 3$ from $x = 0$ to $x = 4$, using the same axes for all three graphs. Show that all the graphs have the same shape.

5. The heat H calories given by a certain electric fire is related to the voltage V volts by the equation $H = 0·1V^2$. Plot a graph of this equation from $V = 100$ to $V = 250$, using $V = 100$, 125, 150, 175, 200, 225, 250. From the graph read off the values of H when $V = 180$ and $V = 240$.

6. A body falling from rest under gravity moves s ft. in t sec., where $s = 16t^2$. Plot a graph of this equation from $t = 0$ to $t = 4$. From the graph find out how long the body takes to drop (a) 100 ft., (b) 200 ft.

7. The resistance R ohms of a certain wire at $t°$ C. is given by $R = 150(1 + 0·004t)$. Draw a graph to show the variation of the resistance of the wire from $t = 0$ to $t = 100$.

8. The effort P lb. wt. required to raise a load W lb. wt. by means of a block and tackle is given by $P = 0 \cdot 15W + 3 \cdot 84$. Draw a graph of P against W from $W = 0$ to $W = 100$. Show that whenever W is increased by 20 lb. wt. P is increased by 3 lb. wt.

9. When a car is accelerating the distance s yds. travelled in t secs. is given by $s = 10t + 0 \cdot 4t^2$. Draw a graph to show the relation between s and t from $t = 0$ to $t = 20$. From the graph find at what instant the car has been accelerating for 100 yds.

10. If a tin box with an open top has a square base of side x ft. and a total surface area of 16 sq. ft., its volume V cu. ft. is given by $V = 4x - \frac{1}{4}x^3$. Draw a graph to show the variation of V from $x = 0$ to $x = 4$. From it find V when $x = 2 \cdot 7$ and find what values of x make $V = 3 \cdot 5$. Find the greatest possible volume the box can have.

Plot the graphs of the following equations :

11. $y = 0 \cdot 2x^2 + 0 \cdot 8$ ($x = 0$ to 6).

12. $y = 10 - 2\sqrt{x}$ ($x = 0$ to 16).

13. $y = \dfrac{1}{x + 8}$ ($x = 0$ to 6).

14. $s = 3t - 0 \cdot 2t^2$ ($t = 3$ to 10).

15. $M = \frac{1}{2}(8 - x)^2$ ($x = 0$ to 8).

16. $l = h + \dfrac{16}{h}$ ($h = 1$ to 7).

17. Plot the graph of $y = x^2 - 4x + 5$ from $x = 0$ to $x = 5$, and find the least value of y and the values of x for which $y = 4$.

18. Plot the graph of $y = x^3 - 9x^2 + 24x$ from $x = 0$ to $x = 6$. Show that the value of y at $x = 2$ is larger than any other value of y between $x = 0$ and $x = 4$, and the value of y at $x = 4$ is smaller than any other value of y between $x = 2$ and $x = 6$. For what values of x is y equal to 17 ?

19. Plot the graph of $y = 10x - x^2$ from $x = 0$ to 10. What is the greatest value y has ?

20. Draw graphs to show how (a) the volume in cu. in., (b) the total surface area in sq. in. of a cube vary as the length of an edge increases from 3 in. to 7 in. From them find the length of an edge of a cube which has (a) a volume of 175 cu. in., (b) a surface of 120 sq. in. Verify your answers by direct calculation.

21. If a body is thrown up vertically at a speed of 80 ft. per sec. its height s ft. after t sec. is given by $s = 80t - 16t^2$. Plot s against

t from $t=0$ to $t=5$. From the graph find at what times the body is 40 ft. high on the way up and on the way down. When does it reach the ground again ?

22. When a certain tank, which contains 1000 gallons, is emptying the volume V cu. ft. left in the tank after t secs. is given by $V=1000(1-0{\cdot}008t)^2$. Plot a graph to show the variation of V for the whole time the tank takes to empty. How long does it take for half the contents to run out ?

23. At constant temperature the pressure of a gas, p lb. per sq. in., and its volume, v cu. ft., are related by the equation $pv=C$, where C is a constant number. Find C if $p=1500$ when $v=10$; and using this value of C plot a graph to show how p varies as v increases from 10 to 20.

24. If a cylinder of length $2l$ in. is cut from a sphere of radius 6 in. its volume is $\pi(72l-2l^3)$ cu. in. Plot a graph to show the volume of the cylinder from $l=0$ to $l=6$. What values of l make the volume 100 cu. in. ? What is the volume of the largest cylinder which can be cut from the sphere ?

25. The capacity C microfarads of a parallel plate condenser with plates of area 20 sq. in. separated by mica of thickness t in. is given by :

$$C=\frac{298}{10^7t}.$$

Draw a graph to show the variation of C as t increases from $0{\cdot}01$ to $0{\cdot}1$. What thickness of mica is required for a condenser of capacity $0{\cdot}0008$ microfarads ?

CHAPTER VI

GRAPHS WITH DIRECTED NUMBERS

Use of scale of directed numbers

The following table gives the anode current i milli-ampères of a wireless valve when the grid voltage is V volts :

V	-8	-6	-4	-2	0	$+2$	$+4$	$+6$	$+8$
i	0·15	0·30	0·47	0·82	1·52	2·10	2·50	2·70	2·72

To represent this table by means of a graph make a scale of directed numbers for the values of V on a horizontal line $x'0x$ with its zero at 0, and make a scale on a vertical line $0y$ for the values of i. Then the point on the graph given by $V = -8, i = 0.15$ is on the vertical line through -8 on the horizontal scale, and the horizontal line through 0.15 on the vertical scale. The points corresponding to $V = -6, -4$, etc., are plotted in a similar way and a smooth curve is drawn through them.

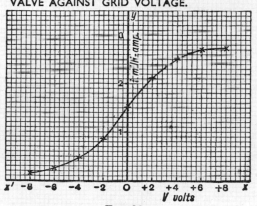

Fig. 18.

In the following example scales of directed numbers are used on both axes.

The table below gives the depth of the water at a port on a certain day at two-hourly intervals from midnight to midnight :

Time after midnight (hr.)	0	2	4	6	8	10	12	14	16	18	20	22	24
Depth of water (ft.)	9	6.8	7.5	11.1	14.2	14.4	10.3	5.8	5.0	8.8	13.2	15.0	11.5

The graph of this table is shown in Fig. 19, using AB, AC as axes.

Instead of measuring the depth of the water from the sea bottom we could measure it from any other zero level, say 10 ft. If this zero is taken, a depth of water 15 ft. becomes

TIDE-CURVE AT A PORT FOR 24 HOURS.

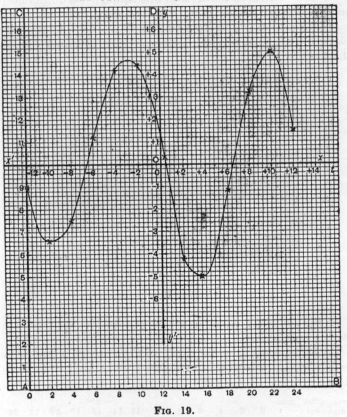

FIG. 19.

$(15 - 10)$ ft., that is 5 ft., and a depth of 8 ft. becomes $(8 - 10)$ ft., that is -2 ft. We could also take noon as our zero of time; then times before noon would be reckoned negative, e.g.,

10.30 a.m. would become $(10\frac{1}{2} - 12)$ hr., that is $-1\frac{1}{2}$ hr. With these new zeros of height and time our table becomes :

Time after noon (t hr.)	-12	-10	-8	-6	-4	-2	0
Depth of water above 10 ft. (D ft.)	-1	$-3\cdot4$	$-2\cdot5$	$+1\cdot1$	$+4\cdot2$	$+4\cdot4$	$+1\cdot3$

Time after noon (t hr.)	$+2$	$+4$	$+6$	$+8$	$+10$	$+12$
Depth of water above 10 ft. (D ft.)	$-4\cdot2$	$-5\cdot0$	$-1\cdot2$	$+3\cdot2$	$+5\cdot0$	$+1\cdot5$

This is equivalent to drawing new axes $x'Ox$ and $y'Oy$ so that 0 corresponds to a depth of 10 ft. at noon. It is easily seen that the graph already drawn is the graph from this new table using scales of directed numbers along both the axes $x'Ox$ and $y'Oy$, taking positive numbers to the right of 0 and negative numbers to the left of 0 on $x'Ox$, and positive numbers above 0 and negative numbers below 0 on $y'Oy$.

In drawing graphs it is often necessary to use directed number scales on both the axes. The following example shows how they are used in plotting the graph of an equation.

Example.—Plot the graph of $y = x^2 - 2x - 5$ from $x = -3$ to $x = +5$ and from it find the values of x which make $y = 0$, and the values of x which make $y = 3\cdot75$.

x	-3	-2	-1	0	$+1$	$+2$	$+3$	$+4$	$+5$
x^2	$+9$	$+4$	$+1$	0	$+1$	$+4$	$+9$	$+16$	$+25$
$-2x$	$+6$	$+4$	$+2$	0	-2	-4	-6	-8	-10
-5	-5	-5	-5	-5	-5	-5	-5	-5	-5
$y = x^2 - 2x - 5$	$+10$	$+3$	-2	-5	-6	-5	-2	$+3$	$+10$

In making this table notice that, when $x = -3$, $-2x = (-2)(-3) = +6$ and similarly for other negative values of x.

To draw a graph from this table we note that x varies from -3 to $+5$, that is x increases by 8 ; in the same way y varies from 10 to -6, that is y varies through a range of 16. Hence the scales on the axes have to be chosen so that there is room for 8 units horizontally and 16 units vertically. Using

4

a sheet of graph paper 7 in. by 9 in., suitable scales in this case are 1 unit to $\frac{1}{2}$ in. horizontally, and 1 unit to 0·4 in.

GRAPH OF $y=x^2-2x-5$

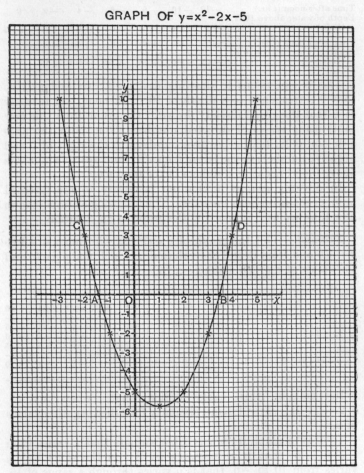

FIG. 20.

vertically. Then the origin O has to be taken so that it is more than 3 units, i.e. $1\frac{1}{2}$ in., from the left hand side of the paper, and more than 5 units, i.e. $2\frac{1}{2}$ in., from the right hand side of the paper ; it has also to be more than 6 units, i.e. 2·4 in. from the bottom of the paper, and more than 10 units, i.e. 4 in., from the top of the paper. A suitable position is $2\frac{1}{2}$ in. from the left of the paper and $3\frac{1}{2}$ in. from the bottom of the paper.*

Draw a horizontal axis $x'Ox$ and a vertical axis $y'Oy$ through O and set out the directed scales along these axes. Then the point on the graph given by $x = -1$, $y = -2$ is the point of intersection of the vertical line through -1 on the horizontal scale, and the horizontal line through -2 on the vertical scale.

$y = 0$ at A and B on the graph, and at these points the values of x are $-1\cdot45$ and $3\cdot45$ respectively. $y = 3\cdot75$ at the points C and D and at these points x has the values $-2\cdot1$ and $4\cdot1$ respectively.

Solution of an equation by means of a graph

At the points where the graph of $y = x^2 - 2x - 5$ cuts the horizontal axis (x axis) $y = 0$, that is, $x^2 - 2x - 5 = 0$. Hence the values of x at these points are the roots of the equation $x^2 - 2x - 5 = 0$. From the graph we saw that these values are $-1\cdot45$ and $3\cdot45$ nearly. As a check these values are substituted in the equation.

When $x = -1\cdot45$, $x^2 - 2x - 5 = (-1\cdot45)^2 - 2(-1\cdot45) - 5$
$$\backsimeq 2\cdot103 + 2\cdot90 - 5 \backsimeq +0\cdot003.$$

When $x = 3\cdot45$, $x^2 - 2x - 5 = (3\cdot45)^2 - 2(3\cdot45) - 5$
$$\backsimeq 11\cdot903 - 6\cdot90 - 5 \backsimeq 0\cdot003.$$

Thus at $x = -1\cdot45$ and at $x = 3\cdot45$ the values of $x^2 - 2x - 5$ are so small that values of x very near to $-1\cdot45$ and $3\cdot45$ respectively must make $x^2 - 2x - 5$ equal to zero.

* Fig. 20 shows a sheet of graph paper 7 in. by 9 in. reduced to half size so that all measurements on it are just half the number of inches in the description above.

Maxima and minima

If on the graph of y against x in Fig. 21 a point P is below points on the graph near to it and on both sides of it the value of y at P is called a "*minimum* [Latin for least] value of y"; in the figure y has a minimum value 1 at P. If a point Q is above the points near to it and on both sides of it the value of y at Q is called a "*maximum* [Latin for greatest] value of y"; in the figure y has a maximum value 2 at Q.

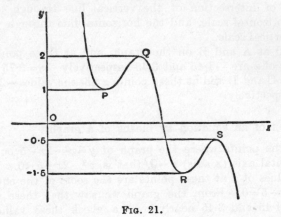

FIG. 21.

It should be noticed, however, that the minimum value of y at P is greater than the maximum value of y at S, so that a minimum value of y is not less than all the other values of y but merely less than the values of y at adjacent points on the graph.

The graph of $y = x^2 - 2x - 5$ in Fig. 20 shows that $x^2 - 2x - 5$ has a minimum value -6 at the point E and this minimum value is given by putting $x = 1$.

Co-ordinates

If the variable quantity x is plotted horizontally and the variable quantity y is plotted vertically, the point given by

$x = 4$, $y = 2$ is said to have co-ordinates 4 and 2. It is called the point (4, 2), writing the horizontal co-ordinate first. The horizontal co-ordinate is called the *abscissa* of the point and the vertical co-ordinate is called the *ordinate* of the point. The figure shows the points (4, 2) ; (-3, -1) and (-2, 3).

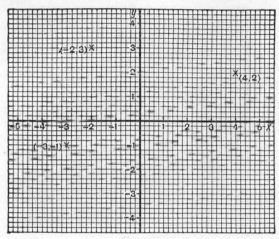

Fig. 22.

Example.—What is the abscissa of the point on the graph of $15x - 12y + 14 = 0$ whose ordinate is 2 ?

If the ordinate is 2, $y = 2$ at the point.

$$\therefore 15x - 24 + 14 = 0.$$
$$\therefore 15x = 24 - 14 = 10.$$
$$\therefore x = \frac{10}{15} = \frac{2}{3}.$$

Straight line graphs

Since a straight line can be drawn when two points on it are known, the graph of an equation like $y = ax + b$, which we have already seen to be a straight line, can be drawn by finding the values of x and y at two points on it.   As a check it is, however, desirable to find the values of x and y at a third point.

Examples.—The graphs of the equations below are shown in Fig. 23.

GRAPH OF $y=3x-2$ AND $2x+4y=13$.

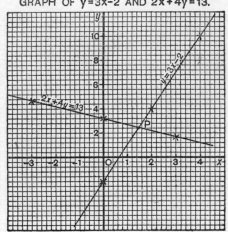

Fig. 23.

$$y = 3x - 2.$$

x	0	2	4
y	-2	4	10

$$2x + 4y = 13.$$

This can be written :

$$4y = -2x + 13.$$

$$\therefore y = -\tfrac{1}{2}x + 3{\cdot}25.$$

x	-3	0	3
$-\tfrac{1}{2}x$	1·5	0	-1·5
y	4·75	3·25	1·75

The last of these examples shows that any equation like $Ax + By + C = 0$ can be written in the form $y = ax + b$, and so its graph is a straight line. In other words, if an equation contains only the first powers of the variable quantities, its graph is a straight line.

Solution of simultaneous equations by using graphs

Consider the equations:

$$3x - y = 2,$$
$$2x + 4y = 13.$$

The first equation can be written $y = 3x - 2$ and so the graphs in Fig. 23 are the graphs of these two equations. These intersect at the point P which has co-ordinates $x = 1.5$, $y = 2.5$. Since the point lies on both lines, these values satisfy both equations. To test this—

$$3 \times 1.5 - 2.5 = 4.5 - 2.5 = 2, \text{ and}$$
$$2 \times 1.5 + 4 \times 2.5 = 3.0 + 10.0 = 13.$$

Thus *the roots of a pair of simultaneous equations are the co-ordinates of the points of intersection of the graphs of the equations.* These equations can easily be solved otherwise and the graphical method is merely an illustration of a method which is used to solve more difficult equations.

Exercise XX

1. The table shows the difference between the average daily water supply of London in each month of a certain year and the daily average throughout the whole year. Show these differences graphically :

Month Difference (millions of gallons)	Apr.	May	June	July	Aug.	Sept.
	−16·9	+2·8	+22·7	+31·0	+28·0	+14·4
Month Difference (millions of gallons)	Oct.	Nov.	Dec.	Jan.	Feb.	Mar.
	+3·4	−4·2	−16·7	−14·8	−22·8	−22·8

2. During the last fortnight of June 1936 the average number of hours of sunshine per day was 8·9. The table below shows the number of hours of sunshine in excess of the average 8·9 for each day of this fortnight. Represent this table by a graph.

Day of Month	17	18	19	20	21	22	23
Excess hours of sunshine	−3·6	−6·3	−8·4	−8·9	−0·9	+5·3	+6·0

Day of Month	24	25	26	27	28	29	30
Excess hours of sunshine	+6·0	−1·6	+4·0	−7·0	+2·5	+5·6	+3·8

3. A newspaper gave the following table to show the fortune of a cabinet minister at elections. The first line gives the date of the election and the second line the number of votes by which he won (positive) or lost (negative) the election. Represent this table graphically.

Election date	1895	1900	1906	1910 (Jan.)	1910 (Dec.)	1919
Majority (thousands of votes) ..	−5·1	−6·3	+7·2	+5·8	+5·5	−14·2

Election date	1921	1922	1923	1924	1929	1931	1935
Majority (thousands of votes) ..	−0·7	+3·2	+3·5	+2·1	+28·7	+6·0	−20·5

4. A ship is y miles North of a point O when it is x miles East of O. It starts to sail from a point $1\frac{1}{4}$ miles West, 6 miles South of O and its subsequent positions are given by the following table. Draw a graph of its course. State the greatest distance the ship goes to the West of O and its distance from O when it is due North of O.

x	−1·25	−1·81	−2·00	−1·81	−1·25	−0·25	1·00	2·75	4·75	7·20	10·00
y	−6	−5	−4	−3	−2	−1	0	1	2	3	4

5. The plate currents of two wireless valves are i_1 and i_2 milliampères when the grid voltage is V volts. Plot graphs of i_1 and i_2 from V = −12 to V = +12, using the same axes and scales for both graphs.

V	−12	−10	−8	−6	−4	−2	0	2	4	6	8	10	12
i_1	0·04	0·05	0·12	0·30	0·65	1·04	1·40	1·70	1·92	2·00	2·00	2·00	2·00
i_2	0	0	0	0	0·03	0·10	0·35	0·68	0·97	1·26	1·50	1·60	1·60

6. The following table gives the temperature in degrees Fahrenheit at two-hourly intervals during the 24 hours of a winter's day. Make a table of y, the number of degrees the temperature is above the freezing point (32°), and plot a graph of y against the time of day. State the probable rise in temperature from 5 a.m. to 1 p.m.

Time of day	..	Midnight.	2 a.m.	4 a.m.	6 a.m.	8 a.m.	10 a.m.	Noon.
Temperature	..	31°	28·5°	28°	30°	33°	35·5°	38°

Time of day	..	2 p.m.	4 p.m.	6 p.m.	8 p.m.	10 p.m.	Midnight.	
Temperature	..	39·5°	40°	39°	37°	34°	28°	

7. A ship 200 ft. long is divided into ten lengths. The table below gives the vertical thrust T ton wt. per ft. of the water on each of the ten lengths, and the load W ton wt. per ft. due to the weight of the hull, cargo, etc. These values are shown below the distance x ft. from the bow to the middle point of each 20 ft. length.

Make a table of the resultant upward force F ton wt. per foot which is given by $F = T - W$. Plot graphs of T, W and F against x, using the same axes for the three graphs.

x	10	30	50	70	90	110	130	150	170	190
T	1·00	2·20	3·25	4·00	4·25	4·25	4·00	3·35	2·13	0·87
W	1·75	2·50	2·78	3·06	3·20	3·53	4·00	4·20	3·00	1·55

8. If a body is thrown vertically upwards at 80 ft./sec. its upward velocity after t sec. is v ft./sec., where $v = 80 - 32t$. Make a table of values of v at intervals of $\frac{1}{2}$ sec. from $t = 0$ to $t = 5$, and draw a graph of v, using this table. What is the meaning of a negative value of v ? At what time is $v = 0$?

9. A light rod AB l ft. long, with a weight w lb. attached to it at B, is freely hinged at A so that it can swing in a vertical plane. If, when the rod is at rest, B is given a velocity u ft./sec. the tension in the rod, when B is h ft. above its lowest position, is T lb. wt., where

$$T = \frac{w}{gl}\{u^2 - g(3h - l)\}$$

Find the relation between T and h when $w = 4$, $g = 32$, $l = 2$, $u = 16$, and draw a graph of it from $h = 0$ to $h = 4$. At what value of h is $T = 0$? What is the meaning of the negative values of T ?

4*

Plot the graphs of the following equations, and read off from them the values of x for which $y = 0$:

10. $y = 12 - x^2$ $(x = -5$ to $+5)$.

11. $y = 4 - x - x^3$ $(x = -4$ to $+4)$.

12. $y = 4 - \sqrt{x}$ $(x = 0$ to $100)$.

13. $y = \dfrac{20}{4 + x} - 7$ $(x = -3$ to $+3)$.

Draw the graphs of the following equations, using the same axes for all the graphs in one question. (For Exercises 14 and 15 suitable scales are $\frac{1}{2}$ in. = unit on x axis, $0 \cdot 2$ in. = unit on y axis.)

14. $y = 3x$, $y = 3x + 2$, $y = 3x - 3$.

15. $y = -2x$, $y = 4 - 2x$, $y = -1 - 2x$.

16. $y = 1 \cdot 4x$, $y = -1 \cdot 4x$, $y = 1 \cdot 4(x - 2)$.

17. $y = 3 + x$, $y = 3 + 3x$, $y = 3 - 2x$.

18. $x + y = 1$, $x + y + 1 = 0$, $x + y = 4$.

19. $2x + 3y = 5$, $2x + 3y + 5 = 0$, $2x - 3y = 5$.

20. $y = \frac{1}{6}(x - 3 \cdot 5)$, $\frac{1}{3}(y - x) = \frac{1}{4}$.

21. $1 \cdot 7x - 2 \cdot 9y = 4 \cdot 2$; $2 \cdot 9x - 1 \cdot 7y = 4 \cdot 2$.

Find the ordinate of the point on each of these graphs whose abscissa is 2 and the abscissæ of the points whose ordinates are each 3.

22. The relation between the temperature $t°$ Centigrade and the absolute temperature $T°$ is $T = t + 273$. Draw a graph of this relation from $t = -273$ to $t = +200$.

23. The relation between the temperature $F°$ on the Fahrenheit scale and the temperature $C°$ on the Centigrade scale is $F = (9/5)C + 32$. Draw a graph to show the variation of F from $C = -100$ to $C = +100$. What Fahrenheit temperature corresponds to $-25°$ Centigrade ?

24. The resistance R ohms of a copper wire at $t°$ C. is given by the equation $R = 10\{1 + 0 \cdot 004(t - 20)\}$. Draw a graph to show the variation of R from $t = -150$ to $t = +150$.

25. Solve the equations in Exs. 1-4 on page 71 graphically.

26. A train leaves Paddington at 9.15 a.m. and reaches Reading at 10 a.m. ; a train leaving Reading at 9.25 a.m. arrives at Paddington at 10.5 a.m. Assuming that the distance between the stations is 36 miles and that the trains travel at uniform speeds, find how far from Paddington and at what time they meet.

27. A train leaves Marylebone at 8.45 a.m., arrives at Nottingham at 11.30 a.m., stops for 5 minutes and arrives at Sheffield at 12.25 p.m. A train leaving Sheffield at 7.30 a.m. reaches Nottingham at 8.20 a.m., stops for 5 minutes and reaches Marylebone at 10.40 a.m. The distance from Marylebone to Nottingham is 125 miles and from Nottingham to Sheffield is 40 miles. Assuming the speeds of the trains to be constant when travelling, find when and where they meet.

Plot the graphs of the following equations and find the maximum and minimum values, if any, of the ordinates :

28. $y = 1 - 2x - x^2$ $(x = -4$ to $+3)$.

29. $y = x^3 - 3x$ $(x = -3$ to $+3)$.

30. $s = 80t - 16t^2$ $(t = 0$ to $5)$.

31. $p = 2 + 3r - r^2$ $(r = -4$ to $+2)$.

32. $x = 6m^2 - 2m^3$ $(m = -2$ to $+4)$.

33. When a ball is thrown out of a window its path is the graph of $y = x - 0.016x^2$, where x ft. is the horizontal distance and y ft. the vertical distance upwards from the point of projection.

Draw a graph of this equation and from it find (a) the greatest height above the point of projection, (b) how far from the house it hits the ground, which is 12 ft. below the point of projection $(y = -12)$.

34. Draw a graph of $y = 4 - 3x - x^2$ from $x = -4$ to $+4$ and find from it (a) the values of y when $x = -1.2$ and 0.8 respectively, (b) the values of x which make $y = 0$, (c) the values of x which make $y = 2$, (d) the maximum value of y.

35. When a beam 10 ft. long is clamped horizontally at its ends A and B, a point x ft. horizontally from the middle point O is y ft. above O, where $y = \dfrac{x^2}{40} - \dfrac{x^4}{2000}$. Plot a graph to show the value of y from $x = -5$ to $+5$. Find the values of x at the points which are 3 in. above O, and find how far the line AB is above O.

36. When a certain metal bar 4 ft. long is clamped horizontally at one end, A, a point on the bar x ft. from A is $\dfrac{x^3}{240}$ ft. below A. If we say that this point is y ft. above A, then $y = -\dfrac{x^3}{240}$. Use this equation to draw a graph showing the shape of the bar from $x = 0$ to $x = 4$.

37. From a plate 10 in. by 8 in. a rectangle is cut out so as to leave a rectangular strip x in. wide. Show that the area A sq. in.

of this strip is given by $A = 36x - 4x^2$. Draw a graph showing the relation between A and x. What is the value of A when x is 1·5 ?

38. Plot the points whose co-ordinates are $(-2, 3)$, $(3, 1)$. If the graph of $y = ax + b$ passes through both these points, find a and b.

39. Plot the points where co-ordinates are $(3, 4)$, $(-3, 4)$, $(-3, -4)$, $(-4, -3)$. Join the last two points by a straight line and find its equation.

40. Draw the graph of the line $x + y = 4$, using 1 in. to represent 1 unit on both axes, and draw a circle centre $(0, 0)$ and radius 3 in. Read off the co-ordinates of the points where the circle cuts the line.

41. Plot the points A, B, whose co-ordinates are $(5, 3)$, $(-1, 7)$. Join them, and find the co-ordinates of the middle point of AB.

42. Using 1 in. to represent a unit on both axes draw two circles, one centre $(0, 0)$ and radius 2·5 in., and the other centre $(2, 3)$ and radius 4 in. Read off the co-ordinates of the points where the circles meet.

CHAPTER VII

INDICES AND LOGARITHMS

By the use of logarithms we are able to reduce time and labour in arithmetical calculations as we can replace multiplication and division by addition and subtraction. They were discovered by a Scotsman, John Napier, who published the first book of logarithms in 1614.

We know that 5×5 is written 5^2, which we read as " five squared."

As $5^2 = 25$, we say that 5 is the square root of 25 and, making use of the symbol $\sqrt{}$ for " square root," we write $\sqrt{25} = 5$.

Similarly $5 \times 5 \times 5 = 5^3$, which we read as " five cubed." Since $5^3 = 125$ we say that 5 is the " cube root " of 125 and, making use of the symbol $\sqrt[3]{}$ for cube root, we write $\sqrt[3]{125} = 5$.

A product of equal numbers such as $5 \times 5 \times 5 \times 5$ is called a *power* of the number. $5 \times 5 \times 5 \times 5 = 5^4$ and we say that

$5 \times 5 \times 5 \times 5$ is 5 to the power 4 or more shortly, 5 to the fourth.

The number 4, which tells us how many equal numbers are multiplied together, is called an *index* (plural—*indices*).

As in arithmetic, we write $a \times a \times a \times a = a^4$, the index 4 indicating the number of a's which are multiplied together.

Since $a^4 = a \times a \times a \times a$ and $a^3 = a \times a \times a$, we see that $a^4 \times a^3 = a \times a \times a \times a \times a \times a \times a$ or a^7, illustrating the rule that *when multiplying together powers of the same number, the indices are added.*

Considering the more general case, we know now that $a^m = a \times a \times a \times \ldots$, the number of a's to be multiplied together being m.

Equally $a^n = a \times a \times a \times \ldots$, the number of a's to be multiplied together being n.

Hence $a^m \times a^n = a \times a \times a \times \ldots$, the number of a's to be multiplied together being $m + n$, which we write a^{m+n}. We can say, therefore, that $a^m \times a^n = a^{m+n}$.

Example.—$5^4 \times 5^3 \times 5^2 = 5^{4+3+2} = 5^9$.

In the case of division, we know that

$$\frac{5^7}{5^3} = \frac{5 \times 5 \times 5 \times 5 \times 5 \times 5 \times 5}{5 \times 5 \times 5} = 5 \times 5 \times 5 \times 5 = 5^4,$$

which illustrates the rule that *when dividing powers of the same number, the index of the denominator is to be subtracted from the index of the numerator.*

Examples.—

1. $\dfrac{5^8}{5^2} = 5^{8-2} = 5^6$.

2. $\dfrac{7^4 \times 7^5}{7^6} = 7^{4+5-6} = 7^3$.

3. $\dfrac{a^5 \times a^2}{a^3} = a^{5+2-3} = a^4$.

4. $(7^3)^2 = 7^3 \times 7^3 = 7^{3+3} = 7^6$.

5. $(a^2)^5 = a^2 \times a^2 \times a^2 \times a^2 \times a^2 = a^{2+2+2+2+2} = a^{10}$.

In examples 4 and 5, in which a power of a number is *raised* to a further power, we *multiply* the indices.

a^1 is a, since a^1 means that there is only one a.

We shall attach meanings to a^0, $a^{\frac{1}{2}}$, $a^{\frac{3}{5}}$, $a^{-\frac{1}{2}}$, a^{-2}, etc., by assuming that the rules of indices stated above still hold, even when the indices are not positive whole numbers.

$a^0 \times a^2 = a^{0+2} = a^2$.

a^2 multiplied by a^0 is still a^2 and therefore a^0 must be unity. Hence we have $a^0 = 1$.

$a^{\frac{1}{2}} \times a^{\frac{1}{2}} = a^{\frac{1}{2}+\frac{1}{2}} = a^1 = a$.

The square of $a^{\frac{1}{2}}$ is thus equal to a and therefore $a^{\frac{1}{2}} = \sqrt{a}$.

$(a^{\frac{1}{3}})^3 = a^{\frac{1}{3} \times 3} = a^1 = a$.

The cube of $a^{\frac{1}{3}}$ is therefore a and $a^{\frac{1}{3}} = \sqrt[3]{a}$.

$(a^{\frac{3}{5}})^5 = a^{\frac{3}{5} \times 5} = a^3$.

$a^{\frac{3}{5}}$ raised to the power 5 is therefore a^3, and $a^{\frac{3}{5}}$ is therefore the fifth root of a^3, or $a^{\frac{3}{5}} = \sqrt[5]{a^3}$.

We can say that when the index of a number is a fraction, the numerator indicates the power to which the number is to be raised and the denominator indicates the root which is to be taken.

$a^{-2} \times a^3 = a^{-2+3} = a$.

Dividing each side by a^3, $\quad a^{-2} = \dfrac{a}{a^3} = \dfrac{1}{a^2}$.

Similarly $a^{-5} = \dfrac{1}{a^5}$.

The relations above can be included in the following statements :

$$a^m \times a^n = a^{m+n}.$$

$$\frac{a^m}{a^n} = a^{m-n}.$$

$$(a^m)^n = a^{mn}.$$

$$a^{\frac{m}{n}} = \sqrt[n]{a^m}.$$

$$a^{-n} = \frac{1}{a^n}.$$

Exercise XXI

Express in the form 10^n where n is a single number :

1. $10^3 \times 10^5$.   2. $10^2 \times 10^4 \times 10^6$.   3. $10^5 \div 10^2$.

4. $10^9 \div 10^3$.   5. $\dfrac{10^4 \times 10^2}{10^3}$.   6. $\dfrac{10^5 \times 10^2 \times 10^4}{10^{11}}$.

7. $10^5 \times 10^{-3}$.   8. $10^{-2} \times 10^{-4}$.   9. $10^2 \times 10^{\frac{1}{2}}$.

10. $10^{-3} \times 10^{\frac{1}{3}}$.   11. $10^{\frac{2}{3}} \times 10^{\frac{1}{10}}$.   12. $\dfrac{10^2}{10^{\frac{1}{2}}}$.

13. $\dfrac{10}{10^{\frac{1}{3}}}$.   14. $(10^{\frac{1}{2}})^2$.   15. $(10^3)^{\frac{1}{3}}$.

16. $(10^8)^{\frac{1}{4}}$.   17. $\dfrac{10^2 \times 10^{\frac{1}{2}}}{10^{\frac{3}{2}}}$.   18. $\dfrac{10^{\frac{1}{3}} \times 10^{\frac{2}{3}}}{10}$.

19. $\dfrac{10}{10^5 \times 10^{\frac{1}{5}}}$.   20. $\dfrac{10^4 \times 10^{\frac{1}{4}}}{10^8 \times 10^{\frac{1}{8}}}$.

Simplify :

21. $a^3 \times a^5$.   22. $b^4 \times b^2 \times b^7$.   23. $\dfrac{x^4 \times x^3}{x^6}$.

24. $x^{\frac{1}{2}} \times x^2$.   25. $\dfrac{p^3 \times p^4}{p^5}$.   26. $\dfrac{c^4 \times c^6}{c^{12}}$.

27. $\dfrac{y^{\frac{1}{3}} \times y^{\frac{1}{4}}}{y^3}$.   28. $\dfrac{y^5 \times y^{\frac{1}{5}}}{y}$.   29. $\dfrac{y^3 \times y^{\frac{1}{3}}}{y^2 \times y^{\frac{1}{2}}}$.

30. $a^{\frac{1}{3}} \times a^{\frac{1}{3}} \times a^{\frac{1}{3}}$.   31. $(a^{\frac{1}{4}})^4$.   32. $(a^{\frac{2}{3}})^3$.

Find the value of x if :

33. $10^x = 1000$.   34. $12^x = 144$.   35. $3^x = 81$.

36. $10^x \times 1 \cdot 2 = 12$.   37. $10^x \times 1 \cdot 2 = 1200$.

Express as a power of 16 :

38. 2.   39. 4.   40. 256.   41. 8.   42. 32.

Express as a power of 10 :

43. $10^3 \times 10^{\cdot 3}$.   44. $10^3 \div 10^{\cdot 3}$.   45. $10^{3 \cdot 4} \times 10^{\cdot 5}$.

46. $10^{\cdot 5} \times 10^{\cdot 5}$.   47. $\sqrt{1000}$.   48. $\sqrt[3]{100}$.

49. $\sqrt{10^{\cdot 6}}$.   50. $10\sqrt[3]{10}$.   51. $\sqrt{10} \times \sqrt[4]{10}$.

52. $10 \times \sqrt{10} \times \sqrt[3]{10}$.

In the following examples, use " root " signs rather than fractional indices :

53. The surface area A sq. in. of a sphere of radius r in. is given by $A = 4\pi r^2$. Express r in terms of A.

54. The volume of a sphere V cu. ft. is given by $V = \frac{4}{3}\pi r^3$, where r feet is the radius. Express r in terms of V.

55. The time period t seconds of a simple pendulum of length l feet is given by $t = 2\pi\sqrt{\dfrac{l}{g}}$, where g is constant. Express l in terms of t and g.

56. The formula $A = \pi(a^2 - b^2)$ gives the area of a ring of flat metal. Make b the subject of the formula.

57. The volume of a hollow sphere is given by $V = \frac{4}{3}\pi(a^3 - b^3)$. Express b in terms of V and a.

58. The formula $s = \dfrac{a}{r^2} - b$ gives the compressive stress in a thick cylinder subjected to large internal pressure. Express r in terms of the other symbols.

59. The area s sq. cm. of the curved surface of a cone is given by $s = \pi r\sqrt{r^2 + h^2}$, where r cm. is the base radius of the cone and h cm. the height. Express h in terms of s and r.

60. The time period of a compound pendulum is given by $t = 2\pi\sqrt{\dfrac{h^2 + k^2}{gh}}$. Make k the subject of the formula.

LOGARITHMS

If 3 be raised to different powers, the following results will be obtained :

$$3^0 = 1 ; \quad 3^1 = 3 ; \quad 3^2 = 9 ; \quad 3^3 = 27 ; \quad 3^4 = 81 ; \text{ etc.}$$

Remembering that 3 is the number which is being raised to different powers, the results may be tabulated as below :

Index ..	0	1	2	3	4
Number ..	1	3	9	27	81

These results are shown on the graph on p. 113.

If this graph be drawn on a larger scale, readings will show that $3^{1\cdot5} \simeq 5\cdot2$, $3^{2\cdot5} \simeq 15\cdot6$; other intermediate values may be read as required.

That $3^{1\cdot5} \simeq 5\cdot2$ may be verified.

$3^{1\cdot5} = 3^{\frac{3}{2}} = \sqrt{27}$; $(5\cdot2)^2 = 27\cdot04$.

$\therefore\ 3^{1\cdot5} \simeq 5\cdot2$.

When a number is expressed as a power of 3, the index is said to be the *logarithm* of the number to the *base* 3.

Since $3^2 = 9$, the logarithm of 9 to the base 3 is 2. This is written $\log_3 9 = 2$ and similarly $\log_3 5\cdot2 \simeq 1\cdot5$.

GRAPH SHOWING RELATION BETWEEN
AN INDEX AND 3 RAISED TO THAT INDEX.

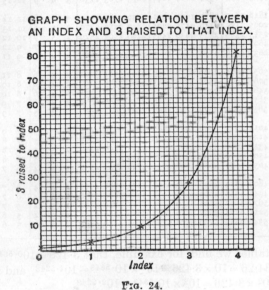

Fig. 24.

The base almost invariably used in numerical calculations is 10. It is usual to write, for example, log 100 = 2, it being understood that the base is 10.

Tables of logarithms to the base 10 are published, most frequently to four places of decimals, and every student should possess a copy. Four figures should be used in calculations, but it should be realized that the fourth figure in the answer cannot be relied on as the neglect of the fifth figure in a series of additions and subtractions may possibly affect the fourth.

An extract from a table of logarithms is shown below :

	0	1	2	3	4	5	6	7	8	9	Differences								
											1	2	3	4	5	6	7	8	9
10	0000	0043	0086	0128	0170	0212	0253	0294	0334	0374	4	8	12	17	21	25	29	33	37
11	0414	0453	0492	0531	0569	0607	0645	0682	0719	0755	4	8	11	15	19	23	26	30	34
12	0792	0828	0864	0899	0934	0969	1004	1038	1072	1106	3	7	10	14	17	21	24	28	31
13	1139	1173	1206	1239	1271	1303	1335	1367	1399	1430	3	6	10	13	16	19	23	26	29
14	1461	1492	1523	1553	1584	1614	1644	1673	1703	1732	3	6	9	12	15	18	21	24	27
15	1761	1790	1818	1847	1875	1903	1931	1959	1987	2014	3	6	8	11	14	17	20	22	25
16	2041	2068	2095	2122	2148	2175	2201	2227	2253	2279	3	5	8	11	13	16	18	21	24
17	2304	2330	2355	2380	2405	2430	2455	2480	2504	2529	2	5	7	10	12	15	17	20	22
18	2553	2577	2601	2625	2648	2672	2695	2718	2742	2765	2	5	7	9	12	14	16	19	21
19	2788	2810	2833	2856	2878	2900	2923	2945	2967	2989	2	4	7	9	11	13	16	18	20
20	3010	3032	3054	3075	3096	3118	3139	3160	3181	3201	2	4	6	8	11	13	15	17	19
21	3222	3243	3263	3284	3304	3324	3345	3365	3385	3404	2	4	6	8	10	12	14	16	18
22	3424	3444	3464	3483	3502	3522	3541	3560	3579	3598	2	4	6	8	10	12	14	15	17
23	3617	3636	3655	3674	3692	3711	3729	3747	3766	3784	2	4	6	7	9	11	13	15	17
24	3802	3820	3838	3856	3874	3892	3909	3927	3945	3962	2	4	5	7	9	11	12	14	16
25	3979	3997	4014	4031	4048	4065	4082	4099	4116	4133	2	3	5	7	9	10	12	14	15
26	4150	4166	4183	4200	4216	4232	4249	4265	4281	4298	2	3	5	7	8	10	11	13	15
27	4314	4330	4346	4362	4378	4393	4409	4425	4440	4456	2	3	5	6	8	9	11	13	14
28	4472	4487	4502	4518	4533	4548	4564	4579	4594	4609	2	3	5	6	8	9	11	12	14
29	4624	4639	4654	4669	4683	4698	4713	4728	4742	4757	1	3	4	6	7	9	10	12	13
30	4771	4786	4800	4814	4829	4843	4857	4871	4886	4900	1	3	4	6	7	9	10	11	13
31	4914	4928	4942	4955	4969	4983	4997	5011	5024	5038	1	3	4	6	7	8	10	11	12
32	5051	5065	5079	5092	5105	5119	5132	5145	5159	5172	1	3	4	5	7	8	9	11	12
33	5185	5198	5211	5224	5237	5250	5263	5276	5289	5302	1	3	4	5	6	8	9	10	12
34	5315	5328	5340	5353	5366	5378	5391	5403	5416	5428	1	3	4	5	6	8	9	10	11

From tables we find, for example, that $3 \cdot 426 = 10^{0 \cdot 5348}$.
Now $34 \cdot 26 = 10 \times 3 \cdot 426 = 10^1 \times 10^{0 \cdot 5348} = 10^{1 \cdot 5348}$, and
$342 \cdot 6 = 10^2 \times 3 \cdot 426 = 10^2 \times 10^{0 \cdot 5348} = 10^{2 \cdot 5348}$.

The integral part of a logarithm is called the *characteristic* and the figures after the decimal point the *mantissa*.

It will be seen from the above examples that logarithms of numbers consisting of the same figures arranged in the same order have the same mantissa.

Use of tables

Example.—Find log $3 \cdot 426$.

Read down the first column of the tables until coming to the figures 34. Read along this line until reaching the column at the head of which is 2 (the third figure of 3426). The number in this position is 5340. Continue along this line to the columns headed " Mean Differences " and stop at the one at the head of which is 6 (the fourth figure of 3426). In this position is a figure 8 which is to be added to 5340, giving the result 5348.

We now know that the mantissa of log 3·426 is 5348. Only the mantissæ of logarithms are given in the tables ; the characteristics have to be inserted.

Since $1 = 10^0$ and $10 = 10^1$, the logarithms of numbers between 1 and 10 are between 0 and 1, i.e. their characteristic is 0.

Hence log $3·426 = 0·5438$.

or $3·426 = 10^{0·5438}$.

As before :

$$34·26 = 10^{1·5438}.$$
$$3426 = 10^{3·5438}.$$
$$34260 = 10^{4·5438}.$$

It will be seen that the characteristic of the logarithm is one less than the number of figures before the decimal point in the original number.

Example.—Evaluate $3·845 \times 29·73$.

$$3·845 \times 29·73 = 10^{0·5849} \times 10^{1·4732} = 10^{2·0581} = 114·3.$$

The last step in the work has been carried out by using the tables in the reverse way to that previously explained. We look for the mantissa 0581 ; the nearest to this in the tables, using the mean differences, is $0569 + 11$ or 0580. Omitting the decimal point, the number of which this is the logarithm is 1143. Since 2 is the characteristic of 2·0581, the number must have three figures before the decimal point. It is therefore 114·3, but the figure 3 cannot be relied on.

As the logarithm of 1·143 is 0·0581, 1·143 is said to be the antilogarithm of 0·0581.

To remove the necessity of using tables in the reverse way, tables of antilogarithms are included. They are read as shown below in a similar way to the tables of logarithms.

To find antilog. 2·0581 we look down the first column until we come to the figures 05 (the first two figures of 0581). We continue along this line until we reach the column headed 8 (third figure of 0581). The number here is 1143. Along the same line, in the mean differences columns, we look for the figure in the column headed 1 (fourth figure of 0581). This figure is 0, meaning that 0 is to be added to 1143. 114·3 is therefore the number whose logarithm is 2·0581.

Example.—Evaluate $6·738^2 \times 13·85 \over 3·971 \times 4·946$.

$$\frac{6·738^2 \times 13·85}{3·971 \times 4·946}$$

$$= \frac{10^{0·8285} \times 10^{0·8285} \times 10^{1·1415}}{10^{0·5989} \times 10^{0·6942}}$$

$$= \frac{10^{[2(0·8285)+1·1415]}}{10^{(0·5989+0·6942)}}$$

$$= \frac{10^{2·7985}}{10^{1·2931}}$$

$$= 10^{(2·7985-1·2931)}$$

$$= 10^{1·5054}$$

$$= 32·02.$$

It will be seen that multiplication of numbers has been replaced by the addition of logarithms and division by the subtraction of logarithms. As calculations become more complicated the work is simplified by writing the logarithms tabulated as shown below.

Number.	Logarithm.	
$6·738^2$	$2 \times 0·8285 = 1·6570$	
13·85	1·1415	
Numerator	2·7985	2·7985
3·971	0·5989	
4·946	0·6942	
Denominator	1·2931	1·2931
32·02		1·5054

Exercise XXII

1. Draw a graph of 2^x for values of x from 0 to 4. From your graph determine the values of :
(i) $2^{1\cdot5}$, $2^{2\cdot8}$, $2^{3\cdot7}$;
(ii) $\log_2 5\cdot7$, $\log_2 8$, $\log_2 10$, $\log_2 14\cdot5$.

2. Make use of tables to express as powers of 10 :
$2\cdot345$, 50, $17\cdot06$, $428\cdot7$, 6359, 57820.

3. With the help of tables, evaluate :
$10^{\cdot2876}$, $10^{\cdot4321}$, $10^{1\cdot4528}$, $10^{2\cdot0007}$, $10^{3\cdot4506}$, $10^{4\cdot7892}$.

Find the values of the following by expressing numbers as powers of 10 ; also write out in tabular form :

4. $14\cdot87 \times 53\cdot26$.

5. $283\cdot5 \times 17\cdot96$.

6. $31\cdot46 \times 52\cdot57$.

7. $\dfrac{17\cdot48}{5\cdot329}$.

8. $\dfrac{1647}{13\cdot96}$.

9. $\dfrac{453\cdot9}{357\cdot8}$.

10. $16\cdot91 \times 2\cdot143 \times 4\cdot118$.

11. $\dfrac{53\cdot84 \times 16\cdot57}{112\cdot8}$.

12. $\dfrac{1\cdot478 \times 0476}{26\cdot45}$.

13. $\dfrac{44\cdot48 \times 9\cdot763}{3\cdot47 \times 5\cdot89}$.

14. $(32\cdot68)^3$.

15. $(4\cdot217)^5$.

16. $(1\cdot041)^{10}$.

17. $(987\cdot6)^2$.

18. $27\cdot91 \times (3\cdot419)^3$.

19. $(1\cdot019)^4 \times 20\cdot98 \times 17\cdot25$.

20. $\dfrac{2\cdot765 \times (13\cdot48)^2}{5\cdot763 \times 7\cdot452}$.

Since $(\sqrt{7})^2 = 7 = 10^{0\cdot8451}$,
$$\sqrt{7} = 10^{\frac{1}{2}(0\cdot8451)} = 10^{0\cdot4226}.$$

This means that the logarithm of $\sqrt{7}$ is half the logarithm of 7. In the same way the logarithm of $\sqrt[3]{7}$ is a third of the logarithm of 7, and the logarithms of other roots are found similarly.

Example.—Express $\sqrt[3]{49\cdot25}$ as a power of 10.
$$49\cdot25 = 10^{1\cdot6924}.$$
$$\therefore \sqrt[3]{49\cdot25} = 49\cdot25^{\frac{1}{3}} = 10^{\frac{1}{3}(1\cdot6924)} = 10^{0\cdot5641}, \text{ or in other words}$$
$$\log(\sqrt[3]{49\cdot25}) = 0\cdot5641.$$

Example.—Evaluate $\dfrac{(17\cdot45)^3 \times 14\cdot82}{24\cdot7 \times \sqrt{3\cdot95}}$.

Number.	Logarithm.	
$(17\cdot45)^3$	$1\cdot2417 \times 3 = 3\cdot7251$	
$14\cdot82$	$1\cdot1709$	
Numerator	$4\cdot8960$	$4\cdot8960$
$24\cdot7$	$1\cdot3927$	
$\sqrt{3\cdot95}$	$0\cdot5966 \times \frac{1}{2} = 0\cdot2983$	
Denominator	$1\cdot6910$	$1\cdot6910$
$1603\cdot$		$3\cdot2050$

Answer 1603.

Example.—The percentage efficiency of an electric motor is given by the formula $\dfrac{2 \times 746\pi n \text{T},}{12 \times 33{,}000\text{VC}}$ where $n =$ number of rev. per min., T in. lb. is the torque, the voltage is V volts, and the current C amp.

Find the percentage efficiency when $n = 734$, $T = 29\cdot7$, $C = 2\cdot85$, $V = 175$.

Efficiency$\% = \dfrac{\cancel{2} \times 746 \times 3\cdot142 \times 734 \times 29\cdot7 \times 1\cancel{00}}{\cancel{12} \times 330\cancel{00} \times 175 \times 2\cdot85.}$
$ 6$

Number	Logarithm	
746	$2\cdot8727$	
$3\cdot142$	$0\cdot4972$	
734	$2\cdot8657$	
$29\cdot7$	$1\cdot4728$	
Numerator	$7\cdot7084$	$7\cdot7084$
6	$0\cdot7782$	
330	$2\cdot5185$	
175	$2\cdot2430$	
$2\cdot85$	$0\cdot4548$	
Denominator	$5\cdot9945$	$5\cdot9945$
$51\cdot75$		$1\cdot7139$

Efficiency $= 51\cdot7\%$.

In many calculations addition, subtraction, multiplication, and division all occur. It must be remembered that addition and subtraction are to be carried out in the ordinary way and that the use of logarithms applies only to multiplication and division, including powers and roots.

Example.—The surface area of a cone s sq. in. is given by the formula $s = \pi r^2 + \pi r \sqrt{r^2 + h^2}$, where r in. is the base radius and h in. the height   Calculate the surface area of a cone of base radius 10·7 in. and height 13·9 in., assuming $\pi = 3\cdot142$.

$$s = \pi(10\cdot7)^2 + \pi \times 10\cdot7\sqrt{(10\cdot7)^2 + (13\cdot9)^2}.$$

	Number		Logarithm
$(10\cdot7)^2 = 114\cdot5.$	$(10\cdot7)^2$	$1\cdot0294 \times 2 = 2\cdot0588$	
$(13\cdot9)^2 = 193\cdot2.$	$(13\cdot9)^2$	$1\cdot1430 \times 2 = 2\cdot286$	
$(10\cdot7)^2 + (13\cdot9)^2 = 307\cdot7$			
$3\cdot142 \times 10\cdot7 \times \sqrt{307\cdot7}$	$3\cdot142$		$0\cdot4972$
	$10\cdot7$		$1\cdot0294$
	$\sqrt{307\cdot7}$	$2\cdot4881 \times \frac{1}{2}$	$1\cdot2440$
	$589\cdot6$		$2\cdot7706$
$3\cdot142 \times (10\cdot7)^2.$	$3\cdot142$		$0\cdot4972$
	$(10\cdot7)^2$		$2\cdot0588$
	$359\cdot7$		$2\cdot5560$

$s = 589\cdot6 + 359\cdot7 = 949\cdot3.$
Area $= 949$ sq. in.

As the data are only given to three significant figures, the answer should not be given to a greater degree of accuracy.

Further tables

Tables of reciprocals, of squares, and of cubes are read as are tables of logarithms ; tables of squares may be read in the reverse way to find square roots, and of cubes to find cube roots. The student must insert any necessary decimal points, the digits only being given in the tables.

Using tables of squares in the example above :

$$s = \pi(10\cdot7)^2 + \pi \times 10\cdot7\sqrt{(10\cdot7)^2 + (13\cdot9)^2}.$$
$$= \pi \times 114\cdot5 + \pi \times 10\cdot7\sqrt{114\cdot5 + 193\cdot2}$$
$$= \pi \times 114\cdot5 + \pi \times 10\cdot7\sqrt{307\cdot7}.$$
$$= \pi \times 114\cdot5 + \pi \times 10\cdot7 \times 17\cdot54.$$

The calculation is then completed by using logarithms.

Exercise XXIII

(Assume that $\pi = 3\cdot142$.)

Evaluate :

1. $\sqrt{2\cdot976}$.　　　　2. $\sqrt{4597}$.　　　　3. $\sqrt[3]{26\cdot77}$.

4. $\sqrt[3]{100}$.　　　　5. $\sqrt[3]{2796}$.　　　　6. $\sqrt[5]{473\cdot8}$.

7. $\dfrac{1}{3\cdot45} + \dfrac{1}{15\cdot62}$.　　　　8. $\dfrac{1}{0\cdot782} + \dfrac{1}{0\cdot359} + \dfrac{1}{0\cdot835}$.

9. $\sqrt{(17\cdot1)^2 + (5\cdot89)^2}$.　　　　10. $\dfrac{1}{\sqrt{(3\cdot97)^2 + (4\cdot21)^2}}$.

11. The area of the curved surface of a cone is πrl sq. in., where r in. is the base radius and l in. the slant height. What is the area when the radius is $5\cdot23$ in. and the slant height $14\cdot7$ in. ?

12. The horse-power of an engine exerting a constant pull P lb. wt. and moving at v ml. per hr. is $\dfrac{Pv \times 22}{550 \times 15}$. Calculate the horse-power when $P = 3227$ and $v = 34$.

13. The surface area A sq. ft. and the volume V cu. ft. of a sphere of radius r ft. are given by $A = 4\pi r^2$, $V = \frac{4}{3}\pi r^3$. Find the surface area and the volume of a sphere of radius $2\cdot89$ feet.

14. The length l ft. of a simple pendulum of period t sec. is given by $l = \dfrac{gt^2}{4\pi^2}$. Find the length of a simple pendulum of period $1\cdot95$ sec. assuming that $g = 32\cdot2$.

15. The resistance R ohms of three wires in parallel of resistances r_1, r_2 and r_3 ohms respectively is given by $\dfrac{1}{R} = \dfrac{1}{r_1} + \dfrac{1}{r_2} + \dfrac{1}{r_3}$. Calculate the resistance of three wires in parallel of resistances $10\cdot5$, $8\cdot74$ and $9\cdot37$ ohms respectively.

16. If V cu. in. is the volume of a cone of height h in. and base radius r in., $V = \frac{1}{3}\pi r^2 h$. Calculate the volume of a cone of height 15·7 in. and radius 11·3 in. Assuming your result to be the volume of a cone of height 15·7 in., find its radius and hence verify your result.

17. The force P lb. wt. on a car weighing W lb. rounding a bend of radius r ft. at v ft. per sec. is given by $P = \frac{Wv^2}{gr}$. What is the force when $W = 875$, $v = 47$, $g = 32·2$, $r = 483$?

18. A racing car travelled 10 kilometres in 3 min. 27·5 sec. Express this speed in ml. per hr., assuming that 1 ml. = 1·609 Km.

19. $\sqrt{s(s-a)(s-b)(s-c)}$ sq. in. is the area of a triangle with sides a, b, c in. respectively, where $s = \frac{a+b+c}{2}$. Find the area of a triangle with sides 9·83 in., 13·45 in. and 19·74 in.

20. Find the radius of a sphere of volume 895·5 c.c. given that the radius of a sphere of volume V cu. in. is $\sqrt[3]{\frac{3V}{4\pi}}$ in.

21. The formula for finding the diameter d in. of a shaft required to transmit H horse-power at R revolutions per minute is $d = \sqrt[3]{\frac{321,400H}{RS}}$, where the safe stress of the material is S lb. per sq. in.

Find the diameter when the shaft is required to transmit 65 horse-power at 325 rev. per min. if the safe stress is 11,000 lb. per sq. in.

22. If water is contained in a hemispherical bowl of radius r in. to a depth h in., its volume is $\pi h^2\left(r - \frac{h}{3}\right)$ cu. in. What is the volume of water in a bowl of radius $13\frac{1}{2}$ in. if the depth of water is $8\frac{1}{2}$ in. ?

23. If a body be thrown vertically upwards with a velocity u ft. per sec., its velocity v ft. per sec. is given by $v^2 = u^2 - 2gs$. Find v when $u = 38·5$, $s = 17·5$, $g = 32·2$.

24. The radius of gyration of a rectangular plate of sides a in. and b in. about an axis through its centre perpendicular to its plane is $\sqrt{\frac{a^2 + b^2}{12}}$ in. Calculate the radius of gyration when the sides are 15·85 and 9·65 in. in length.

25. The inner radius of a flat circular ring of area A sq. in. is $\sqrt{a^2 - \dfrac{A}{\pi}}$ in., where a in. is the outer radius. What is the inner radius when the area is 127·6 sq. in. and the outer radius is 8·75 in. ?

26. The height h metres of a segment of a circle of radius r metres is given by $h = r - \sqrt{r^2 - a^2}$, where $2a$ metres is the length of the chord. Find the height of the segment when the radius is 4·37 m. and the chord is of length 3·49 m.

Negative characteristics

We know from tables that $3·426 = 10^{0·5348}$.

$$0·3426 = \frac{3·426}{10} = 10^{-1} \times 3·426 = 10^{-1+0·5348}.$$

Similarly $0·03426 = 10^{-2+0·5348}$.

Hence log $0·3426 = -1 + 0·5348$.

log $0·03426 = -2 + 0·5348$.

log $0·003426 = -3 + 0·5348$.

$-1 + 0·5348$ is written $\overline{1}·5348$ and is read " bar one 0·5348."

$-2 + 0·5348$ is written $\overline{2}·5348$ and is read " bar two 0·5348."

We see that the logarithms of numbers less than 1 are negative but are written with negative characteristics and positive mantissæ. Thus $-0·4537$ would be written as $-1 + 0·5463$ or $\overline{1}·5463$.

All numbers between 0·1 and 1 are between 10^{-1} and 10^0. Their logarithms will therefore lie between -1 and 0, i.e. will be $-1 +$ a positive decimal. Similarly the logarithms of numbers between 0·01 and 0·1 will be $-2 +$ a positive decimal. Proceeding in this way we may deduce that the negative characteristic of the logarithm of a decimal will be numerically 1 more than the number of 0's before the first significant figure.

Thus log $0·00003426 = \overline{5}·5348$ since four 0's follow the decimal point in the number before the first significant figure.

Example.—Evaluate $(0.4728)^7$

Number.   Logarithm.

$(0.4728)^7$ $7 \times \bar{1}.6746 = 7(-1 + 0.6746) = -7 + 4.7222$

0.005274 $= \bar{3}.7222$

$\therefore (0.4728)^7 = 0.005274.$

Example.—Evaluate $\sqrt[5]{0.04597}$

Number.   Logarithm.

$\sqrt[5]{0.04597}$ $\dfrac{\bar{2}.6625}{5} = \dfrac{-5 + 3.6625}{5} = -1 + 0.7325$

0.5401 $= \bar{1}.7325$

$\therefore \sqrt[5]{0.04597} = 0.5401.$

NOTE.—To divide $\bar{2}.6625$ by 5, we write it with a negative characteristic, -5; thus $-2 + 0.6625 = -5 + 3.6625.$

Example.—If r cm. is the radius of a copper cylinder of height h cm. weighing W gm., $r = \sqrt{\dfrac{W}{8.94\pi h}}$. Find the radius of a copper cylinder of height 3.26 cm. weighing 69.4 gm. assuming that $\pi = 3.142$.

$$r = \sqrt{\dfrac{69.4}{8.94 \times 3.142 \times 3.26}}.$$

Number.	Logarithm.	
69.4	1.8414	
Numerator		1.8414
8.94	0.9513	
3.142	0.4972	
3.26	0.5132	
Denominator	1.9617	1.9617
	$\frac{1}{2}(\bar{1}.8797)$	$\bar{1}.8797$
0.8706	$\bar{1}.9398$	

Radius $= 0.87$ cm.

Exercise XXIV

Evaluate :

17·18 1. 0.8735×19.67. *4317* 2. $.5829 \times .7406$.

24·83 3. $\dfrac{10.86}{.4374}$. *1·917* 4. $\dfrac{0.9876}{0.5437}$.

·9317 5. $\dfrac{0.7983}{0.8567}$. *4·697* 6. $\dfrac{5.678 \times 0.7938}{0.9596}$.

·6561 7. $3.142 \times (0.457)^2$. *·7698* 8. $\sqrt{0.5927}$.

·6580 9. $\sqrt[3]{.2849}$. *·2695* 10. $\sqrt{.0726}$.

2·809 11. $\sqrt{\dfrac{3.576}{0.4529}}$. *·8030* 12. $\sqrt{\dfrac{0.4836}{0.7497}}$.

187·1 13. If W lb. is the weight of an iron cylinder of diameter d ft. and height h ft., $W = \dfrac{7.79 \times 62.3 \pi d^2 h}{4}$. Find the weight of an iron cylinder of diameter 0·76 ft. and height 0·85 ft.

14. During an adiabatic expansion of a gas from a volume v_1 cu. in. at a pressure p_1 lb. per sq. in. to a volume v_2 cu. in. at a pressure p_2 lb. per sq. in. the work done by the gas is $\dfrac{p_1 v_1 - p_2 v_2}{c - 1}$ in. lb., where c is a constant. Calculate the work done by 24·7 cu. in. of gas at 17·4 lb. per sq. in. in expanding to 31·9 cu. in. at 12·3 lb. per sq. in. if $c = 1.42$.

15. From the formula $t = 2\pi \sqrt{\dfrac{l}{g}}$ for the period of a simple pendulum, find t when $l = 7.39$ and $g = 32.2$. *3·009*

16. A cast iron flywheel of mean radius r ft. makes n rev. per min. If S lb. be the stress in the rim and W lb. its weight, $S = 0.00005427 W r n^2$. Find the stress when the weight is 38·7 lb., the mean radius 4·93 ft. and $n = 213$.

469·8

17. $d = 0.36 \sqrt{\dfrac{v}{\sqrt{2g(h + h_1)}}}$ gives the diameter d ft. of the discharge pipe of a centrifugal pump, where v cu. ft. = volume of water pumped per minute, h ft. = height of suction and h_1 ft. = height of discharge. Find d when $v = 12.5$, $h = 14$, $h_1 = 19$, $g = 32$. *·1878*

18. The diameter d in. of a steel wire forming a helical spring which will carry a load of P lb. is given by $d = \sqrt[3]{\dfrac{2.55 P d_1}{s}}$, where

5066 IN.

d_1 in. is the mean diameter of the spring and s lb. per sq. in. the safe tensile stress. Find the diameter of the wire if the maximum load is 850 lb., the mean diameter of the spring $4\frac{1}{2}$ in. when the tensile stress must not exceed 75,000 lb. per sq. in.

19. The formula $d = \sqrt{\dfrac{Ta}{0\cdot85Ps}}$ gives the cylinder diameter of a locomotive engine. Find d when $T = 29,000$, $a = 58$, $P = 195$, $s = 22$.   *21·48*

20. The weight W lb. of steam per min. which will flow through a pipe 2 in. in diameter can be found from the formula

$$W = 52\cdot7 \sqrt{\frac{w(P - P_1)d^5}{l}},$$

where w lb. is the weight per cu. ft. of steam at initial pressure P lb. per sq. in., P_1 lb. per sq. in. is final pressure, d in. is diameter, and l ft. length of pipe. Find W when initial pressure is 42 lb. per sq. in., final pressure is 36 lb. per sq. in., $w = \cdot0972$ and $l = 95$.   *23·35*

21. The weight of a steel ball of radius r cm. is $\frac{4}{3} \times 7\cdot76\pi r^3$ gm. Find the radius of a steel ball weighing $\cdot64$ gm.   *·2701 CM.*

22. If V c.c. is the volume of a spherical shell of external radius a cm. and internal radius b cm. $a = \sqrt[3]{b^3 + \dfrac{3V}{4\pi}}$. Find the external radius of a shell of volume $2\cdot95$ c.c. with internal radius $\cdot58$ cm.   *·9652 CM*

23. If a cylinder of radius r cm. and length l cm. be making small oscillations about a horizontal diameter of one end, the period is $2\pi \sqrt{\dfrac{3r^2 + 4l^2}{6\,gl}}$ sec. Find the period when $r = 4\cdot7$ and $l = 9\cdot3$, given that $g = 981$.   *·545 SEC.*

24. Rankine's formula for the volume of steam at a given pressure is $PV^{\frac{17}{16}} = 475$. Find P when $V = 3\cdot86$.   *113·1*

25. The formula $v = \cdot0757cd^{\frac{2}{3}}\left(\dfrac{h}{l}\right)^{\frac{1}{2}}$ occurs in connection with the discharge of water through pipes. Find v when $c = 160$, $d = 1\cdot63$, $h = 68$, $l = 1980$.   *3·109*

Slide rule

An instrument in common use by technical men for carrying out calculations quickly is the " slide rule." This is a practical application of logarithms in which the graduations are spaced according to the logarithms of numbers. A book of instructions is usually supplied by the makers with each rule; a study of the book and use of the rule would be interesting and profitable to the student.

The slide rule is a rule in which the central part, called the slide, can be moved parallel to the length of the rule. On

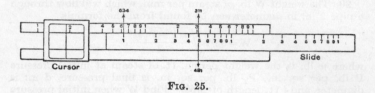

Fig. 25.

both the fixed part of the rule and on the slide there are similar scales in which the graduations are spaced according to the logarithms of the numbers.

Since the logarithm of 1 is 0, the zero on each scale is marked 1 and the distances from this point to the points marked 2, 3, 4, etc., are the logarithms of 2, 3 and 4 respectively.

Examples of use of the rule

1. Evaluate $63\cdot4 \times 0\cdot491$.

First find an approximate answer; $63\cdot4 \times 0\cdot491 \backsimeq 30$. Place 1 on the slide against 634 on the rule and read off on the rule the number 311, which is opposite 491 on the slide. By this operation we have added the lengths, which are the logarithms of 634 and 491, and found that their sum is the logarithm of a number starting with the figures 311. Our approximate answer shows that the decimal point comes after 31 and hence $63\cdot4 \times 0\cdot491 \backsimeq 31\cdot1$.

Notice that in using the rule we disregard the position of the decimal point absolutely; its position is always fixed by finding a rough answer.

2. Evaluate $\dfrac{31\cdot1}{0\cdot491}$.

Rough answer $= \dfrac{300}{5} = 60$.

Place 491 on the slide opposite 311 on the rule and read off the quotient 634 on the rule opposite to 1 on the slide. This is just the reverse of the procedure in the first example.

The cursor

To enable the position of a point on the rule or slide to be kept while the slide is moved, a piece called the " cursor " (see Fig. 25) is provided which slides on the outside of the rule and contains a hair line which can be placed over any number on the rule or slide. The cursor is useful in long calculations such as the one below.

Example.—Evaluate $\dfrac{24\cdot7 \times 0\cdot35 \times 0\cdot591}{1\cdot27 \times 456}$.

Rough answer $= \dfrac{25 \times 6 \times \frac{1}{2}}{400} = \dfrac{75}{400} = 0\cdot2$.

Place 127 on the slide opposite 247 on the rule. Move the cursor line to 635 on the slide. Then place 456 on the slide opposite the cursor line and move the cursor to 591 on the slide. Then the number 160 on the rule under the cursor line is the required answer, apart from the decimal point. Hence answer $= 0\cdot160$.

By the above procedure we have started with log 247, subtracted log 127, added log 635, subtracted log 456 and finally added log 591. So that we must finish with the logarithm of the answer.

Work out Exercises 4–13 inclusive, on p. 117, by using a slide rule.

CHAPTER VIII

FURTHER ALGEBRAIC PROCESSES

Products of simple expressions

In Chapter III we saw that $(a+b)c = ac+bc$.

If, in this equation, we put $c+d$ instead of c, we get
$$(a+b)(c+d) = a(c+d) + b(c+d).$$
$$= ac + ad + bc + bd.$$

Thus the product of $(a+b)$ and $(c+d)$ is the sum of the products of each term of $a+b$ with each term of $c+d$. The terms of the product are the areas of the four small rectangles in the figure below, the area of the whole figure being $(a+b)(c+d)$.

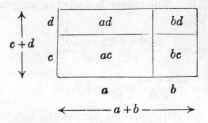

Example.—Multiply $2x+3$ by $4x+5$.
$$(2x+3)(4x+5) = 2x(4x+5) + 3(4x+5)$$
$$= 8x^2 + 10x + 12x + 15$$
$$= 8x^2 + 22x + 15.$$

If we write this product $(2x+3)(4x+5)$, then we see

that the terms $8x^2$ and 15 are obtained by multiplying the first terms of each bracket and the last terms of each bracket respectively, i.e. the terms linked by the curved lines above the brackets ; also the term $22x$ is the sum of the products $10x$ and $12x$ of the terms linked by curves below the brackets,

With a little practice the " x^2 " terms, the " x " term and the term without x can be picked out in this way.

In the product of $(a+b)(c+d)$ there is no restriction on the numbers a, b, c, d. They can be positive or negative.

Example.—Multiply $2p-5q$ by $3p+8q$.

$$(2p-5q)(3p+8q) = 2p(3p+8q) -5q(3p+8q)$$
$$= 6p^2 + 16pq - 15pq - 40q^2$$
$$= 6p^2 + pq - 40q^2.$$

Example.—Multiply $3-2y$ by $3y-4$.

$$(3-2y)(3y-4) = 3(3y-4) - 2y(3y-4)$$
$$= 9y - 12 - 6y^2 + 8y$$
$$= -6y^2 + 17y - 12.$$

Multiplication can be set out as in arithmetic. To multiply $(3y-4)$ by $(3-2y)$ we write $3-2y$ with the y term first, that is, as $-2y+3$, underneath $3y-4$. We multiply $3y-4$ first by $-2y$ and then by 3, placing like terms under like.

$$\begin{array}{l} 3y-4 \\ -2y+3 \\ \hline -6y^2+8y \\ +9y-12 \\ \hline -6y^2+17y-12 \end{array}$$

this line $= -2y(3y-4)$.
this line $= +3\ (3y-4)$.

Formulæ for $(a+b)^2$, $(a-b)^2$ and $(a+b)(a-b)$.

Just as a^2 stands for $a \times a$, so $(a+b)^2$ stands for $(a+b) \times (a+b)$.

$$\therefore (a+b)^2 = (a+b)(a+b) = a(a+b) + b(a+b) = a^2 + ab + ab + b^2.$$
$$\therefore\ (a+b)^2 = a^2 + 2ab + b^2.$$

In the same way :

$$(a-b)^2 = a^2 - 2ab + b^2.$$
$$(a+b)(a-b) = a^2 - b^2.$$

These products are so important that they should be remembered.

5

Example.—Simplify $(l-x)^2-(l-2x)(l+2x)$.

By the formulæ above :

$$(l-x)^2 = l^2 - 2lx + x^2,$$
$$(l-2x)(l+2x) = l^2 - (2x)^2 = l^2 - 4x^2.$$
$$\therefore (l-x)^2 - (l-2x)(l+2x) = l^2 - 2lx + x^2 - (l^2 - 4x^2)$$
$$= l^2 - 2lx + x^2 - l^2 + 4x^2$$
$$= -2lx + 5x^2,$$
$$\text{or } 5x^2 - 2lx.$$

Factors

30 has factors 2, 3 and 5, because $2 \times 3 \times 5 = 30$.

In the same way abc has factors a, b and c because abc means $a \times b \times c$.

We have seen that $ab + ac = a(b+c)$. This shows that a and $b+c$ are factors of $ab+ac$, and by writing $ab+ac$ in the form $a(b+c)$ we are said to have factorized it.

Simple expressions can be factorized by finding the highest common factor of each term.

Example.—Factorize $3x - 15y$.

$$3x = 3 \times x \text{ and } 15y = 3 \times 5 \times y.$$

Hence the highest common factor of $3x$ and $15y$ is **3**.

$$\therefore 3x - 15y = 3(x - 5y).$$

Example.—Factorize $2l^2x - lx^2$.

$$2l^2x = 2 \times l \times l \times x.$$
$$lx^2 = l \times x \times x.$$
$$\therefore \text{ H.C.F.} = lx.$$
$$\therefore 2l^2x - lx^2 = lx \times 2l - lx \times x.$$
$$= lx(2l - x).$$

An expression may have factors even when its terms have no common factor.

Example.—Factorize $xy - xz + ay - az$.

$$xy - xz + ay - az = x(y - z) + a(y - z)$$
$$= (x + a)(y - z).$$

The formula $a^2 - b^2 = (a+b)(a-b)$ can be used to factorize the difference of any two squares, and it is often useful in calculating the difference of two squares.

Example.—Factorize $p^2 - 4q^2$.
$$p^2 - 4q^2 = p^2 - (2q)^2 = (p + 2q)(p - 2q).$$

Example.—Find $\sqrt{150^2 - 144^2}$.
$$150^2 - 144^2 = (150 + 144)(150 - 144)$$
$$= 294 \times 6 = 49 \times 6 \times 6 = 7^2 \times 6^2.$$
$$\therefore \ \sqrt{150^2 - 144^2} = 7 \times 6 = 42.$$

Example.—Factorize $(x + 2a)^2 - 9a^2$.
$$(x + 2a)^2 - 9a^2 = (x + 2a)^2 - (3a)^2$$
$$= (x + 2a + 3a)(x + 2a - 3a)$$
$$= (x + 5a)(x - a).$$

Factors of $x^2 + px + q$

By multiplication :
$$(x + 3)(x + 2) = x(x + 2) + 3(x + 2)$$
$$= x^2 + 2x + 3x + 2 \times 3$$
$$= x^2 + (2 + 3)x + 2 \times 3$$
$$= x^2 + 5x + 6.$$

Notice that in the last line $5 = 2 + 3$ and $6 = 2 \times 3$.

To factorize $x^2 + 5x + 6$ we have to find two numbers whose sum is 5 and whose product is 6, so that we can write out the steps above in the reverse order. To do this write down the pairs of numbers whose product is 6, namely 6×1 and 2×3 and pick out the pair, in this case 2 and 3, whose sum is 5. Then we can factorize $x^2 + 5x + 6$ as follows :
$$x^2 + 5x + 6 = x^2 + (2 + 3)x + 2 \times 3$$
$$= x^2 + 2x + 3x + 2 \times 3$$
$$= x(x + 2) + 3(x + 2)$$
$$= (x + 3)(x + 2).$$

Example.—Factorize $x^2 + 8x + 12$.

$12 = 12 \times 1$ or 6×2 or 4×3. The only pair whose sum is 8 is 6 and 2. Hence we write $8 = 6 + 2$ and $12 = 6 \times 2$. Then :
$$x^2 + 8x + 12 = x^2 + 6x + 2x + 6 \times 2$$
$$= x(x + 6) + 2(x + 6)$$
$$= (x + 2)(x + 6).$$

Example.—Factorize $x^2 - 8x + 12$.

In this example we split up 8 and 12 in the same way :

$$x^2 - 8x + 12 = x^2 - 6x - 2x + 6 \times 2$$
$$= x(x - 6) - 2(x - 6)$$
$$= (x - 2)(x - 6).$$

Now consider the product $(x + 3)(x - 2)$.

$$(x + 3)(x - 2) = x(x - 2) + 3(x - 2)$$
$$= x^2 - 2x + 3x - 3 \times 2$$
$$= x^2 + (3 - 2)x - 3 \times 2$$
$$= x^2 + x - 6.$$

So to factorize an expression like $x^2 + x - 6$, where the numerical term is negative, we have to find two numbers, in this case 2 and 3, whose product is 6 and whose *difference* is 1.

Example.—Factorize $l^2 - 7l - 18$.

$18 = 18 \times 1$ or 9×2 or 6×3. The difference of 9 and 2 is 7 so we write $7l = (9 - 2)l$ and $18 = 9 \times 2$.

$$\therefore \quad l^2 - 7l - 18 = l^2 - (9 - 2)l - 9 \times 2$$
$$= l^2 - 9l + 2l - 9 \times 2$$
$$= l(l - 9) + 2(l - 9)$$
$$= (l + 2)(l - 9).$$

The method used is the same for an expression like $p^2 - 10pq + 16q^2$, which contains two letters.

$16 = 16 \times 1$ or 8×2 or 4×4. The sum of 8 and 2 is 10.

$$\therefore \quad p^2 - 10pq + 16q^2 = p^2 - (8 + 2)pq + 8 \times 2q^2$$
$$= p^2 - 8pq - 2pq + 8 \times 2q^2$$
$$= p(p - 8q) - 2q(p - 8q)$$
$$= (p - 2q)(p - 8q).$$

If $x^2 - 10x + 7 = (x - a)(x - b)$ the numbers a and b cannot be whole numbers because there are no two whole numbers whose sum is 10 and whose product is 7. We shall see in page 134a that values of a and b can nevertheless be found. In this example they are approximately 0·757 and 9·24. It is

FURTHER ALGEBRAIC PROCESSES

133

easy to verify this because $0.757 + 9.24 = 10.00$ and 0.757×9.24
$= 7.00$, both to two decimal places.   Hence—
$$x^2 - 10x + 7 \approx (x - 0.757)(x - 9.24).$$

Simplification of fractions

Fractions can often be simplified by factorizing the
numerator and denominator.

Example.—Simplify $\dfrac{2p^2 - 8p}{p^2 - 16}$.

$$2p^2 - 8p = 2p(p-4) \text{ and } p^2 - 16 = (p+4)(p-4).$$

$$\therefore \frac{2p^2 - 8p}{p^2 - 16} = \frac{2p(p-4)}{(p+4)(p-4)} = \frac{2p}{p+4}.$$

Example.—Simplify $\dfrac{x^2 + 6x + 5}{x^2 + 3x - 10}$.

$$\frac{x^2 + 6x + 5}{x^2 + 3x - 10} = \frac{(x+1)(x+5)}{(x+5)(x-2)} = \frac{x+1}{x-2}.$$

Equations with two roots

Example.—A piece of fencing is 36 ft. long.   It is required to
divide it into three parts BC, CD, DA, which, when placed in
contact with a wall so as to form a rectangle ABCD, shall

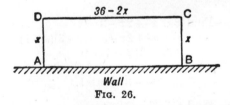

Wall

Fig. 26.

enclose an area of 64 sq. ft.   Find the lengths of the parts
into which it should be divided.

The figure shows the rectangle formed by the fencing.   Let
the length of each of the sides BC and AD be x ft.   Then the
length of CD is $(36 - 2x)$ ft., and so the area of the rectangle is

$x(36 - 2x)$ sq. ft. This is given to be 64 sq. ft. and hence x is given by the equation :

$$x(36 - 2x) = 64.$$
$$\therefore \; 36x - 2x^2 = 64.$$
$$\therefore \; 18x - x^2 = 32.$$
$$\therefore \; 18x - x^2 - 32 = 0.$$
$$\therefore \; x^2 - 18x + 32 = 0.$$

Now $x^2 - 18x + 32$ has factors $x - 16$ and $x - 2$, so we can write the equation :

$$(x - 16)(x - 2) = 0.$$

This is true if, either $x - 16 = 0$, or $x - 2 = 0$, i.e. $x = 16$ or $x = 2$. No other value of x will make it true. For instance, $x = 20$ makes $(x - 16)(x - 2) = 4 \times 18$.

Hence BC and AD must be either 16 ft. each, or 2 ft. each.

If BC and AD are 16 ft., then CD is $36 - 2 \times 16$ ft. $= 4$ ft., and if BC and AD are 2 ft. then CD is $36 - 2 \times 2$ ft. $= 32$ ft.

Therefore either BC and AD are 16 ft. and CD is 4 ft.,
         or BC and AD are 2 ft. and CD is 32 ft.

The point to notice in the solution of the above problem is that an equation like $x^2 + px + q = 0$, which is called a quadratic equation, can be solved by splitting $x^2 + px + q$ into factors. Some further examples of this method of solution are given below.

Example.—Find x if $x^2 + 2x - 3 = 0$.
$$x^2 + 2x - 3 = (x + 3)(x - 1)$$
$$\therefore (x + 3)(x - 1) = 0$$
$$\therefore \; x + 3 = 0 \text{ or } x - 1 = 0$$
$$\therefore \; x = -3 \text{ or } x = 1.$$

Example.—Find t if $66 = t^2 - 5t$.
$$-t^2 + 5t + 66 = 0$$
$$\therefore \; t^2 - 5t - 66 = 0$$
$$\therefore \; (t + 6)(t - 11) = 0$$
$$\therefore \; t + 6 = 0 \text{ or } t - 11 = 0$$
$$\therefore \; t = -6 \text{ or } t = 11.$$

Solution by completing the Square.

Another method of solving the equation $x^2 + 2x - 3 = 0$ (see example on p. 134) is as follows :

First write the equation $x^2 + 2x = 3$ and then, because $x^2 + 2x + 1 = (x + 1)^2$, add 1 to both sides of the equation.

Thus $\qquad\qquad x^2 + 2x + 1 = 3 + 1$

$\qquad\qquad\qquad \therefore (x + 1)^2 = 4.$

Hence, because $2^2 = 4$ and $(-2)^2 = 4$,

either $\qquad\qquad x + 1 = 2$ or $x + 1 = -2.$

Therefore $\qquad\quad x = 2 - 1 = 1$ or $x = -2 - 1 = -3.$

The same method can be used when there are no easy factors as in the following example.

Example.—Solve the equation $x^2 - 10x + 7 = 0.$

Subtracting 7 from both sides

$$x^2 - 10x = -7.$$

Now $x^2 - 10x + 25 = (x - 5)^2$, so add 25 to both sides

$$x^2 - 10x + 25 = -7 + 25 = 18,$$

i.e. $\qquad\qquad (x - 5)^2 = 18.$

$\therefore$ either $\qquad x - 5 = \sqrt{18} = \sqrt{9 \times 2} = 3\sqrt{2} = 4 \cdot 243$

or $\qquad\qquad x - 5 = -\sqrt{18} = -4 \cdot 243.$

i.e. $\quad x = 5 + 4 \cdot 243 = 9 \cdot 243$ or $x = 5 - 4 \cdot 243 = 0 \cdot 757.$

We note that in each case the number which has to be added to both sides is the square of half the coefficient of x ; in the first equation above it is $\left(\dfrac{2}{2}\right)^2 = 1$ and in the second equation

it is $\left(\dfrac{-10}{2}\right)^2 = 5^2 = 25.$

If $x^2 - 10x + 7 = (x - a)(x - b)$, then $x^2 - 10x + 7 = 0$ when $x = a$ or b and hence a and b are $9 \cdot 24$ and $0 \cdot 757$ as stated on page 132.

In the following example the method of completing the square is used in solving a quadratic equation which occurs in a problem in physics.

Example.—If a tube, of length l cm., with one end closed is immersed vertically in water with the open end downwards until this end is at a depth y cm. below the surface of the water, the length of the column of air in the tube becomes x cm., where x is given by

$$x^2 + (76 + l - y)x = 76l.$$

Find x when $l = 8$ and $y = 10$.

Substituting these values

$$x^2 + (76 + 8 - 10)x = 760$$
$$\therefore \quad x^2 + 74x = 760$$
$$\therefore \quad x^2 + 74x + \left(\frac{74}{2}\right)^2 = 760 + \left(\frac{74}{2}\right)^2$$
$$\therefore \quad (x + 37)^2 = 760 + 1369 = 2129$$

$$\therefore \text{ either} \qquad x + 37 = \sqrt{2129} \backsimeq 46 \cdot 14$$
$$\text{or} \qquad x + 37 = -\sqrt{2129} \backsimeq -46 \cdot 14$$
$$\therefore \qquad x \backsimeq 9 \cdot 14 \text{ or } -83 \cdot 14.$$

Hence the length of the column of air is $9 \cdot 14$ cm., the negative value being impossible.

Exercise XXV

Express the following products without brackets:

1. $(l + 2)(l + 3)$.   2. $(a + 1)(a + 2)$.

3. $(x + 7)(x + 9)$.   4. $(x - 1)(x + 5)$.

5. $(t - 4)(t - 11)$.   6. $(2y - 1)(3y + 1)$.

7. $(p - q)(p + 2q)$.   8. $(2x + 7y)(3x - y)$.

9. $(2 - 3x)(4 + 5x)$.   10. $(4 - t)(2 - 3t)$.

Multiply the following expressions by using brackets and also by placing one expression beneath the other and multiplying as in arithmetic :

11. $a + 2$ and $a + 6$.   12. $2x + 1$ and $3x + 4$.

13. $l + m$ and $2l - m$.   14. $1 - y$ and $2 - 4y$.

15. $p + 2q$ and $p - 2q$.   16. $2t + T$ and $3t - T$.

Express without brackets:

17. $(x + 2y)^2$.　　**18.** $(2l - 5m)^2$.　　　　**19.** $(z - 6)^2$.

20. $(1 + 3k)^2$.　　**21.** $(t^2 + 1)^2$.　　　　**22.** $(\sqrt{x} - 2)^2$.

23. $(2x - y)(2x + y)$.　　　**24.** $(a - 7b)(a + 7b)$.

Fill in the brackets in the following equations:

25. $x^2 - 4x = x ($　　　$)$.　　**26.** $2xy^2 - 3x^2y = xy ($　　　$)$.

27. $ax + bx - ay - by = x ($　　　$) - y ($　　　$) = (x - y)($　　　$)$.

28. $x^2 - 4l^2 = (x + 2l)($　　　$)$.

29. $R^2 - r^2 = (R - r)($　　　$)$.

30. $x^2 + 6x + 5 = (x + 1)($　　　$)$.

31. $x^2 - 5x + 6 = (x - 3)($　　　$)$.

32. $K^2 - K - 2 = (K - 2)($　　　$)$.

33. $T^2 - 3T - 10 = (T + 2)($　　　$)$.

Factorize:

34. $t^2 + 3t$.　　　　**35.** $l^2 - lm$.　　　　**36.** $2p^4 + p^2q^2$.

37. $x^2y - x^2y^2$.　　**38.** $6abc - 9bc^2$.　　**39.** $4kl + 5kl^3$.

40. $x^2 + 4x + 3$.　　**41.** $t^2 + 7t + 6$.　　**42.** $l^2 + 7l + 10$.

43. $p^2 + 8p + 15$.　　**44.** $p^2 + 16p + 15$.　　**45.** $x^2 + 7x + 12$.

46. $p^2 - 3p + 2$.　　**47.** $x^2 - 11x + 10$.　　**48.** $x^2 - 7x + 10$.

49. $y^2 - 8y + 12$.　　**50.** $y^2 - 7y + 12$.　　**51.** $k^2 - 13k + 36$.

52. $x^2 - x - 2$.　　**53.** $y^2 - 3y - 10$.　　**54.** $t^2 - 5t - 6$.

55. $t^2 - t - 6$.　　**56.** $m^2 - m - 12$.　　**57.** $m^2 - 4m - 12$.

Simplify the expressions:

58. $\dfrac{l^2 - l}{l - 1}$.　　**59.** $\dfrac{t^2 - 2t}{t^3 - 2t^2}$.　　**60.** $\dfrac{x^2 - x}{x^2 - 1}$.

61. $\dfrac{(l - m)^2}{l^2 - m^2}$.　　**62.** $\dfrac{x^2 - 3x + 2}{x^2 - 4}$.　　**63.** $\dfrac{y^2 - 6y + 8}{y^2 - y - 2}$.

64. $\dfrac{m^2 - n^2}{m^2 + mn}$.　　**65.** $\dfrac{(k + 4)^2 - k^2}{k^2 + 5k + 6}$.

5*

Solve the equations :

66. $x^2 - 4x - 5 = 0$.   **67.** $x^2 + 6x + 5 = 0$.

68. $x^2 - 3x - 10 = 0$.   **69.** $t^2 + 10t - 11 = 0$.

70. $l^2 - 6l = 16$.   **71.** $2 + k = k^2$.   **72.** $m^2 - 9 = 0$.

73. $x^2 - 5x = 0$.   **74.** $(x+4)^2 = 6 + x$.

75. The area of a rectangle is 15 sq. in. and the sum of the lengths of its sides is 16 in. Find the lengths of its sides.

76. When a cable x ft. long is stretched between two points at the same level, the sag z ft. is given by the equation $z^2 - (T/w)z + x^2/4 = 0$ where T lb. wt. is the tension at the ends and w lb. wt. is the weight per unit length. Find z (i) when T $= 2600$, $w = 4$, and $x = 160$, (ii) when T $= 200$, $w = 2$, and $x = 80$.

77. When a wooden bar 10 ft. long and specific gravity s floats partly in water the upper end being supported by a string, x ft. of the bar is immersed, where x is given by $x^2 - 2lx + sl^2 = 0$. Find x if $l = 10$ and $s = \frac{16}{25}$.

78. If one arm of a **U**-tube containing mercury is sealed leaving a column of air of length 6 in., and 8 in. more of mercury are poured into the open end, the mercury rises x in. in the closed end, where x is given by $x^2 - 25x + 24 = 0$. Find x.

79. Solve the equations in Questions 66, 67, 68, 69 by completing the square.

Solve the following equations giving the roots to three significant figures.

80. $x^2 + 2x = 14$.   **81.** $y^2 - 4y + 1 = 0$.

82. $x^2 - 42x - 150 = 0$.   **83.** $t^2 + 28t = 54$.

84. If, in Question 77, $l = 20$, $s = 0 \cdot 4$, find x.

85. If, in Question 76, T $= 3600$, $w = 4$ and $x = 600$, find z.

86. If $s = ut + \frac{1}{2}ft^2$ find t when $s = 20$, $u = 18$, and $f = -2$.

Miscellaneous exercises in Algebraic processes.

Simplify :

87. $\frac{1}{3}\pi r^3 h \div (\frac{1}{2}\pi r h)$.   **88.** $(1 + 2a)(1 - 2a) + (\frac{1}{2}a)(8a)$.

89. $\dfrac{2a}{b} + \dfrac{(a-b)^2}{b^2}$.   **90.** $(1 + \frac{1}{2}x)^2 - (x + 1)$.

CHAPTER IX

RATIO, PROPORTION AND VARIATION

Ratio and proportion

On page 22 we saw that, if one quantity is expressed as a fraction of another, the fraction measures the ratio of the two quantities. Suppose two cans hold 2 and 3 gallons respectively, then the volume of the smaller can is $\frac{2}{3}$ the volume of the larger can, that is, the ratio of their volumes is $\frac{2}{3}$. To express that this is a ratio it is often written $2:3$. Similarly if the cans held a and p gallons respectively the ratio of the volume of the former to that of the latter is $\frac{a}{p}$ or $a:p$. If $\frac{a}{p} = \frac{b}{q}$, the ratio of a to p is the same as the ratio of b to q. Another way of writing this is $a:p::b:q$, which is read " a is to p as b is to q "; here " is to " stands for " is in the same ratio to."

When $\frac{a}{p} = \frac{b}{q}$ the four numbers a, p, b, q are said to form a proportion and the numbers a and b to be proportional to p and q respectively. Similarly if $\frac{a}{p} = \frac{b}{q} = \frac{c}{r} = \frac{d}{s}$, etc., the numbers a, b, c, d, etc., are proportional to p, q, r, s, etc., respectively.

A common example of proportion occurs in making a map of a town. The length of every line on the map has to be proportional to the length of the road, river or railway, which it represents. If, for instance, a map is drawn to a scale of $\frac{1}{2}$ in. to 1 ml., and if lengths p, q, r miles are represented by a, b, c inches on the map, then

$$\frac{a}{p} = \frac{b}{q} = \frac{c}{r} = \frac{1}{2}.$$

Hence $a = \frac{1}{2}p$, $b = \frac{1}{2}q$, $c = \frac{1}{2}r$.

$\therefore a + b + c = \frac{1}{2}p + \frac{1}{2}q + \frac{1}{2}r = \frac{1}{2}(p + q + r)$.

$\therefore \dfrac{a+b+c}{p+q+r} = \frac{1}{2}$, which equals $\dfrac{a}{p}$, $\dfrac{b}{q}$ and $\dfrac{c}{r}$.

The meaning of this result is that the total length $(a + b + c)$ inches on the map represents the total length $(p + q + r)$ miles in the town to the same scale as a in. represents p ml.

This is clearly true whatever the scale of the map, and so whenever $(a/p) = (b/q) = (c/r)$ each ratio equals the ratio $(a + b + c)/(p + q + r)$.

If a and b are proportional to p and q,

$$\frac{a}{p} = \frac{b}{q}, \quad \therefore aq = bp \quad \therefore \frac{a}{b} = \frac{p}{q}.$$

and hence a and p are proportional to b and q.

Example.—It is required to divide a piece of wood 6 ft. long into two parts so that the ratio of their lengths shall be 2:3. Find the lengths of the two parts. Also find their lengths if the length of the wood is a ft. and the ratio of the parts is l:m.

Mark off $2 + 3$, i.e. 5 equal lengths, each 6/5 ft. on the wood, and cut it so that there are two of these lengths in one part and three in the other. Then the lengths of the two parts are 2(6/5) ft. and 3(6/5) ft., which are 2·4 ft. and 3·6 ft. respectively, and their ratio is clearly 2:3.

Now we will work out the same problem using algebra. Let the length of the shorter part be x ft., then the length of the other part is $(6 - x)$ ft.

Hence the ratio of the parts is $x : (6 - x)$

$$\therefore \frac{x}{6-x} = \frac{2}{3}$$

$$\therefore 3x = 2(6 - x) = 12 - 2x$$

$$\therefore 3x + 2x = 12$$

$$\therefore 5x = 12$$

$$\therefore x = 2·4 \text{ and } 6 - x = 3·6.$$

If the parts are in the ratio l/m and the length of the wood is a ft.,

$$\frac{x}{a-x} = \frac{l}{m}$$
$$\therefore \ mx = l(a-x) = la - lx$$
$$\therefore \ lx + mx = la$$
$$\therefore \ x = \frac{la}{l+m}.$$

Variation

If a body moves s ft. in t sec. at a uniform speed of 6 ft. per sec., $s/t = 6$. Suppose it moves s_1 ft. in t_1 sec., s_2 ft. in t_2 sec., s_3 ft. in t_3 sec., and so on, then :

$$\frac{s_1}{t_1} = \frac{s_2}{t_2} = \frac{s_3}{t_3} = 6.$$

Thus s_1, s_2, s_3 are proportional to t_1, t_2, and t_3 respectively. In fact every value of s is proportional to the corresponding value of t.

When two variable quantities s and t are such that the ratio s/t is the same for all pairs of corresponding values of s and t we say that s varies as t, and we write $s \propto t$ as short for " s varies as t."

It follows that $s \propto t$ means $s/t = k$, where k is a fixed number; k is 6 in the above example.

We have seen that the graph of $s - kt$ is a straight line through the point (O, O). Conversely, if the graph of s against t is a straight line through the point (O, O), $s \propto t$.

It often happens that we know that one quantity varies as another but we do not know the fixed number k until we have made an experiment. For instance, if the electrical resistance of a piece of wire of uniform cross section and length l ft. is R ohms, it is known that $R \propto l$, that is, $R = kl$. Suppose an experiment with a certain wire gives $R = 6$ when $l = 20$, then—

$$6 = 20k, \ \therefore \ k = 0\cdot3$$

Hence the relation between R and l for wire of this particular cross section is $R = 0·3l$. From this relation, which is called " the law of variation of R," the resistance of any length of this wire can be calculated.

Let R_1, R_2 ohms be the resistances of l_1, l_2 ft. of wire respectively, then—

$$\frac{R_2}{R_1} = \frac{0·3l_2}{0·3l_1} = \frac{l_2}{l_1}.$$

Therefore, when $R \propto l$, if l is altered in a certain ratio, R is altered in the same ratio. If l is doubled, R is doubled ; if l is trebled, R is trebled, and so on.

It often happens that two related quantities in science or engineering are such that one quantity varies as some power of the other. For instance, when an electric fire is plugged into a circuit of voltage V, the heat produced by the fire in one minute varies as V^2. If the heat produced is H British Thermal Units, $H \propto V^2$, that is $H = kV^2$, where k is a constant. Suppose that an experiment shows that $H = 12,960$ when $V = 200$, then k is given by $12,960 = k \times 200^2$.

$$\therefore k = \frac{1·296}{4} = 0·324.$$

Hence the law connecting H and V is :

$$H = 0·324V^2.$$

This law can be used to calculate H for any other mains voltage.

For a voltage of 230 :

$$H = 0·324 \times 230^2 = 17,140.$$

If in a relation of this kind we change the units in which the variable quantities are measured, the constant in the law of variation will have a different value. Suppose the heat produced by the fire is H calories instead of H British Thermal Units, then since 1 B.T.U. $= \frac{5}{9}$ calorie, at 200 volts the heat of the fire will be given by—

$$H = 12,960 \times \tfrac{5}{9} = 7200.$$

If in this case :

$$H = k'V^2,$$
$$7200 = k' \times 200^2.$$
$$\therefore k' = \frac{7200}{200^2} = \frac{0.72}{2} = 0.18.$$
$$\therefore H = 0.18V^2$$

is the formula, which gives the heat in calories.

Other examples of one quantity varying as a power of another are :

" The area of a circle varies as the square of its radius."

" The period of one oscillation of a simple pendulum varies as the square root of the length of the pendulum."

" The current produced in a wire by a cell of a given voltage varies as the reciprocal of the resistance of the wire."

" The time of the exposure of a photographic plate varies as the square of the stop used."

" The candle-power of one electric lamp varies as a power of the voltage, the power depending on the type of lamp used."

When $y \propto x$ we say that " y varies directly as x " in order to distinguish this type of variation from examples where y varies as some power of x.

If $y \propto x^2$, $y = kx^2$, where k is a constant number and so the graph of y against x is not a straight line but a curve. In fact, if y varies as any power of x, other than the first, the graph of y against x is a curve. But, if we write X for x^2, then $y = kX$, which has a straight line graph if we plot y against X. Consequently, if we plot x^2 horizontally instead of x, the graph of $y = kx^2$ is a straight line.

Example.—A beam is supported at points l ft. apart at the same level, and a fixed load is hung from the centre. The distance of the centre below the ends is then found to be y in.

In an experiment y was measured for 6 values of l and the following values of y were obtained :

l	..	2	4	6	8	10	12
y	..	0.03	0.22	0.75	1.77	3.47	6.00

Plot a graph of y against l, and show that y does not vary directly as l. Then plot a graph of y against l^3, and show that $y \propto l^3$, and find the equation connecting y and l.

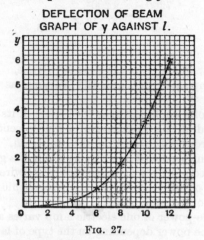

DEFLECTION OF BEAM
GRAPH OF y AGAINST l.

FIG. 27.

The graph of y against l is shown in Fig. 27. It is not a straight line, and hence y does not vary as l.

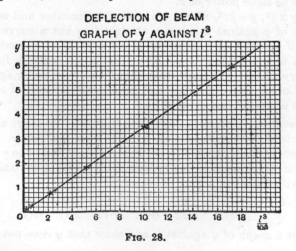

DEFLECTION OF BEAM
GRAPH OF y AGAINST l^3.

FIG. 28.

To draw the graph of y against l^3 we require a table of values of l^3 :

| l^3 | .. | 8 | 64 | 216 | 512 | 1000 | 1728 |
| y | .. | 0·03 | 0·22 | 0·75 | 1·77 | 3·47 | 6·00 |

The graph of y against l^3 is shown in Fig. 28. For convenience the values of $l^3/100$ are given on the horizontal scale, This graph is a straight line through the origin. Hence $y \propto l^3$, that is, $y = kl^3$. Substituting the values $y = 3·47$ when $l^3 = 1000$, we find $k = 0·00347$.

$$\therefore y = 0·00347l^3.$$

Exercise XXVI

1. Express $l : m :: 7 : 5$ as an equation. Use the equation to find the value of $(l + m)/(l - m)$.

2. If $6y = 11x$ what is the ratio of x to y ? Find the value of $(x + 2y)/(3x - y)$.

3. If a length of 2 miles is represented on a map by $\frac{1}{2}$ in., how many inches will represent lengths of 5 ml., $\frac{2}{3}$ ml. and n miles respectively ?

4. A set of picture frames has to be made in which the ratio of the height h in. to the breadth b in. is 4/3. What is the formula connecting h and b ? If the height of one frame is double that of another, what is the ratio of their areas ?

5. The centre of gravity of a uniform triangular plate ABC is at a point G on the line joining A to D the middle point of BC, such that the ratio of AG to GD is 2. Find the ratio of AG to AD.

6. The centre of gravity of two weights W_1 lb. wt. and W_2 lb. wt. placed at A and B respectively is at a point G which divides AB so that $AG/GB = W_2/W_1$. Find the lengths of AG and GB if AB is l in.

7. If a point C on AB produced is such that the ratio of AC to BC is 7/6 find the ratio of AC to AB. Also find the ratio of AC to AB when the ratio of AC to BC is p/q.

8. Lengths p and q miles on the ground are represented by a and b in. on a map. How many inches on the map will represent $(p - q)$ and $(lp + mq)$ miles on the ground ? Deduce that, if $a/p = b/q$, each ratio equals $(a - b)/(p - q)$ and $(la + mb)/(lp + mq)$.

9. A, B C, D are four points in a straight line. The ratio of AB to BD is 2/5 and the ratio of AC to CD is 5/9. Find the ratio of BC to AD. If the ratio of AB to BD is k and the ratio of AC to CD is l, show that the ratio of BC to AD is $\dfrac{l-k}{(k+1)(l+1)}$.

10. The linear dimensions of a rectangular block are each n times the corresponding dimensions of another block. What is the ratio of (a) their volumes, (b) their surface areas ?

11. If in the figure the ratio of AB to EF is k and the ratio of BC to FG is l, what is the ratio of the area between the two rectangles to the area of ABCD ?

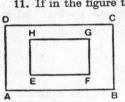

FIG. 29.

12. If $y \propto x$ and $y = 4$ when $x = 5$, find the relation between y and x and draw its graph.

13. If the current in a wire is i ampères when the potential difference between its ends is V volts, $i \propto V$. If $i = 15$ when V = 230, find the relation between i and V. From it calculate the values of i when V is 100, 200, 250 respectively. Draw a graph of the relation between i and V.

14. If a horizontal force of F lb. wt. is required to pull a load W lb. wt. along a rough horizontal plane, $F \propto W$. With a certain plane it is found that F = 70 when W = 250. Find the equation connecting F and W, and draw its graph. Find the values of F when W is 100, 200, 300 respectively.

15. When a load W lb. wt. is hung from a wire the extension of the wire x in. is proportional to W. If the wire extends 0·02 in. when a load of 3 lb. wt. is hung from it, find the relation between x and W. What will be the extension for a load of 20·5 lb. wt. ?

16. If a light beam AB is supported at its ends at the same level the distance d in. of its middle point below AB, when a load W lb. wt. is hung from the middle point, varies as W. If $d = 0·3$ when W = 25, find the relation between d and W.

17. The exposure E secs. required for a photograph varies as the square of the stop f used. If $E = \frac{1}{25}$ when $f = 4·5$, find E when f is = 6·3, 8·0, 11·0 respectively. State the equation connecting E and f.

18. If the volume of a gas is V cu. ft. when its pressure is p lb. per sq. in. $p \propto \dfrac{1}{V}$, when the temperature is kept constant. If

$p = 40$ when $V = 200$, find the law connecting p and V. Calculate the values of p when V is 150, 100, 50 respectively.

19. If a body is falling under gravity the speed v ft./sec. is proportional to the square root of the distance fallen s ft. If v is 16 when it has fallen 4 ft., what is the relation between v and s ? How fast will it be moving when it has fallen 24 ft., 40 ft., 56 ft. respectively ?

20. When water is flowing out of a tap at the bottom of a tank the rate at which it flows out, V cu. ft. per min., is proportional to the square root of the depth h ft. If $V = 42 \cdot 5$ when $h = 9$, find the relation between V and h.

21. If $y \propto x^3$ and $y = 10$ when $x = 2$, find the relation between y and x. From it calculate the value of x when $y = 100$.

22. When a current is switched through the primary of a transformer, the graduation θ of a ballistic galvanometer connected with the secondary, is found to have the following values when the secondary has n turns :—

n	20	40	60	80	100
θ	5·41	10·82	10·22	21·65	27·03

Show by a graph that $\theta \propto n$. The charge Q coulombs, which passes through the secondary, is proportional to θ. Deduce that $Q \propto n$.

23. Draw a graph of y against x from the following table. Show from it that y does not vary directly as x. Then plot a graph of y against x^2, show that $y \propto x^2$ and find the relation between y and x. Use it to find the value of y when $x = 3 \cdot 5$.

x	0	1·5	3·0	4·0	4·5	5·0
y	0	9	36	64	81	100

24. In an experiment on a simple pendulum the following values of the time T sec. of a single oscillation, and the length l in. were found :

l	5	10	20	30	40	50	60
T	0·717	1·013	1·433	1·757	2·028	2·263	2·480

Plot a graph of T against l and show that T does not vary as l. Then plot a graph of T against $\sqrt{l}$ and show that $T \propto \sqrt{l}$ and use this graph to find the relation between T and l. Use this relation to find l when $T = 1$.

GEOMETRY

CHAPTER X

It is now generally agreed that the origin of Geometry is to be found in Egypt. From time to time the Nile floods swept away landmarks, and it therefore became necessary to have some system of land survey. Men were employed to draw right angles who made use of the fact that a triangle whose sides are three lengths of rope in the ratios 3 : 4 : 5, has a right angle opposite to the longest side. The Ahmes papyrus in the British Museum, written about 1700 B.C. and believed to be a copy of a much earlier work, is the main source of knowledge of Egyptian geometry. In this work Ahmes gives the volumes of several barns and attempts to find the area of a circle.

Although the Greeks derived their early knowledge of geometry from the Egyptians, the practical aspect of the subject made less appeal to them and they began to treat the subject as an abstract science. The earliest of the Greek geometers of whom we have knowledge was Thales, whose main work was done during the first half of the sixth century B.C. He is believed to have studied geometry and astronomy in Egypt while engaged there in commerce. On his return to Miletus he founded the Ionian school.

At the time of Thales' death, about 550 B.C., Pythagoras was a young man of twenty. The Pythagorean school was a society bound by oath not to reveal its secrets. It was an object of suspicion and was broken up, but re-established itself and flourished at Tarentum for about 150 years. How many of the discoveries of the school, including Pythagoras' theorem, are to be attributed to him it is impossible to say. Much of the work during this period developed from attempts to solve

146

three famous problems, the construction of a square equal in area to a given circle, the trisection of an angle, and the construction of a cube with twice the volume of a given cube, three problems which it has long been realized are impossible of solution by ruler and compasses only.

By the end of the fifth century B.C. Athens had become the chief city of Greece and the Athenian school was founded as a centre of mathematics and philosophy. Its most famous members were Plato and Aristotle, but their interests were chiefly philosophical and from the mathematical standpoint they are more to be remembered for their influence on their contemporaries.

After the death of Alexander the Great in 323 B.C. his empire was divided and Alexandria became the centre of learning. The third century B.C. was perhaps the most brilliant in Greek mathematics, producing the work of Euclid, Archimedes, and Apollonius. Euclid's *Elements* was a standard text-book in geometry until the end of the nineteenth century, though in the opinion of one of the foremost authorities, Sir Thomas Heath, it probably contained little that was new.

The work at Alexandria was partially interrupted by the military disturbances affecting the Roman world, but from the beginning of the Christian era until 641, when it was destroyed by the Arabs, it was a centre of cultural activity. Two geometers of note were Ptolemy, who in the second century showed the application of geometry to astronomy, and Pappus, famed near the end of the third century for his *Collections*. This book contained a synopsis of Greek mathematics, a number of original contributions, and essentially all the propositions normally found in a present-day technical course.

Interest in geometry declined and was not seriously revived until the end of the sixteenth century, largely due to the influence of the German, Kepler. Its development then passed to France, where it was extended by Desargues and Pascal, though suffering partial eclipse as a result of the introduction of analytical geometry by Descartes in 1637. In the eighteenth century Monge, when at the military training school at Mézières, submitted a solution of a problem which was at first rejected by the officer in charge, on the grounds that the calculations could not have been carried out in so short a time. Monge's solution was the result of his discovery of descriptive geometry, the basis of the work in the modern drawing office.

FUNDAMENTAL IDEAS

In geometry we call any object a *solid* which occupies a certain amount of space. With this definition we see that a football or an empty box is a solid ; each has a definite *volume*.

The boundary of a solid is a *surface*. We sometimes read in catalogues that all exposed surfaces are chromium-plated. The surface, we see, separates the solid from the surrounding space. A surface has no thickness and consequently no volume ; it has an *area*.

The boundary between two surfaces or between two parts of the same surface is a *line*. Adjoining counties on a map are painted in different colours ; they are separated by a line. A line has neither thickness nor breadth but only *length*.

The intersection of two lines is a *point*. It has neither thickness nor breadth nor length.

A line may be either straight or curved. Straight lines are usually drawn by using a ruler or some other drawing instrument with a straight edge. The straightness of the edge of a ruler may be tested in the following way. Draw a line making use of the edge of the ruler. Reverse the ruler and bring the same edge into contact with the line. If the edge is now in contact with the line throughout the whole of its length, the edge is straight.

A surface may be either *plane* or curved. A carpenter tests the planeness of a surface by means of a straight edge. He puts the edge on the surface in a number of different positions. If the edge is in contact with the surface throughout its length and in all positions, the surface is plane.

The intersection of two plane surfaces is a straight line, e.g. the intersection of two walls of a room.

Most solids are irregular in shape, but some of the regular solids frequently seen are shown below.

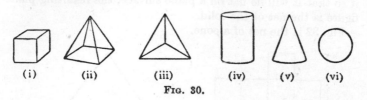

(i)   (ii)   (iii)   (iv)   (v)   (vi)

FIG. 30.

The first is a *cube*. The surface consists of six *faces*, each of which is a *square*. Any two adjoining faces meet in an *edge*.

[A square will be defined later.]

The second solid is a *square pyramid*. Its base is a square and each of the other faces is a *triangle*, i.e. a *plane figure bounded by three straight lines*.

The third solid is a *triangular pyramid*; it is also called a *tetrahedron*, the latter name being derived from two Greek words meaning four faces. Each of its four faces is a triangle. The face on which it rests is its base and the corner above is its *vertex*. It is clear that the solid could rest on any of the other faces and each corner is a vertex. The corners of solids are frequently called its vertices (plural of vertex).

The fourth solid is a *cylinder*. Its total surface consists of two plane ends joined by a curved surface. Each end is a *circle*, i.e. *a plane figure bounded by a curved line every point of which is the same distance from the point called its centre*.

The fifth solid is a *cone*. Its surface consists of a circular base and a curved surface which contains every straight line obtained by joining the vertex to points on the edge of the base.

The sixth solid is a *sphere*. It is bounded by a curved

surface, every point of which is the same distance from a point within, called its centre.

If a piece of stiff paper of the shape shown in Fig. 31 be suitably folded about the dotted lines, the result will be a cube. In this case, the plane figure is called the *net* of the cube.

If a solid be made of stiff paper and it be possible to unfold it so that it will lie flat on a plane surface, the resulting plane figure is the net of the solid.

Fig. 32 is the net of a cone.

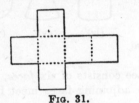

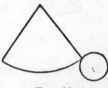

FIG. 31.   FIG. 32.

If a cone or a cylinder be placed with its curved surface on a table, the solid and the table will be in contact along a line. If a sphere be placed on a table, it will touch the table at one point only.

It is possible to draw the net of a cone or of a cylinder but not of a sphere.

Exercise XXVII

State whether you consider each of the following to be a solid, a surface, or a line :

1. Brick.   2. Petrol can.   3. Jug.
4. Gas pipe.   5. Balloon.   6. Soap bubble.
7. Sponge.   8. Tinfoil.   9. Sheet of paper.
10. Coat of transparent varnish.   11. Piece of string.
12. A hair.

Draw the net of ɩ

13. A square pyramid.   14. A tetrahedron.
15. A cylinder   16. A closed box.

17. A box without lid.   **18.** A house.

19. A jam jar.   **20.** A " Royal Sovereign " pencil
                                          before sharpening.

21. Cut out in stiff paper the *net* shown in Fig. 33.
Fold to form a regular solid with eight faces.
The solid so formed is called an octahedron.

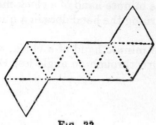

FIG. 33.

22. Sketch an octahedron.

23. Complete the table below, showing the number of faces,
vertices and edges in the case of each solid named :

	Number of—		
	Faces	*Vertices*	*Edges*
	F	V	E
Cube	6	8	12
Square Pyramid			
Tetrahedron			
House			
" Royal Sovereign " pencil (unsharpened)			
Octahedron			

24. Show that in each case in Ques. 23, $F + V - E = 2$.

25. Sketch the plane figure which would be obtained if you were
to cut off the top of a (i) square pyramid, (ii) tetrahedron, (iii)
cylinder, (iv) cone, (v) sphere.

Angles

When a drill instructor gives the order " Left turn," each
man does the same amount of turning and faces a new direction. If the order be repeated, each man will then face in a
direction opposite to his original. If the order be again twice

repeated, each man will have made a complete turn or a revolution.

Fig. 34 indicates a man's direction after each successive order. He has turned through the same amount four times in order to make one revolution. One quarter of a revolution is called a *right angle*.

In one hour, the minute hand of a clock makes a revolution. The amount of turning the hand does in a quarter of an hour is a right angle.

Considering the minute hand of a clock, we see that in ten minutes it will turn through an angle less than a right angle,

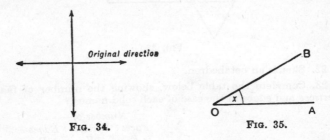

FIG. 34.   FIG. 35.

in twenty minutes through an angle greater than a right angle.

An angle is represented by two lines meeting in a point. The lines are called the *arms* of the angle and the point where they meet the *vertex* of the angle.

Three letters are often used to refer to an angle, one on each arm and one at the vertex, e.g. the angle AOB (or BOA) in Fig. 35, the middle letter being always at the vertex. Two symbols for an angle are in common use. The angle AOB is written $\angle AOB$ or $\widehat{AOB}$. A single small letter will often be used to represent an angle when there is no doubt as to which angle it refers. Thus x might be used to denote the angle AOB.

An angle is measured by the amount of turning one arm must do to coincide with the other. The lengths of the arms

do not affect the angle.   In ten minutes the minute hand of
" Big Ben " turns through the same amount as the minute
hand of a wrist-watch.

The direction of rotation from one arm to the other is often
shown by an arrow as in Fig. 36 below.

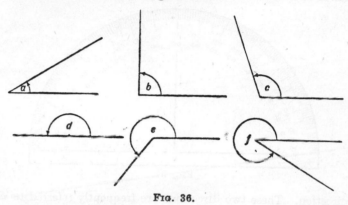

FIG. 36.

Angle *a* is less than a right angle, and is called an *acute*
angle.

Angle *b* is a *right* angle.

Angle *c* is greater than one right angle and less than two
right angles ; it is called an *obtuse* angle.

Angle *d* is two right angles and is called a *straight* angle.

Angles *e* and *f* are greater than two right angles and less
than four right angles ; they are called *reflex* angles.

An instrument to measure angles is a protractor, a common
form of which is shown in Fig. 37.

Each right angle is divided into 90 equal angles, each one of
which is called a *degree*.   The symbol ° is used for degrees,
90 degrees being written 90°.

1 right angle = 90° ;
2 right angles = 180°.

NOTE —When very accurate measurement is necessary,
each degree is divided into 60 minutes (written 60′), and when

still greater accuracy is required, each minute is divided into 60 seconds (written 60″).

The divisions on a protractor are marked with two numbers, one series indicating rotation in the direction of motion of the hands of a clock and the other series motion in the opposite

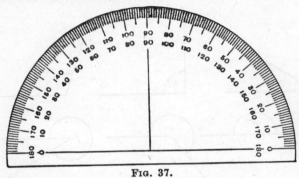

FIG. 37.

direction. These two directions are frequently referred to as clockwise and anti-clockwise directions.

Construction of an angle of given magnitude.

Suppose we are required to construct an angle of 75°. A straight line is drawn, e.g. *OA*. The protractor is then placed so that the middle point of its straight edge is at *O*, and the edge along *OA*. A point *B* is marked on the paper at the

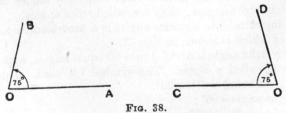

FIG. 38.

division numbered 75 on the protractor, counting from *OA*, which is marked *O*. *OB* is joined and the angle *AOB* is 75°.

The other division marked 75 on the protractor would give the angle *COD* as shown in Fig. 38.

There should never be any confusion as to which numbered division to consider in any particular case as it will be quite clear whether or not the angle is less or greater than a right angle.

The protractor may be likewise employed to measure a given angle. It is placed so that its straight edge lies along one arm of the angle, with the middle point of the straight edge at the vertex. The other arm will then indicate on the numbered scale the magnitude of the angle in degrees.

Vertical and horizontal lines and planes

When a builder wishes to know if a wall is upright, he uses a plumb line, i.e. a piece of string with a weight attached to the end of it. The weight would of course fall to the earth if not held by the string and the line of the string is such that it would pass through the centre of the earth if produced ; in this case the string is vertical.

A *vertical line* is a line which passes through the centre of the earth. A *vertical plane* is a plane which passes through the centre of the earth.

It is assumed that the line is produced as far as necessary and that the plane is extended as far as necessary.

A *horizontal line* through a point is at right angles to the vertical line through the point.

If two horizontal lines be drawn through the same point, a plane passing through the two lines is a *horizontal plane* through the point.

To determine whether or not a plane is horizontal, a carpenter uses a spirit level.

When two lines are at right angles they are said to be *perpendicular*.

If the sum of two angles is 90°, they are said to be *complementary* ; 75° and 15° are complementary. Each is the complement of the other. If the sum of two angles is 180°, they are *supplementary*; 110° and 70° are supplementary angles. Each is the supplement of the other. Two angles on

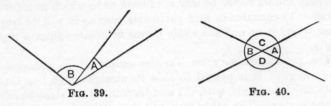

| FIG. 39. | FIG. 40. |

opposite sides of a common arm, such as *A* and *B* in Fig. 39 are *adjacent* angles.

If two lines intersect, as in Fig. 40, the opposite angles

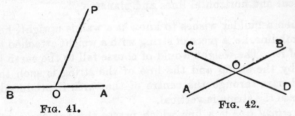

| FIG. 41. | FIG. 42. |

A and *B* are called *vertically opposite angles*. The angles *C* and *D* are also vertically opposite angles.

Draw an angle *POA* of 75° and on the opposite side of *PO* an angle *POB* of 105° (Fig. 41). Test the line *AOB* for straightness.

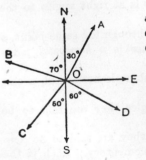

FIG. 43.

It will be found that *AOB is a straight line as the sum of the adjacent angles POA and POB is a straight angle.*

Draw two intersecting lines *AOB* and *COD* (Fig. 42).

By measurement it will be found that *vertically opposite angles are equal.*

A surveyor gives directions with reference to a North–South line.

A direction *OA* in Fig. 43 is

'given as N. 30° E., indicating that the direction is 30° to the East of North.

Direction of *OB* is N. 70° W., of *OC* is S. 50° W., and of *OD* is S. 60° E.

Exercise XXVIII

1. Draw two triangles such as *ABC* and *DEF*, on a larger scale, one of which has an obtuse angle. Measure the angles *A*, *B*, *C*

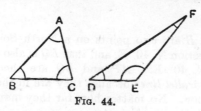

FIG. 44.

and add them together. Do likewise for the angles *D*, *E*, *F*. Do you notice anything about the sum in each case?

2. Draw on a larger scale a triangle *ABC* and produce *BC* to *D*. Measure the angles *A* and *B* and add them together; measure

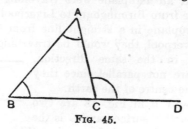

FIG. 45.

the angle *ACD*. Do you notice anything striking about the results?

3. Through what angle does each hand of a clock turn between one o'clock and half-past two?

4. What is the time if the minute hand of a clock has turned through 75° since two o'clock?

5. A man walks 200 yards due E., then 100 yards N. 25° E. and finally 150 yards N. 30° W. Make a scale drawing and hence determine his distance and direction from the starting point.

6. Two towns B and C are S. 30° E. and S. 60° W. respectively from A. If B is 3 miles from A and C is 2 miles from A, find by drawing to scale, the distance and bearing of B from C.

7. Draw a line BC 3 inches in length. Construct an angle BCA of 60° and an angle CBA of 60°. Measure the angle BAC and the lengths of AB and of AC.

8. Draw a line QR 8 cm. in length. Construct any acute angle QRP and an angle RQP so that the two angles are complementary. Measure the angle QPR.

Parallel lines

Suppose A, B are two points on a North–South line, that AP is in a direction N. 40° E. and that BQ is also in a direction

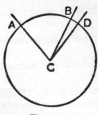

N. 40° E. AP and BQ are then said to be *parallel lines* because they are in the same direction. No matter how far they may be produced they will not meet.

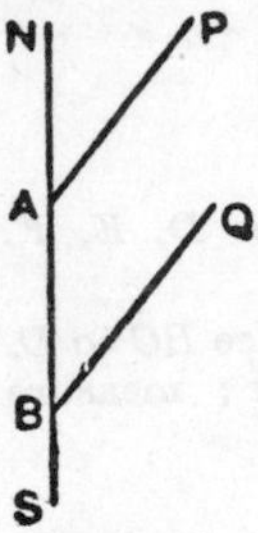

Arrows on two straight lines which don't meet, as in Fig. 47, are often used to indicate that the lines are parallel.

If an aeroplane were travelling in a straight line from Birmingham to Liverpool and a second aeroplane in a straight line from Manchester to Liverpool, they would be travelling to the same

Fig. 46.

place but *not* in the same direction. Vertical lines are not parallel since they pass through the centre of the earth.

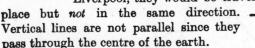

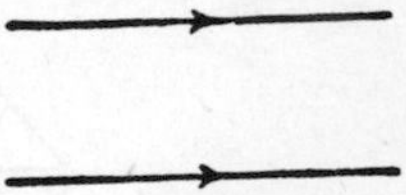

Suppose A and B in Fig. 48 are two points on the earth's surface and C is the

Fig. 47.

centre of the earth. CA and CB are not parallel. A vertical line in Bombay, for example, will not be parallel to a vertical line in London. If D is a point near to B then CB and CD are more nearly parallel. For all practical purposes, two vertical lines through points near together, e.g. in the same room, may be assumed to be parallel as the point at which they

Fig. 48.

meet, viz. the centre of the earth, is approximately 4000 miles away.

One of the instruments used in drawing is a set square. It is in the shape of a triangle in which one angle is a right angle and a second angle is either 45° or 60°.

Place a set square ABC with one of its edges AB in contact with an edge PQ of a ruler, Fig. 49. Draw a line along AC. Keep the ruler fixed and slide the set square along it until it takes up a new position $A_1B_1C_1$. Draw a line along A_1C_1. AC and A_1C_1 are parallel straight lines. They make equal angles with PQ; these angles are called *corresponding angles*.

When a straight line intersects two other straight lines, it is called a *transversal*.

The angles between two straight lines and a transversal are

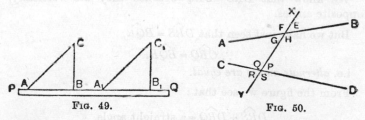

FIG. 49.   FIG. 50.

named as below. AB and CD, Fig. 50, are two straight lines met by a transversal XY.

G and P are *alternate angles*, as are also H and Q.

E and P are *corresponding angles*, as are also F and Q, G and R, H and S.

G and Q are *interior angles* on the same side of the transversal, as are also H and P.

We have seen already that *when a transversal intersects two parallel lines, corresponding angles are equal.*

This fact may also be illustrated in the following way.

Suppose AB and CD are two parallel roads (Fig. 51) running due East and that PS is a road crossing AB and CD at Q and R respectively.

A man walks from A along AB until he reaches Q, when he

6

decides to turn right along PS. He therefore turns from the

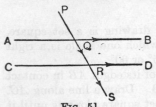

FIG. 51.

direction E, i.e. QB, to the direction QR; in other words he turns through the angle BQR. He now walks along the road PS until he reaches R, when he decides to turn left along RD, i.e. in a direction due E. In doing this he turns through the angle SRD. He is now walking in his original direction, viz. due E. The angle through which he turns back to due E. must therefore be equal to the angle through which he turned away from due E., i.e.

$$B\widehat{Q}R = D\widehat{R}S.$$

We know that $D\widehat{R}S = C\widehat{R}Q$ because they are vertically opposite angles.

But we have just seen that $D\widehat{R}S = B\widehat{Q}R$.

$$\therefore\ C\widehat{R}Q = B\widehat{Q}R.$$

i.e. *alternate angles are equal.*

From the figure we see that:

$$D\widehat{R}S + D\widehat{R}Q = \text{a straight angle.}$$

$$\text{But } D\widehat{R}S = B\widehat{Q}R.$$

$$\therefore\ B\widehat{Q}R + D\widehat{R}Q = \text{a straight angle}$$
$$= \text{two right angles.}$$

Hence *two interior angles on the same side of the transversal are together equal to two right angles.*

The Greek letters a, β, γ (read alpha, beta, gamma) are often used to denote angles.

In Fig. 52, the angles marked a are equal; the angles marked β are equal, and $a + \beta =$ two right angles.

Suppose $PQRS$ is a straight line meeting two straight lines AB and CD in Q and R respectively, and making the alternate angles BQR and CRQ equal.   We can then show that the lines AB and CD are parallel.   (Fig. 53).

$\widehat{CRQ} = \widehat{DRS}$ because they are vertically opposite angles.

But we are told that $\widehat{CRQ} = \widehat{BQR}$.

$$\therefore \widehat{BQR} = \widehat{DRS}.$$

These are corresponding angles.   They show that the change of direction from PS to QB is the same as the change of

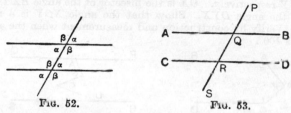

FIG. 52.   FIG. 53.

direction from PS to RD.   Hence QB and RD are in the same direction, i.e. they are parallel.

It is also true that the lines AB and CD are parallel if

$$\widehat{BQR} + \widehat{DRQ} = 2 \text{ right angles.}$$

For $\widehat{DRS} + \widehat{DRQ} = 2$ right angles and

$$\therefore \widehat{BQR} = \widehat{DRS}.$$

Hence, as before, the lines are parallel.

We will now tabulate our results, which should be known by every student.

1. *If two straight lines intersect, the vertically opposite angles are equal.*

2. *If a transversal meets two parallel straight lines,* (i) *the corresponding angles are equal,* (ii) *the alternate angles are equal,* (iii) *two interior angles on the same side of the transversal are together equal to two right angles.*

3. *If a transversal meets two straight lines and* (i) *the corresponding angles are equal,* or (ii) *the alternate angles are equal,* or (iii) *two interior angles on the same side of the transversal are together equal to two right angles, the two straight lines are parallel.*

Exercise XXIX

1. Construct an angle ABC of 60°; make BA 8 cm. and BC 6 cm. in length. Through C draw a line CD parallel to BA by making an angle BCD of 120°. Make CD 8 cm. in length and through D draw DE parallel to CB. Make DE 6 cm. in length, so that B and E are on the same side of CD. What do you notice about the points A and E ?

2. PQ is a transversal meeting two parallel lines AB and CD in X and Y respectively. OX is the bisector of the angle BXY and OY of the angle DYX. Show that the angle XOY is a right angle. Verify by construction and measurement when the angle BXY is 100°.

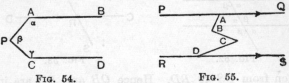

FIG. 54.   FIG. 55.

3. In Fig. 54, AB and CD are parallel lines. Find, by supposing a further parallel line to be drawn through P (or otherwise) the relation between the angles α, β, γ.

4. In Fig. 55, PQ and RS are parallel lines. Show that $\widehat{A} + \widehat{B} = \widehat{C} + \widehat{D}$.

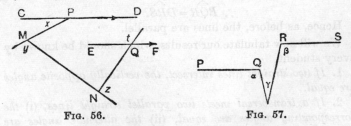

FIG. 56.   FIG. 57.

5. In Fig. 56, CD and EF are parallel lines. Show by considering the total change in direction in traversing the path $DPMNQE$ that the sum of the angles x, y, z, t is four right angles.

6. In Fig. 57, $\widehat{\alpha} + \widehat{\beta} = 180° + \widehat{\gamma}$; show that PQ and RS are parallel.

Definitions

Triangles are classified with reference to their angles and also with reference to their sides.

In Fig. 58, *ABC* is an *acute-angled triangle,* as all its angles are acute.

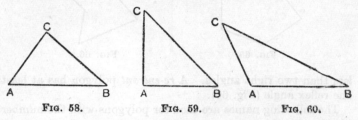

Fig. 58.	Fig. 59.	Fig. 60.

In Fig. 59, *ABC* is a *right-angled triangle,* as one angle, viz. *A,* is a right angle. In this case the side *BC*, opposite to the right angle, is called the *hypotenuse.*

In Fig. 60, *ABC* is an *obtuse-angled triangle,* as one angle, viz. *A,* is an obtuse angle.

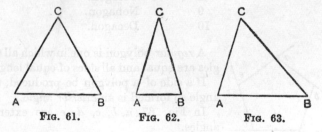

Fig. 61.	Fig. 62.	Fig. 63.

An *equilateral triangle* has three equal sides (Fig. 61).

An *isosceles triangle* has two sides equal (Fig. 62).

A *scalene triangle* has three unequal sides (Fig. 63).

A plane figure bounded by four straight lines is a *quadrilateral. ABCD* is a quadrilateral and the lines *AC* and *BD* joining opposite vertices are its *diagonals.*

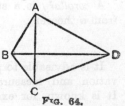

Fig. 64.

A *polygon* is a plane figure bounded by any number of straight lines.

Fig. 65 is a *convex* polygon because each of its angles is

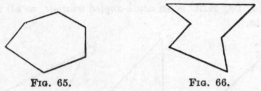

FIG. 65.　　　　　　　　FIG. 66.

less than two right angles. A *re-entrant* polygon has at least one reflex angle (Fig. 66).

The following names are used for polygons with the number of sides stated.

Number of sides.		Name.
5	..	Pentagon.
6	..	Hexagon.
7	..	Heptagon.
8	..	Octagon.
9	..	Nonagon.
10	..	Decagon.

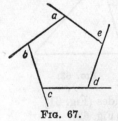

FIG. 67.

A *regular* polygon is one in which all angles are equal and all sides of equal length.

If a side of a polygon be produced, the angle so formed is an *exterior* angle.

In Fig. 67, *a, b, c, d, e* are exterior angles.

A statement of a geometrical fact is a *theorem.*

A *corollary* is a statement which may easily be deduced from a theorem.

THEOREMS

It is advisable to prove a theorem when possible, as observation and measurement may sometimes lead us astray. It is known, for example, from the Ahmes papyrus in the

British Museum, that the Egyptians used formulæ in their
practical work, derived most likely from observation and
measurement, some of which have since been proved to be
wrong.

The example below will show the student how necessary it
is to prove statements rather than to rely on observation.

On graph paper draw a square with each side 8 units in
length (Fig. 68). Cut the square into four pieces A, B, C, D

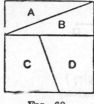

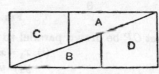

FIG. 68.   FIG. 69.

along the lines shown. Fit these together as in Fig. 69, to
form a rectangle of sides 13 and 5 units in length.

A square of area 64 sq. units has become a rectangle of
area 65 sq. units, thus apparently showing that 64 = 65. The
student will find that only by very accurate drawing on a large
scale and most careful cutting is it possible to see that the
pieces A, B, C, D of the square do not exactly fit together to
form the rectangle.

We have seen from measurement of the angles of several
triangles that the sum of the angles of each of these triangles
is approximately 180° and it is natural to suspect that the sum
of the angles of any triangle is exactly 180°. We cannot show
this by drawing since we cannot measure the angles with
absolute accuracy and in any case, we cannot draw all triangles.
We shall, however, now show that it is possible to prove this
statement.

Theorem.—If a side of a triangle be produced, the exterior
angle is equal to the sum of the two interior opposite angles.
The sum of the three angles of a triangle is two right angles.

ABC is a triangle with *BC* produced to *D*.

To prove that (i) $A\widehat{C}D = x + y$; (ii) $x + y + z = 180°$.

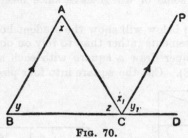

FIG. 70.

Let *CP* be drawn parallel to *BA*.

(i) $x_1 = x$. (Alt. angles.)

$y_1 = y$. (Corr. angles.)

By addition $x_1 + y_1 = x + y$,

i.e. $A\widehat{C}D = x + y$.

(ii) $x + y = x_1 + y_1$. (Proved.)

To each add *z*.

$\therefore x + y + z = x_1 + y_1 + z$

$= 180°$.

Corollary : If two angles of one triangle are equal respectively to two angles of another, the third angles of the triangle are equal.

This follows at once from the theorem, since the sum of the angles in each triangle is 180°.

Corollary : If a side of a triangle be produced the exterior angle is greater than either of the interior and opposite angles.

NOTE.—The statement before the figure is the *general enunciation* ; the statement of the facts to be proved with reference to the particular figure is the *particular enunciation.*

Each statement in a proof should be written on a separate line with the reason given as concisely as possible in brackets.

When possible the complete proof should be given on one page ; if it is necessary to turn over, the figure should be repeated.

Theorem.—The sum of the angles of a convex polygon of n sides is $2n - 4$ right angles.

Let a point O inside a polygon of n sides be joined to each vertex.

n triangles are now formed.

The sum of the angles in each triangle is 2 right angles.

∴ the sum of the angles in the n triangles is $2n$ right angles.

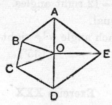

FIG. 71.

These angles together make up the angles of the polygon and the angles at O.

But the angles at $O = 4$ right angles.

∴ angles of polygon $+ 4$ right angles $= 2n$ right angles.

∴ angles of polygon $= 2n - 4$ right angles.

Theorem.—If the sides of a convex polygon be produced in order, the sum of the exterior angles is 4 right angles.

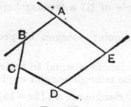

FIG. 72.

Sum of exterior and interior angles at each vertex $= 2$ right angles.

Since there are n vertices, sum of all interior and exterior angles $= 2n$ right angles.

6*

But sum of interior angles + 4 right angles
$$= 2n \text{ right angles.} \quad \text{(Proved.)}$$
∴ sum of exterior angles = 4 right angles.

Example.—What is the angle of a regular octagon ?
In this case $n = 8$.
∴ sum of 8 angles $= 2 \times 8 - 4$ right angles.
$$= 12 \text{ right angles.}$$

Since angles are equal,
$$\text{each angle} = \tfrac{12}{8} \text{ right angles.}$$
$$= 135°.$$

Exercise XXX

1. Draw a regular hexagon.

2. Draw a regular octagon.

3. Two angles of a triangle are 57° and 74° respectively. What is the third angle ?

4. Could a triangle have angles of (i) 50°, 55°, 48° ; (ii) 125°, 35°, 20° ?

5. What is the fourth angle of a quadrilateral with angles of 70°, 85°, 95° ? Is this a convex quadrilateral ?

6. What are the angles of an isosceles right-angled triangle ?

7. What is the angle of (i) a regular heptagon, (ii) a regular nonagon ?

8. If a side of a regular decagon be produced, what is the exterior angle ?

9. One angle of a triangle is equal to the sum of the other two angles. Prove that the triangle is right-angled.

10. The angles of a triangle are $x°$, $(2x - 15)°$, $(3x - 9)°$; find the angles.

11. Two angles of a quadrilateral are 76° and 124° ; the other two angles are equal. Find these angles.

12. A, B, C, D, E are the angles of a pentagon. $A = B = C = 2D = 2E$. Find the angles.

CHAPTER XI

SYMMETRY, CONGRUENCE AND SIMILARITY

In Fig. 73, ABC is a triangle and $A_1B_1C_1$ its reflexion as seen in a mirror MN. If the paper were folded about the line MN, the triangle ABC (Fig. 73) would coincide exactly with the triangle $A_1B_1C_1$.

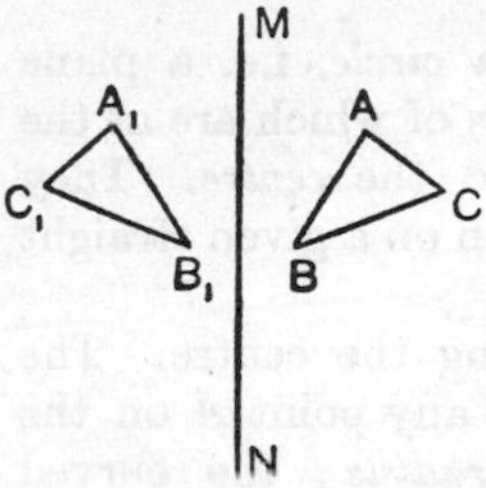

Each point of one figure is the "image" or "reflexion" of the corresponding point of the other; each line of one figure is the image of the corresponding line of the other. In such cases figures are said to be *symmetrical* and the line MN is the *axis of symmetry*.

FIG. 73.

When two figures are symmetrical *corresponding lines and corresponding angles are equal*.

Two figures which are alike in all respects are said to be *congruent*. It is now usual to extend the word congruent to

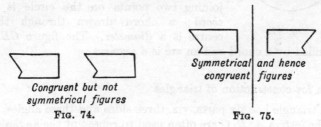

Congruent but not symmetrical figures

FIG. 74.

Symmetrical and hence congruent figures

FIG. 75.

include symmetrical, since symmetrical figures have corresponding lengths and corresponding angles equal.

Figures which are alike in shape but of different size are said to be *similar*.

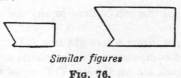

Similar figures

FIG. 76.

A plan of a field, such as is used by an architect, is similar in shape to the original field. It is a copy drawn on a much smaller scale.

Use of compasses

Compasses may be used to describe a *circle*, i.e. a plane figure bounded by a curved line, all points of which are at the same distance from a fixed point called the *centre*. They may also be used to mark a required length on a given straight line when dividers are not available.

A circle is shown in Fig. 77, *O* being the centre. The distance from *O* to any point *A* on the curved line is the *radius*; the curved bounding line is the *circumference* of the circle. A part of the circumference, e.g. *AB*, is an *arc* of the circle. The figure *AOB* bounded by two radii and an arc is a *sector*. A line *CD* joining two points on the circle is a *chord*; a chord drawn through the centre is a *diameter*. The figure *CED* bounded by a chord and an arc is a *segment*.

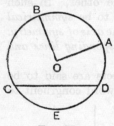

Fig. 77.

Data for construction of triangles

A triangle has six parts, viz. three sides and three angles.

The letters *A*, *B*, *C* are often used to represent the angles of a triangle *ABC*, and the small letters *a*, *b*, *c* to represent the sides opposite to *A*, *B*, *C* respectively.

Suppose that *ABC* is a triangle of which we wish to make an exact copy.

We shall see that this can be done in any one of the following three ways.

I.—With a ruler, draw a straight line *DX*.

Open a pair of compasses until the points are at a distance *BC* apart and mark *DF* on the line *DX*, equal to *AC*.

With a protractor make the angle *FDY* equal to the angle *CAB*.

Mark the distance *DE* on the line *DY* equal to *AB*.   Join *EF*.

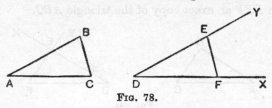

Fig. 78.

The triangle *DEF* is now an exact copy of the triangle *ABC*.

$$AB = DE \; ; \quad AC = DF \; ; \quad B\widehat{A}C = E\widehat{D}F.$$

The angle *BAC* between the sides *AB* and *AC* is called the included angle.

We see that *two triangles are congruent if two sides and the included angle of one triangle are equal respectively to two sides and the included angle of the other.*

II.—As before, make *DF* equal to *AC*. With centre *D* and radius *AB* describe an arc of a circle ; every point on this arc will be at a distance *AB* from *D*. With centre *F* and radius *CB* describe an arc ; every point on this arc will be at

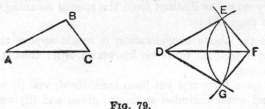

Fig. 79.

a distance *CB* from *F*.   Let the two arcs intersect at *E* and *G*. The triangles *DEF* and *DGF* are symmetrical, *DF* being the axis of symmetry and each triangle is congruent with the triangle *ABC*.

We see that *two triangles are congruent if three sides of one triangle are equal respectively to three sides of the other.*

III.—Again make *DF* equal to *AC*. Construct an angle *XDF* equal to the angle *BAC* and an angle *YFD* equal to the angle *BCA*. Let *DX* and *FY* intersect in *E*. Once more we have in *DEF* an exact copy of the triangle *ABC*.

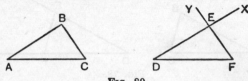

Fɪɢ. 80.

Suppose we are required to construct a triangle *DEF* in which *DF* = 5 cm., $\widehat{DEF}$ = 71° and $\widehat{EDF}$ = 65°. As we know that the sum of the angles of a triangle is 180°, $\widehat{EFD}$ = (180 – 71 – 65)° = 44°. We can now proceed as before. Given, therefore, one side of a triangle and any two angles, it is possible to construct it.

Thus *two triangles are congruent if a side and two angles of one triangle are equal respectively to a side and two corresponding angles of the other.*

(Noᴛᴇ.—The word " corresponding " is here used in the ordinary sense, as distinct from the special meaning attached to it on page 159.)

From the above consideration it would appear that three parts of a triangle must be known in order that it may be constructed.

Two cases have not yet been considered, viz. (i) when two sides and a non-included angle are given and (ii) when three angles are given.

Two sides and a non-included angle

Suppose we are required to construct a triangle *ABC* in which *A* = 45°, *a* = 4 cm., *b* = 5 cm.

Construct an angle *CAX* equal to 45° with *AC* 5 cm. in

length.   With centre C and radius 4 cm., draw an arc intersecting AX in the two points B_1 and B_2.   Each of the triangles
AB_1C and AB_2C then satisfies the requirements.

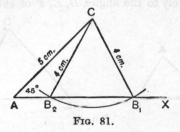

FIG. 81.

When, as above, it is possible to construct two triangles
given two sides and a non-included angle, we have what is
known as the *ambiguous case*.

When A, a and b are given but $a > b$, the triangle ABC is
uniquely determined, as will be seen from Fig. 82.

When the non-included angle A is a right angle, as in Fig.
83, there are two triangles, AB_1C and AB_2C, but these are
symmetrical about the axis CA and are therefore congruent.

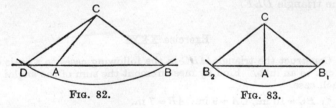

FIG. 82.   FIG. 83.

We can say now that—

(i) *Two right-angled triangles will be congruent if two sides of
one triangle are equal respectively to the two corresponding sides
of the other;*

(ii) *Two triangles will be congruent when two sides and a
non-included angle of one triangle are equal respectively to the
two corresponding sides and non-included angle of the other
only if the side opposite the given angle in each case is greater
than the other given side.*

Three angles of a triangle

In Fig. 84 the angles A, B, C of the triangle ABC are equal respectively to the angles D, E, F of the triangle DEF.

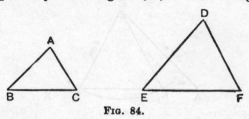

FIG. 84.

The angles of a triangle determine its shape but not its size and in this case the triangles are *similar*. If EF be made twice BC in length, DE will be twice AB and DF twice AC.

In general, if the angles A, B, C of a triangle ABC are equal respectively to the angles D, E, F of a triangle DEF, the sides are proportional, i.e. $\dfrac{BC}{EF} = \dfrac{CA}{FD} = \dfrac{AB}{DE}$.

The triangle ABC may be considered as a scale drawing of the triangle DEF.

Exercise XXXI

Construct the triangle ABC in the following cases to a scale of 1 cm. to an inch. Find by measurement the sum of the angles in each case.

1. $BC = 10$ in., $CA = 9$ in., $AB = 7$ in.

2. $AB = 9$ in., $AC = 14$ in., $B\widehat{A}C = 35°$.

3. $BC = 8·5$ in., $A\widehat{B}C = 74°$, $ACB = 57°$.

4. $AB = 8·5$ in., $A\widehat{B}C = 74°$, $ACB = 57°$.

5. $AB = 9$ in., $AC = 15$ in., $A\widehat{B}C = 90°$.

6. Draw the two possible triangles in which $AB = 4$ in., $BC = 3·5$ in., $B\widehat{A}C = 50°$. Measure the two angles C. What do you notice about their sum ?

7. Draw a triangle in which $AB = 4$ in., $BC = 5$ in., $B\widehat{A}C = 50°$ and find by measurement the sum of the angles.

If you were asked to make a triangular template and were given the following measurements, would you say in each case that it was impossible, and if so, why ?

8. $BC = 13$ in., $CA = 7$ in., $AB = 5$ in.

9. $AB = 5$ in., $BC = 3$ in., $B\widehat{A}C = 40°$.

10. $AB = 5$ in., $BC = 4$ in., $B\widehat{A}C = 40°$.

11. $\widehat{A} = 70°$, $\widehat{B} = 60°$, $\widehat{C} = 50°$.

12. Draw any triangle. Make a copy in as many different ways as you can by making in each case three measurements only on the original triangle. Mark the parts on each copy which you measured. Measure the lengths of the sides of each copy and compare with the original triangle.

13. Draw a straight line AB. Through A draw a line AC and on it mark points P, Q, R, S, T so that AP, PQ, QR, RS, ST are of equal length. Use an edge of a set square to join TB and, by sliding the set square along a ruler, draw lines SH, RG, QF, PE parallel to TB, meeting AB in H, G, F, E respectively. Measure the lengths AE, EF, FG, GH, HB.

Since PE is parallel to TB, the triangles APE and ATB are similar. $AP = \frac{1}{5}AT$; hence $AE = \frac{1}{5}AB$. Similarly $AF = \frac{2}{5}AB$, $AG = \frac{3}{5}AB$, etc. AE, EF, FG, GH, HB are therefore equal in length.

NOTE.—*The above illustrates a method of dividing a line of given length into a required number of equal parts.*

14. Draw a convex quadrilateral $ABCD$ in which $AB = 4·7$ cm., $BC = 3$ cm., $CD = 2·3$ cm., $DA = 4$ cm. and the diagonal $AC = 5$ cm. Draw a line PQ near to but not intersecting the quadrilateral and not parallel to any side or to a diagonal. Construct a quadrilateral which shall be symmetrical with the given quadrilateral about the line PQ. Measure the sides of the second quadrilateral.

15. Draw Fig. 85 and the symmetrical figure about the axis AB.

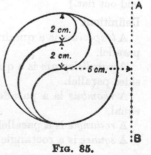

FIG. 85.

Questions 16–23 should be answered by drawings to scale.

16. A bob at the end of a string 3·5 feet long, the upper end of which is fixed, swings through an angle of 28° on either side of the vertical. How many inches does it rise above its lowest position ?

17. An aeroplane flies 60 miles N.E. then 80 miles in a direction S. 15° E. and then straight home. What is the distance of the return journey and in what direction does it head ?

18. Two aeroplanes leave an aerodrome at the same time, one flying due N. at 120 m.p.h. and the other in a direction N. 30° W. After half an hour they are 35 miles apart. What are the possible average speeds of the second aeroplane ?

19. A, B are two points on one bank of a river which may be assumed to be straight, and P is a point on the opposite bank. P is sighted from A and B and the angles PAB and PBA found to be 79° and 75° respectively. AB is 32 yards. What is the width of the river.

20. A 15-ft. ladder rests against a vertical wall. When a man has walked 6 ft. up the ladder his feet are 5 ft. 8 in. from the ground. How far up the wall does the ladder reach ?

21. Two walls are 20 ft. apart. A ladder with its foot 12 ft. from one wall reaches 16 ft. up the wall. If it is now turned about its foot to the opposite wall, how far up this wall will it reach ?

22. To climb a hill a horse zig-zags from side to side, each straight path being 25 ft. and the width of the road 20 ft. After crossing from side to side four times the horse has climbed a vertical distance of 10 ft. What is the inclination of the road to the horizontal in degrees ?

23. The dimensions of a room are length 20 ft., width 16 ft., height 10 ft. What is the shortest path by which an insect can crawl from one corner of the floor to the diagonally opposite corner on the ceiling ? [Imagine the walls hinged to the floor and laid out flat.]

Definitions

A *trapezium* is a quadrilateral with one pair of opposite sides parallel.

A *parallelogram* is a quadrilateral with both pairs of opposite sides parallel.

A *rhombus* is a parallelogram with a pair of adjacent sides equal.

A *rectangle* is a parallelogram with one angle a right angle.

A *square* is a rectangle with a pair of adjacent sides equal.

Symbols.

The following symbols are often used :

Symbol.		Meaning.
$\|^l$	..	Parallel.
$\perp$ '	..	Perpendicular.
rt. $\angle$	..	Right angle.
$\equiv$	..	Is congruent with.
$\triangle$	..	Triangle.
$\square^m$	..	Parallelogram.
$\odot^{le}$	..	Circle.

CONSTRUCTIONS

The following constructions can be carried out, using a straight edge and compasses only

Construction.—Construct an angle equal to a given angle.

Let x be the given angle.

With centre A and any radius, draw an arc intersecting AB at P and AC at Q.

Draw a straight line ED.

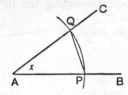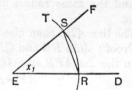

FIG. 86.

With centre E and radius AP, draw an arc RT intersecting ED at R.

With centre R and radius PQ, draw an arc intersecting the arc RT at S.

Join ES and produce it to F.

Then x_1 is the required angle.

Proof : Join PQ and RS.

In the $\triangle$s APQ and ERS,

$$AP = ER. \quad \text{(Constr.)}$$
$$AQ = ES. \quad \text{(Constr.)}$$
$$PQ = RS. \quad \text{(Constr.)}$$
$$\therefore \triangle APQ \equiv \triangle ERS \text{ (Three sides.)}$$
$$\therefore x = x_1.$$

Construction.—Bisect a given angle.

Let BAC be the given angle.

With centre A and any radius, draw an arc intersecting AB at P and AC at Q.

With centre P and any radius, draw an arc, and with centre

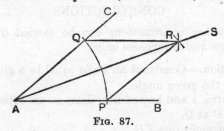

FIG. 87.

Q and the same radius draw an arc intersecting the former at R.

The line ARS then bisects the angle BAC.

Proof : Join PR and QR.

In the $\triangle$s APR and AQR,

$$AP = AQ. \quad \text{(Constr.)}$$
$$PR = QR. \quad \text{(Constr.)}$$
$$AR = AR.$$
$$\therefore \triangle APR \equiv \triangle AQR. \quad \text{(Three sides.)}$$
$$\therefore \widehat{RAP} = \widehat{RAQ}.$$

i.e RA bisects $B\widehat{A}C$.

(NOTE.—It could be deduced from symmetry that the triangles APR and AQR are congruent, AR being the axis of symmetry.)

Construction.—Draw the perpendicular bisector of a given line.

Let AB be the given line.

With centres A and B, draw arcs with the same radius, greater than half the length of AB, to intersect at P and Q.

Join PQ, intersecting AB in M.

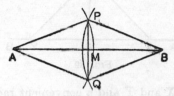

FIG. 88.

Then PQ is the perpendicular bisector of AB.

Proof · In the $\triangle$s APQ and BPQ,

$$AP = BP. \quad \text{(Constr.)}$$
$$AQ = BQ. \quad \text{(Constr.)}$$
$$PQ = PQ.$$
$$\therefore \triangle APQ \equiv \triangle BPQ. \quad \text{(Three sides.)}$$

$$\therefore A\widehat{P}M = B\widehat{P}M.$$

In the $\triangle$s APM and BPM.

$$AP = BP. \quad \text{(Constr.)}$$
$$PM = PM.$$

$$A\widehat{P}M = B\widehat{P}M. \quad \text{(Proved.)}$$
$$\therefore \triangle APM \equiv \triangle BPM. \quad \text{(Two sides and inc. } \angle.)$$
$$\therefore AM = BM \text{ and } AB \text{ is bisected at } M.$$

Also $P\widehat{M}A = P\widehat{M}B$ and since the sum of these angles is two right angles, each is a right angle.

$\therefore PM$ is the perpendicular bisector of AB.

Construction.—Draw a line perpendicular to a given straight line from a point in it.

Let P be a point in the line AB.

With centre P and any radius draw arcs intersecting AB at X and Y.

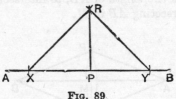

FIG. 89.

With centres X and Y and a convenient radius, draw arcs intersecting at R.

Then RP is $\perp^r$ to AB.

The proof is left to the student.

Construction.—From a point outside a line, draw a perpendicular to it.

Let P be a point outside the line AB.

With centre P and a convenient radius, draw an arc intersecting AB at X and Y.

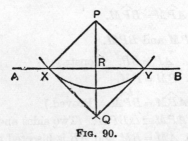

FIG. 90.

With centres X, Y and a convenient radius, draw arcs intersecting at Q.

Then PQ is $\perp^r$ to AB.

The proof is left to the student.

Converse

From given data we can often make a deduction. If from the statement in the deduction, we can deduce the original data, we have proved the *converse*.

The student should clearly understand that when a deduction has been made, the converse may or may not be true.

Consider the following examples :

(i) It is raining.

∴ the roofs of the houses are wet.

The converse would be :

The roofs of the houses are wet.

∴ it is raining.

We know that this is not necessarily true.

(ii) If the sides of one triangle are equal respectively to the sides of another, the angles of the one triangle are equal respectively to the corresponding angles of the other.

The converse would be :

If the angles of one triangle are equal respectively to the corresponding angles of the other, the sides of the one triangle are equal respectively to the sides of the other.

We know that the latter is not necessarily true as the triangles may be only similar and not congruent.

Deductions from the use of congruent triangles

Theorem.—The angles at the base of an isosceles triangle are equal.

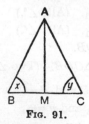

FIG. 91.

Let ABC be an isosceles triangle in which $AB = AC$.

Prove that $x = y$.

Join A to the mid-point M of BC.

In the $\triangle$s ABM and ACM,

$$AB = AC. \quad \text{(Given.)}$$
$$BM = CM. \quad \text{(Constr.)}$$
$$AM = AM.$$
$$\therefore \triangle ABM \equiv \triangle ACM. \quad \text{(Three sides.)}$$
$$\therefore x = y.$$

The proof of the converse, which is also true, is left to the student.

Theorem.—The opposite sides and also the opposite angles of a parallelogram are equal.

Let $ABCD$ be a parallelogram.

Prove that $AB = DC$, $AD = BC$, $\widehat{A} = \widehat{C}$, $\widehat{B} = \widehat{D}$.

Proof : Join BD.

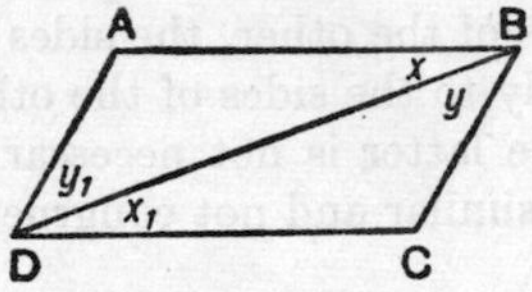

FIG. 92.

In the $\triangle$s ABD and CDB,

$$x = x_1. \quad \text{(Alt. } \angle^s.)$$
$$y = y_1. \quad \text{(Alt. } \angle^s.)$$
$$BD = DB.$$
$$\therefore \triangle ABD \equiv \triangle CDB. \quad \text{(Two } \angle^s \text{ and side.)}$$
$$\therefore AB = CD, \ AD = CB \text{ and } \widehat{A} = \widehat{C}.$$

Also since $x = x_1$ and $y = y_1$,

$$x + y = x_1 + y_1,$$

i.e. $\widehat{B} = \widehat{D}$.

The following are left as exercises to the student :

The diagonals of a parallelogram bisect each other.

If the ends of two equal and parallel straight lines be joined to form a quadrilateral, the quadrilateral is a parallelogram.

If the diagonals of a quadrilateral bisect each other, it is a parallelogram.

If the diagonals of a parallelogram are—

(1) Equal, it is a rectangle ;
(2) Perpendicular, it is a rhombus ;
(3) Equal and perpendicular, it is a square.

Exercise XXXII

Without using a protractor construct angles of :

1. 90°.   2. 45°.   3. 60°.   4. 30°.   5. 67½°.   6. 195°.

7. Construct an equilateral triangle with a given side.

8. Construct a square with a given side.

9. Construct a parallelogram with sides 3 in. and 2½ in. including an angle of 60°. Measure the obtuse angle between two adjacent sides. Draw the diagonals and measure the distances from their point of intersection to the vertices.

10. Construct a rhombus with diagonals 4 in. and 3 in. in length respectively.

11. Draw any triangle *ABC* and bisect each side. Join the vertices to the mid-points of opposite sides. (These lines are the *medians* of the triangle.) They should intersect at a point *O*. Measure the distance *OA* and the distance from *O* to the mid-point of the side opposite to *A*. What do you notice about these distances ?

12. Draw a triangle *ABC* in which *A* is an obtuse angle. Draw the perpendiculars *AP*, *BQ*, *CR* to the sides *BC*, *CA*, *AB*. What do you notice about these perpendiculars if *PA* is produced ?

13. Draw a triangle *ABC* and bisect the angles *B* and *C* by lines *IB*, *IC*. Join *IA* and measure the angles *IAB* and *IAC*. They should be equal. Draw *IP* perpendicular to *BC*. With centre *I* and radius *IP* describe a circle. What do you notice about this circle ?

14. Draw a triangle *ABC*. Draw the perpendicular bisectors

of AB and AC intersecting in O.   Draw also the perpendicular bisector of BC.   With centre O and radius OA describe a circle. What do you notice about this circle ?

15. AB and CD are two non-intersecting lines. P, Q are points on AB and R, S points on CD.   Bisect the angles APR and CRP by lines meeting in X ; bisect the angles BQS and DSQ by lines meeting in Y.   Produce the lines AB, CD and XY until they intersect.   What do you notice ?

16. Draw a pentagon $ABCDE$.   By construction find a point P in AB such that $\dfrac{AP}{BP} = \dfrac{4}{3}$ and a point S in AE such that $\dfrac{AS}{ES} = \dfrac{4}{3}$. Through P draw a line parallel to BC to meet AC in Q ; through Q a line parallel to CD to meet AD in R, and through R a line parallel to DE.   Does this pass through S ?

17. Construct a parallelogram with diagonals 10 cm. and 7 cm. in length respectively, including an angle of 120°.

18. Construct a triangle in which the perpendicular from the vertex to the base is $2\frac{1}{2}$ in. long and divides the vertical angle into two angles of 45° and 30° respectively.   Measure the base angles of the triangle.

In Questions 19–26, proofs are required.

19. P is any point on the bisector of the angle BAC.   Prove that the perpendiculars from P to the arms AB and AC are equal.

20. Two lines, PQ and RS, intersect and bisect each other at O. Prove that $PS = QR$.

21. If the opposite sides of a quadrilateral are equal, prove that it is a parallelogram.

22. The diagonals of a parallelogram $PQRS$ intersect at O.   A line through O meets PQ at X and RS at Y.   Prove that $OX = OY$.

23. ABC is an isosceles triangle in which $AB = AC$. AB is produced to D and AC to E, so that $BD = CE$.   Prove that $BE = CD$.

24. ABC is a triangle.   Equilateral triangles APB and AQC are described exterior to ABC.   Prove that $PC = QB$.

25. $ABCD$ and $ABEF$ are parallelograms.   Prove that $CDFE$ is a parallelogram.

The following statements are true.   State the converse in each case and say whether or not it is true.

26. All boys under eight years of age are children.

27. All Englishmen are Europeans.

28. If three angles of a quadrilateral are known, the fourth angle is known.

29. If the sides of a rectangle are 3 inches and 4 inches, its area is 12 square inches.

30. If a quadrilateral is a square, its four angles are equal.

31. If a man is a good engineer, he will earn more than two pounds a week.

32. All engines in new Rolls Royce cars develop more than 10 horse-power.

33. All isosceles triangles have two equal angles.

CHAPTER XII

AREAS

Theorem.—Area of parallelogram = base × height.

Let $ABCD$ be a $\square^m$.
Draw $\perp^{rs}$ AP and BQ to the line CD.
Then $ABQP$ is a rectangle.
$\triangle APD \equiv \triangle BQC$ (2 sides and rt. $\angle$.)
$\therefore$ area APD = area BQC.

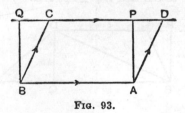

Fig. 93.

To each add the area $ABCP$.

Then area of $\square^m$ $ABCD$ = area of rect. $ABQP = AB \times AP$
= base × height of $\square^m$.

Corollary : Parallelograms on the same base and of equal area are between the same parallels.

Theorem.—Area of triangle $= \dfrac{\text{base} \times \text{height}}{2}$.

Let ABC be a triangle.

Draw $AD \parallel^{l}$ to CB and $BD \parallel^{l}$ to CA.

Then $CBDA$ is a $\square^{m}$.

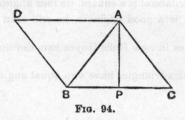

Fig. 94.

Draw $AP \perp^{r}$ to BC.

Diagonal AB bisects the $\square^{m}$ $CBDA$.

$\therefore$ area of $\triangle ABC = \frac{1}{2}$ area of $\square^{m}$ $CBDA = \dfrac{BC \times AP}{2}$.

Theorem.—Area of trapezium

$$= \frac{(\text{sum of parallel sides}) \times (\text{perp. dist. between them})}{2}.$$

$ABCD$ is a trapezium.

Draw $BP \perp^{r}$ to CD and $DQ \perp^{r}$ to AB.

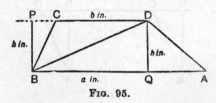

Fig. 95.

Let $AB = a$ inches, $CD = b$ inches, $DQ = h$ inches.

Area of $ABCD =$ area $ABD +$ area BCD.

$= \frac{1}{2}ah + \frac{1}{2}bh$ sq. in.

$= \dfrac{(a+b)h}{2}$ sq. in.

A rectilineal figure is a plane figure bounded by straight lines, i.e. a polygon.

The area of a rectilineal figure may be found by joining two vertices and drawing perpendiculars from the other vertices

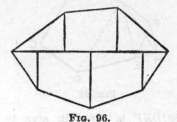

FIG. 96.

on to the joining line as in Fig. 96. The original area is then equal to a sum of areas, each of which is either a triangle or a trapezium.

Construction.—Construct a triangle equal in area to a given quadrilateral.

ABCD is a quadrilateral.

Draw *BE* parallel to *AC* to meet *DC* produced in *E*. Join *AE*.

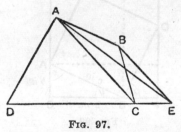

FIG. 97.

ADE is the required triangle.

Area of $\triangle ABC$ = area of $\triangle AEC$.   (Same base and between same parallels.)

To each add area *ACD*.

Then area of quadrilateral *ABCD* = area of triangle *ADE*.

By use of the above construction, a triangle can be constructed equal in area to any rectilineal figure. In Fig. 98

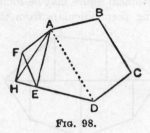

FIG. 98.

the hexagon *ABCDEF* is equal in area to the pentagon *ABCDH* ; applying the same method a quadrilateral of equal area can be constructed and then a triangle.

Pythagoras' theorem

The square on the hypotenuse of a right-angled triangle is equal to the sum of the squares on the other two sides.

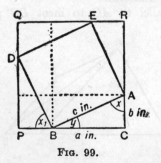

FIG. 99.

ABC is a triangle with *C* a right angle.

Let $BC = a$ in., $CA = b$ in., $AB = c$ in.

Produce *CA* to *R* so that $AR = CB$ and *CB* to *P* so that $BP = CA$.

Complete the square *CPQR*.

Take a point D on PQ and a point E on QR such that $PD = QE = a$ in.

Then $DQ = ER = b$ in.

The $\triangle$s ABC, BDP, DEQ and EAR are congruent. (2 sides including rt. $\angle$.)

$$\therefore AB = BD = DE = EA.$$

Also $x = x_1$.

But $x + y = 90°$. $(\widehat{ACB} = 90°.)$

$$\therefore x_1 + y = 90°.$$

$$\therefore \widehat{ABD} = 90°.$$

$$\therefore ABDE \text{ is a square.}$$

Area of sq. $CPQR =$ area of inner sq. $ABDE +$ area of $4 \triangle$s
$$= \text{area of } ABDE + 4 \text{ (area of } ABC).$$

$$\therefore (a+b)^2 = c^2 + 4\frac{ab}{2}.$$

$$a^2 + 2ab + b^2 = c^2 + 2ab.$$

$$\therefore a^2 + b^2 = c^2, \text{ which proves the theorem.}$$

Corollary : The perpendicular is the shortest distance from a given point to a given straight line.

The above is one of the most widely known theorems in geometry. Its discovery is generally attributed to Pythagoras, who died just before the beginning of the fifth century B.C., but the special case in which the sides of a triangle are in the ratios $3 : 4 : 5$ was known earlier to the Egyptians. The proof (not the above) given by Euclid in his *Elements*, which was written about 300 B.C., is still frequently given.

Converse.—If the square on one side of a triangle is equal to the sum of the squares on the other two sides, the triangle is right-angled.

ABC is a triangle in which $AB^2 = AC^2 + BC^2$.

Prove that $A\widehat{C}B$ is a right angle.

Construct a right angle ACD and make $CD = CB$.

Join AD.

Proof : $AD^2 = AC^2 + DC^2$.   ($A\widehat{C}D$ is rt. $\angle$.)

$$AB^2 = AC^2 + BC^2. \quad \text{(Given.)}$$

But $DC = BC$.   (Constr.)

$$\therefore \ AD^2 = AB^2.$$

$$\therefore \ AD = AB.$$

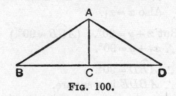

FIG. 100.

In the $\triangle$s ACB and ACD,

$$AC = AC.$$

$$CB = CD. \quad \text{(Constr.)}$$

$$AB = AD. \quad \text{(Proved.)}$$

$$\therefore \ \triangle ACB \equiv \triangle ACD. \quad \text{(Three sides.)}$$

$$\therefore \ A\widehat{C}B = A\widehat{C}D = \text{right angle.}$$

Corollary. The .... is the distance from a given point to a given straight line.

The above is one of the most widely known theorems in geometry. Its discovery is usually attributed to Pythagoras.

In the ratio 3 : 4 : 5 was known ....

Exercise XXXIII

1. *AP, BQ* are the perpendiculars from the vertices *A, B* to the opposite sides of a triangle *ABC.* $AC = 9$ cm., $BC = 10$ cm., $AP = 8 \cdot 2$ cm.   Find *BQ.*

2. Construct a trapezium in which the parallel sides are of lengths 8 cm. and 4 cm. respectively at a distance 3·5 cm. apart and a third side is 3·8 cm. long.   Calculate (i) its area, (ii) the length of the second side of a rectangle of equal area with one side 6 cm., (iii) the side of a square of equal area.   Construct a triangle equal in area to the trapezium and calculate its area, making any necessary measurements.

3. Draw a convex polygon *ABCD* in which $A\widehat{B}C = 72°$, $AB = 2$ in., $BC = 4$ in., $CD = 3 \cdot 5$ in., $DA = 2 \cdot 5$ in.   Calculate its area, making any necessary measurements.   Construct a triangle equal in area to the polygon and calculate its area, making any necessary measurements.

4. From a field book the following details are taken :

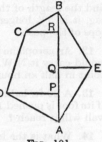

Fig. 101.

	Yards	
	To B	
	225	
To C 70	175	
	125	80 to E.
To D 100	85	
	From A	

The meaning is as below.

A base line AB is taken and distances measured from A towards B. $AP = 85$ yd., $AQ = 125$ yd., $AR = 175$ yd., $AB = 225$ yd. Offsets are taken at P, Q, R, perpendicular to AB. $PD = 100$ yd., $QE = 80$ yd., $RC = 70$ yd.

It will be seen that the area is divided into a trapezium and four triangles. Calculate the area from the data given.

5.

	Links	
	To B	
	1600	
To C 500	1300	
	1000	700 to F
To D 900	500	
	200	500 to E
	From A	

Draw a plan of the field from the given data and calculate its area in square yards, given that 100 links = 22 yards.

6. Draw a triangle with sides 9, 7 and 5 cm. in length respectively and an isosceles triangle of equal area on a base of 7 cm. Measure the sides.

7. Draw a triangle with sides 3 in., 3·2 in., 2·4 in. Construct an isosceles triangle of equal area with each of the equal sides 3 in. in length. Measure the third side.

8. Draw a parallelogram of area 50 sq. cm. with sides 10 cm. and 5·2 cm. in length. Draw a second parallelogram of equal area with one side 10 cm. and with an angle of 60°. Measure the other side.

9. Is a triangle with sides 12·5 cm., 30 cm., 32·5 cm. in length right-angled ?

10. Find the side and area of a rhombus with diagonals 20 and 21 cm. in length respectively.

7

11. A tightly stretched wire joins the tops of two vertical posts 13 ft. apart. If the posts are 5 ft. and 13 ft. high respectively, find the length of the wire correct to the nearest ¼ ft. if, owing to sag, it is 5% longer than the straight line distance between the tops of the posts.

12. An aeroplane is heading N.E. at 160 m.p.h. in a wind which would carry it N.W. at 36 m.p.h. How far is it from its starting point in half an hour ?

13. A 20-ft. ladder rests with its foot 5 ft. from a vertical wall. If its foot is pushed 1 ft. nearer to the wall, how much higher up the wall will it reach ?

14. What is the length of the longest straight rod which can be put into a box 4·8 ft. long, 3·6 ft. wide and 2·5 ft. high ?

15. Draw a right-angled triangle ABC and the squares on the sides as in Fig. 102. Cut the square on AB into parts I, II, III, IV,

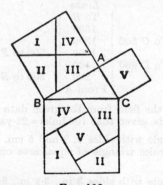

FIG. 102.

as shown, cutting lines being parallel and perpendicular to BC through the centre of the square. Fit the parts together with the square on AC to form the square on BC and thus verify Pythagoras' theorem.

16. Construct lines $\sqrt{2}$, $\sqrt{5}$, $\sqrt{6}$ in. long respectively.

17. Construct a square of area 7 sq. in.

18. Given two squares, construct a square equal in area to the sum of the given squares.

19. ABC is a triangle in which A is an obtuse angle. CD is perpendicular to AB. $BC=a$ in., $CA=b$ in., $AB=c$ in., $AD =h$ in. By applying Pythagoras' theorem to the triangles BDC and ADC, prove that $a^2=b^2+c^2+2ch$.

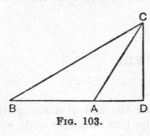

Fig. 103.

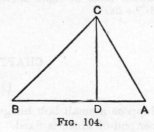

Fig. 104.

20. In Fig. 104, if $AD=h$ in., show that $a^2=b^2+c^2-2ch$.

If the sides of a triangle are a cm., b cm., c cm., determine if the following triangles are obtuse or acute-angled :

21. $a=15$, $b=12$, $c=8.5$.

22. $a=13.5$, $b=11.7$, $c=9.9$.

23. Construct a triangle ABC in which $AB=10$ cm., $AC =6$ cm., $\widehat{BAC}=60°$. Take a point P on AC produced so that $AP=9$ cm. Find a point Q on AB such that the area of the triangle APQ is equal to the area of ABC. Measure AQ.

In the following questions, proofs should be given :

24. P is a point on the diagonal AC of a parallelogram $ABCD$. Show that the triangles APB and APD are equal in area.

25. P and Q are the mid-points of the sides AB and AC of a triangle ABC. Prove that the triangles BPC and BQC are equal in area and hence that PQ is parallel to BC. Deduce that if R is the mid-point of BC, $PQRB$ is a parallelogram and hence that $2PQ=BC$.

26. P and Q are points on opposite sides of AB and the triangles APB and AQB are equal in area. Prove that AB bisects PQ.

27. ABC is a triangle with P a point in AC. M is the mid-point of AB and a line through C parallel to PM meets AB in Q. Prove that the area of the triangle APQ is half the area of the triangle ABC.

28. ABC is an equilateral triangle and AP perpendicular to BC. Prove that $3AC^2=4AP^2$.

29. Prove that the sum of the squares of the sides of a rhombus is equal to the sum of the squares of the diagonals.

30. The opposite sides, AB and DC, of a quadrilateral when produced meet at right angles at P. Prove that $AD^2 + BC^2 = AC^2 + BD^2$.

CHAPTER XIII

LOCI

Suppose a small bob hangs from the end of a string, the upper end of which is fixed. If the bob be pulled aside with the string taut and then allowed to fall, it will describe an arc of a circle. This arc is said to be the *locus* of the bob, moving so that it is always a fixed distance from a fixed point.

If a point moves in a plane so that it is always a fixed distance from a given straight line, the locus is two parallel lines, one on each side of the given line and at the fixed distance from it.

If the point could move in space so as to be always a fixed distance from a given line, the locus would be a cylinder with the given line as axis and the fixed distance as radius.

We may say that the locus of a point is the curve (or surface) on which the point must lie when it moves, subject to some given conditions.

In determining a locus, consideration must be given to two aspects of the problem. We first find the curve (or surface) on which the point must lie ; we must then determine if the complete curve (or surface) or only part of it is the locus.

In the case of a swinging bob moving so as to be a fixed distance from a fixed point, the curve would be a circle. But in the case first discussed above, the conditions are such that only an arc of the circle is the locus.

NOTE.—The word " circle " is often used as a short way of writing " circumference of a circle."

Theorem.—The locus of a point which moves so that it is equidistant from two fixed points is the perpendicular bisector of the line joining them.

Let A, B be two fixed points and P any position of a point such that $PA = PB$.

Fig. 105.

Prove that the locus of P is the perpendicular bisector of AB.

Join P to the mid-point M of AB.

In the $\triangle$s PMA and PMB,

$$PA = PB. \quad \text{(Given.)}$$
$$AM = BM. \quad \text{(Constr.)}$$
$$PM = PM.$$
$$\therefore \triangle PMA \equiv \triangle PMB. \quad \text{(Three sides.)}$$
$$\therefore x = y.$$

But $x + y = 180°$.

$$\therefore x = 90°.$$

$\therefore P$ lies on the perpendicular bisector of AB.

Every point on the perpendicular bisector is equidistant from A and B and it is therefore the locus.

Theorem.—The locus of a point which moves so that it is equidistant from two given intersecting straight lines is the pair of lines bisecting the angles between the given lines.

Let the given lines AB and CD intersect in O and let P be any position of the point. If PM and PN be the perpendiculars to the given lines, $PM = PN$.

Prove that the locus of P is the pair of lines bisecting the angles between AB and CD.

Join PO.

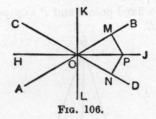

Fig. 106.

In the $\triangle$s POM and PON,

$$PM = PN. \quad \text{(Given.)}$$
$$PO = PO.$$

$$\widehat{PMO} = \widehat{PNO} = \text{rt. } \angle. \quad \text{(Given.)}$$
$$\therefore \triangle POM \equiv \triangle PON. \quad \text{(2 sides and rt. } \angle.)$$

$\therefore \widehat{POM} = \widehat{PON}$ and P lies on a bisector of the angle between AB and CD.

Conversely it can be shown that any point on HJ or KL (the bisectors of the angles between AB and CD) is equidistant from AB and CD.

$\therefore$ the lines HJ and KL are the required locus.

Theorem.—The locus of a point which moves so that it forms with a fixed line of given length a triangle of constant area, is a pair of lines parallel to and on either side of the fixed line.

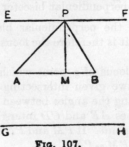

Fig. 107.

Let AB be the given line and P one position of the point such that the triangle PAB is of constant area.

Prove that the locus of P is a pair of lines parallel to and on either side of AB.

Draw $PM \perp'$ to AB.

Area of $\triangle PAB = \frac{1}{2}AB.PM = \text{const.}$

But AB is given.

$\therefore PM$ is of constant length.

$\therefore P$ moves so that it is always a fixed distance from the line AB, i.e. on the lines EF and GH, parallel to AB and at a distance PM from AB.

Every point on these lines forms with AB a triangle of the given area.

$\therefore$ these lines are the locus of P.

Exercise XXXIV

1. What is the locus of the mid-points of radii of a given circle ?

2. A point moves so that it is always 1 in. from the nearest side of a square of side 3 in.   What is its locus ?

3. $ABCD$ is a parallelogram of given area on a fixed base AB. What is the locus of C (i) in a plane, (ii) in space ?

4. What is the locus of the centre of a football in the case of a straight ground pass ?

5. A circle of given radius rolls round a fixed circle.   What is the locus of the centre of the rolling circle ?

6. What is the locus of the centre of the front wheel of a bicycle ridden round a circular track at the same distance from the edge ?

7. A tight belt passes round two equal pulleys, one vertically above the other.   What is the locus of a point on the belt ?

8. What are the loci of the ends of a connecting rod cranked to a fixed centre ?

9. O is a fixed point and P moves along a fixed straight line. What is the locus of the mid-point of OP ?

10. A rod has a small ring attached to each end.   The rings slide along two fixed horizontal bars.   What is the locus of a fixed point on the rod ?

11. A triangular template ABC rotates with AB fixed. What is the locus of C ?

12. What type of curve is described by the end of a propeller of an aeroplane travelling with constant speed in a straight line ?

13. A, B are two fixed points. Draw a line through A and with a 60° set-square find a point P on the line such that $\widehat{APB} = 60°$. Draw a number of lines through A and on these lines find the corresponding points P. Through these points draw a curve. Describe how a point must move to give this curve for locus.

Construct the perpendicular bisector of AB and of one of your lines AP and let them meet in O. With centre O and radius OA draw an arc APB. What do you notice about this arc ?

14. S is a fixed point and AB a fixed line. Find a number of points P such that PS is equal to the perpendicular distance of P from AB. Draw a curve through these points.

This curve is a parabola ; it is the section of a searchlight mirror by a plane through its axis.

15. Draw the curve described by P when $\dfrac{PS}{PM} = \dfrac{3}{2}$, where S is a fixed point and PM the perpendicular distance of P from a fixed line AB. This curve is a hyperbola.

16. Fix two pins vertically at two points A, B. Make loops at the end of a piece of thread and pass one loop over each pin. With your pencil describe the curve which you obtain by keeping the thread taut and as near to the paper as possible. This curve is an ellipse.

Remove the pins and thread and draw a line through A and B to meet the curve in C and D. On CD as diameter describe a circle. Take a point P on the circle and draw a line PQM perpendicular to AB and meeting the ellipse in Q. Measure QM and PM and express $\dfrac{QM}{PM}$ as a decimal. Do this for a number of corresponding points, P, Q. What do you deduce ?

17. Fasten one end of a piece of thread to a circular disc. Make a loop at the other end of the thread and pass the thread round the disc. Hold the disc flat on your paper and pass your pencil point through the loop. Draw the curve which you obtain by unwinding the thread while keeping it taut.

This curve is the involute of a circle and is used in constructing gear teeth.

18. Hold a penny flat on the paper and in contact with a straight line. Mark the point P on the penny in contact with the line. Roll the penny along the line and mark a number of points which are the positions of P as the penny rolls. Join these points by a curve. This curve is a cycloid and is used in connection with gear teeth.

CHAPTER XIV

THE CIRCLE

A circle is symmetrical about any diameter.

The following facts may be deduced from symmetry :

1. A line joining the centre of a circle to the mid-point of a chord is perpendicular to the chord.

2. A line through the centre of a circle perpendicular to a chord bisects the chord.

3. Equal chords of a circle are equidistant from the centre.

4. Chords which are equidistant from the centre are equal.

The student should prove each of the above statements as an exercise on congruent triangles.

A, B, C, D are four points on the circumference of a circle, centre O. $\widehat{BAD}$ is said to be an angle at the circumference *standing on the arc* BCD. The arc BCD is said to *subtend* the angle BAD at the circumference and the angle BOD at the centre. The points A, B, C, D are *concyclic*, since a circle passes through them, and $ABCD$ is a *cyclic* quadrilateral, since its vertices lie on the circumference of a circle.

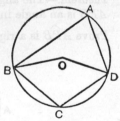

FIG. 108.

Theorem.—The angle at the centre of a circle is twice the angle at the circumference standing on the same arc.

AB is an arc of a circle and P a point on the remaining part of the circumference.

Prove $\widehat{AOB} = 2\widehat{APB}$.

7*

Join *PO* and produce to any point *S.*

$$OA = OP,$$

$$\therefore \ O\widehat{A}P = O\widehat{P}A.$$

But ext. $S\widehat{O}A =$ sum of int. $\angle$s OAP and $OPA.$

$$\therefore \ S\widehat{O}A = 2O\widehat{P}A.$$

Similarly $S\widehat{O}B = 2O\widehat{P}B.$

FIG. 109 (*a*).

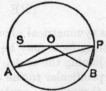

FIG. 109 (*b*).

Adding these results in Fig. 109 (*a*) and subtracting them in Fig. 109 (*b*), $A\widehat{O}B = 2A\widehat{P}B.$

Corollary : Angles at the circumference of a circle standing on the same arc are equal.

Theorem.—The angle in a semicircle is a right angle.

APB is an angle in a semicircle.

Prove $A\widehat{P}B$ is a right angle.

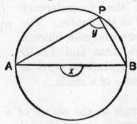

FIG. 110.

$$x = 2y. \quad \text{(Theorem.)}$$

$$x = 2 \text{ rt. } \angle \text{s.}$$

$$\therefore \ y = 1 \text{ rt. } \angle.$$

Theorem.—The opposite angles of a cyclic quadrilateral are supplementary.

Let $ABCD$ be a cyclic quadrilateral.

Prove $\widehat{A} + \widehat{C} = 180°$.

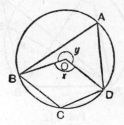

FIG. 111.

Join OB and OD, where O is the centre of the circle.

$$x = 2\widehat{A}. \quad \text{(Theorem.)}$$

$$y = 2\widehat{C}. \quad \text{(Theorem.)}$$

By addition $x + y = 2A + 2C$.

But $x + y = 360°$.

$\therefore A + C = 180°$.

Corollary : If a side of a cyclic quadrilateral be produced, the exterior angle is equal to the interior opposite angle.

We shall now prove the converses of two previous theorems.

Theorem.—If the line joining two points subtends equal angles at two other points on the same side of it, the four points are concyclic.

Let A, B be two points and C, D two points on the same side of AB such that $x = y$.

Prove that A, B, C, D are concyclic.

Suppose a circle to be drawn through A, B, C.

If it does not pass through D, let it intersect BD (or BD produced, if necessary) in E.

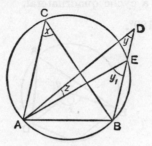

FIG. 112.

$x = y$.   (Given.)

$x = y_1$.   (On same arc AB.)

$\therefore y_1 = y$.

But $y_1 = y + z$.   (Ext. angle theorem.)

$\therefore z = 0$.

$\therefore$ the line AE coincides with the line AD and the circle passes through D.

Theorem.—If the opposite angles of a quadrilateral are supplementary, the quadrilateral is cyclic.

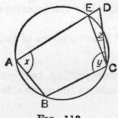

FIG. 113.

Let $ABCD$ be a quadrilateral in which $x + y = 180°$.

Prove that $ABCD$ is cyclic.

Suppose a circle to be drawn through A, B, C. If it does not pass through D let it intersect AD (or AD produced) in E.

$$x + y = 180°. \quad \text{(Given.)}$$
$$x + y - z = 180°. \quad (ABCE \text{ is cyclic quad.})$$
$$\therefore z = 0.$$

$\therefore$ CE and CD coincide and the circle passes through D.

Exercise XXXV

1. Draw a circle centre O and two triangles APB, AQB with their vertices on the circumference. Measure the angles AOB, APB, AQB and verify that :

(i) the angle at the centre is twice the angle at the circumference standing on the same arc ;

(ii) angles in a circle standing on the same arc are equal.

2. Draw a diameter AB of a circle and take points P, Q, R on the circumference. Measure the angles APB, AQB, ARB and verify that the angle in a circumcircle is a right angle.

3. Draw a quadrilateral $ABCD$ with its vertices on the circumference of a given circle. Measure the angles A, B, C, D and verify that opposite angles of a cyclic quadrilateral are supplementary.

4. With the help of a protractor construct three equal angles APB, AQB, ARB. Draw the perpendicular bisectors of AB and AP, meeting in O. With centre O and radius OA describe a circle and verify that points subtending equal angles at two given points lie on an arc of a circle.

5. With the help of a protractor draw a quadrilateral $ABCD$ in which $\widehat{A} + \widehat{C} = 180°$. Draw the perpendicular bisectors of AB and AD meeting in O. With centre O and radius OA describe a circle and verify that a quadrilateral with a pair of opposite angles supplementary is cyclic.

6. ABC is a triangle inscribed in a circle, centre O. $\widehat{BOC} = 164°$ $\widehat{ABC} = 51°$. Find the angles A and C.

7. $ABCD$ is a quadrilateral inscribed in a circle, centre O. $\widehat{BOD} = 150°$, $\widehat{ABC} = 106°$. Find the remaining angles of the quadrilateral.

8. $ABCD$ is a cyclic quadrilateral with diagonals AC and BD intersecting in O. $\widehat{BAC} = 40°$, $\widehat{BOC} = 85°$, $\widehat{OBC} = 63°$. Calculate the angles of the quadrilateral.

9. *ABCDEFGH* is a regular octagon. Calculate the angles of the triangle *GBC*.

10. *BAC* is a triangle with *A* a right angle. The perpendicular to *BC* through any point *P* in *BC* meets *AB* in *Q*. Prove that *ACPQ* is a cyclic quadrilateral.

11. *ABCD* is a quadrilateral $B\widehat{C}D = 90°$, $B\widehat{D}C = 47°$, $D\widehat{A}C = 43°$. Prove that the circle on *BD* as diameter passes through *A* and *C*.

12. *AB* and *AC* are two straight lines. The circles on *AB* and *AC* as diameters intersect at *D*. Prove that *BDC* is a straight line.

13. Two circles intersect at *A* and *B*. A line through *A* meets one circle at *P* and the second at *Q*. A line through *B* meets the first circle at *R* and the second at *S*. Prove that *PR* and *QS* are parallel.

14. What is the locus of a point which moves so that it subtends a constant angle at two fixed points ?

15. *ABC* is a triangle. The perpendiculars *BQ* and *CR* from *B* and *C* to the opposite sides meet in *O*. *AO* produced meets *BC* in *P*. Prove that *AROQ* and *BRQC* are cyclic quadrilaterals. Deduce that the angle *RAP* is equal to the angle *RCP* and hence that *RACP* is a cyclic quadrilateral. Hence show that *APC* is a right angle and that therefore the perpendicular from *A* to *BC* also passes through *O*.

(The intersection of the perpendiculars from the vertices to the opposite sides of a triangle is called the *orthocentre* of the triangle.)

Prove that the angle *BOC* is 180° − *A* and hence find the locus of the orthocentre of a triangle with fixed base and constant vertical angle.

Tangent and Secant to a circle

A line intersecting a circle in two points is a *secant*. In Fig. 114, *CD* is a secant.

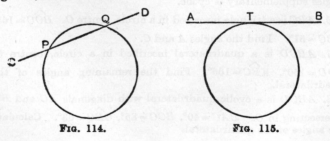

FIG. 114.　　　　　　　　　　　FIG. 115.

A line which, however far it may be produced, meets a circle in one point only is a *tangent*. In Fig. 115, AB is a tangent. AB touches the circle at T, which is the point of contact.

ATB is the tangent at T to a circle. C and C_1 are points on the circle, C_1 being nearer than C to T. It will be seen that if C moves along the circle, through C_1, nearer and nearer to T, the secant TC will move nearer and nearer to the tangent ATB and that ultimately the secant and the tangent will coincide. This we state by saying that the tangent at a point on a circle is the limiting position of a secant through the point. This definition will apply to a tangent to any curve.

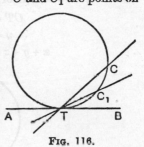

Fig. 116.

The notation $C \to T$ is used, meaning C approaches T.

Theorem.—The radius of a circle to the point of contact of a tangent is perpendicular to the tangent.

Let T be the point of contact of a tangent AB to a circle, centre O.

Prove OT is $\perp^r$ to AB.

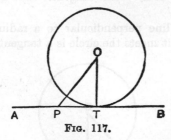

Fig. 117.

Let P be any other point on AB.
Then P is outside the circle
$\therefore\ OP > OT$.

∴ *OT* is the shortest distance from *O* to a point on *AB*.

∴ *OT* is ⊥ʳ to *AB*.

A second proof is given using the idea that a tangent is the limiting position of a secant.

Let *TQ* be a secant of the circle.

$$OT = OQ \text{ (radii.)}$$
$$\therefore y = z.$$
$$x + y + z = 180°. \quad (\angle^s \text{ of a } \triangle.)$$

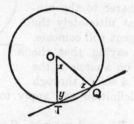

FIG. 118.

As $Q \to T$, $x \to 0$;
$$\therefore y + z \to 180°.$$
Since $y = z$, $\therefore y \to 90°$.

Hence, in the limiting position, when the secant becomes the tangent at *T*, *OT* is ⊥ʳ to the tangent.

Theorem.—A line perpendicular to a radius of a circle at the point where it meets the circle is a tangent to the circle.

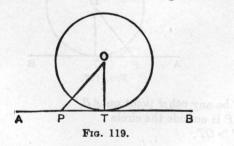

FIG. 119.

Let OT be a radius of a circle and AB the perpendicular through T.

Prove that AB is a tangent to the circle.

Let P be any other point on AB.

OP is the hypotenuse of a right-angled triangle OTP.

$\therefore OP > OT$.

$\therefore$ any point on AB except T is outside the circle and AB meets the circle in one point only.

$\therefore AB$ is a tangent to the circle.

Theorem.—If a tangent be drawn to a circle and a chord be drawn through the point of contact, the angle between the tangent and the chord is equal to the angle in the alternate segment.

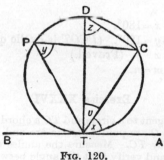

Fig. 120.

Let CT be a chord of a circle through the point of contact T of a tangent AB.

Prove that $x = y$.

Draw TD a diameter of the circle and join CD.

$$T\widehat{C}D = 90°. \quad \text{(Angle in semicircle.)}$$

$$\therefore z + v = 90°.$$

$$\text{But } x + v = 90°. \quad \text{(Radius is } \perp^r \text{ to tangent.)}$$

$$\therefore x = z.$$

$$\text{But } z = y. \quad (\angle^s \text{ on arc } CT.)$$

$$\therefore x = y.$$

$\widehat{CTB}$ is the obtuse angle between the tangent and chord and $\widehat{CQT}$ is the angle in the alternate segment.

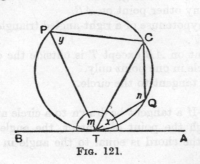

FIG. 121.

Prove that $m = n$.

$$m + x = 180°.$$
$$n + y = 180°. \quad (PCQT \text{ is cyclic quad.})$$
$$\text{But } x = y. \quad (\text{Proved.})$$
$$\therefore m = n.$$

Exercise XXXVI

1. ATB is a tangent to a circle and TC a chord through the point of contact T. P, Q are points on one arc and R, S points on the other arc cut off by TC. Measure the angles CTA, CTB, TPC, TQC, TRC, TSC and verify that the angle between a tangent to a circle and a chord through the point of contact is equal to the angle in the alternate segment.

2. TAP is a tangent to a circle at A and TBC a line meeting the circle in B and C. $\widehat{TAB} = 35°$, $\widehat{PAC} = 45°$. Find the angles of the triangle TAC.

3. ABC is a triangle inscribed in a circle. The tangents to the circle at A, B, C form a triangle PQR. If $\widehat{A} = 51°$ and $\widehat{B} = 47°$, find the angles of the triangle PQR.

4. TAP and TBQ are tangents to a circle at A and B. TCD is a line meeting the circle at C and D. If $\widehat{PAD} = 63°$ and $\widehat{QBD} = 49°$, find the angles ACB and ADB.

5. If TA and TB are tangents to a circle at A and B, prove that $TA = TB$.

6. ABC is a triangle inscribed in a circle and AT the tangent at A. A line through C parallel to BA meets AT in D. Prove that $A\widehat{C}B = A\widehat{D}C$.

7. TA is a tangent to a circle and TCD a line meeting the circle at C and D. Prove that the triangles TAC and TDA are similar.

8. The tangent at A to a circle meets the diameter BC produced at P. AM is perpendicular to BC. Prove that CA bisects the angle MAP.

9. Two circles touch at C (i.e. they have the same tangent at C). A line PCQ meets one circle at P and the other at Q; a line RCS meets the first circle at R and the second at S. Prove that PR and SQ are parallel.

10. Two circles intersect at A and B. A line CD touches one circle at C and the other at D. A line through C parallel to DB meets the circle CAB again in E. Prove that EB is a tangent to the circle drawn through C, B, D.

Construction.—Find the centre of a circle of which an arc is given.

Let A, B, C be any three points on the given arc. Draw MO, the perpendicular bisector of AB, and NO, the perpendicular bisector of BC. Then O is the centre of the circle.

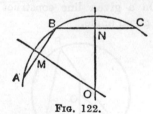

Fig. 122.

Proof : Since O is on the perpendicular bisector of AB,
$$OA = OB.$$
Similarly $OB = OC$.
$$\therefore OA = OB = OC \text{ and the circle centre}$$
O and radius OA also passes through B and C.

The above construction shows how to draw a circle through any three points not in line.

Construction.—Draw a tangent to a circle from a point outside it.

Let O be the centre of the given circle and P a point outside it.

On OP describe a semicircle intersecting the given circle at T.

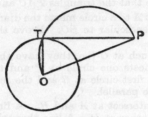

Fig. 123.

PT is a tangent to the circle.

Proof : Join OT.

$\widehat{OTP}$ is a rt. $\angle$. (Angle in semicircle.)

$\therefore PT$ is $\perp^r$ to the radius OT and is therefore a tangent to the circle.

Construction.—On a given line construct a segment of a circle containing a given angle.

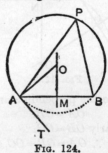

Fig. 124.

Let AB be the given line.

Construct an angle BAT equal to the given angle.

Draw $AO \perp^r$ to AT and MO the perpendicular bisector of AB.

With centre O and radius OA describe the arc APB.

Then APB is the required segment.

Proof : Since OM is the perpendicular bisector of AB, $OA = OB$ and the arc passes through B.

$\widehat{BAT}$ between tangent and chord $= \widehat{APB}$ in alternate segment.

$\therefore \widehat{APB} =$ given angle.

Circumcircle and incircle of triangle

If ABC is a triangle, the circle passing through A, B, C is the *circumcircle* and the circle touching the sides BC, CA, AB is the *incircle* of the triangle.

The radius of the circumcircle is the circum radius and the radius of the incircle the in-radius.

Construction.—Construct the circumcircle and the incircle of a triangle ABC.

Circumcircle

The circle through three given points has already been constructed.

Incircle

Bisect the angles B and C of the triangle ABC and let the bisector meet in O. Draw OP, OQ, $OR \perp^r$ to the sides BC CA, AB of the triangle.

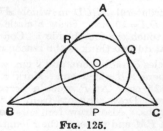

FIG. 125.

$$OP = OR. \quad (O \text{ is on the bisector of } \overset{\frown}{B}.)$$

$$OP = OQ. \quad (O \text{ is on the bisector of } \overset{\frown}{C}.)$$

$$\therefore OP = OQ = OR.$$

∴ circle centre O and radius OP passes through Q and R.

Since BC, CA, AB are $\perp^r$ to radii of the circle, they are tangents to the circle.

∴ PQR is the required circle.

Exercise XXXVII

1. Draw a triangle and its inscribed and circumscribed circles.

2. Draw a triangle ABC and produce AB and AC to P and Q respectively. Bisect the angles PBC and QCB and let the bisectors meet in E. Draw EX perpendicular to BC. With centre E and radius EX describe a circle. This circle should touch AP and AQ, say at Y and Z. Measure the sides of the triangle and hence find its perimeter ; also measure AY and AZ. What is the relation between AY or AZ and the perimeter ?

3. Draw a circle and two tangents to it from an external point. Construct a circle to touch both tangents and the given circle.

4. CM is the perpendicular to AB from its mid-point M. $AM = 4$ in., $CM = 2$ in. Calculate the radius of the circle through ACB. Draw the circle and measure its radius.

5. Draw a quadrilateral $ABCD$ in which $\overset{\frown}{A} = 105°$ and $\overset{\frown}{C} = 75°$. Construct the circle through ABC. Why does this circle pass through D ?

6. Draw a circle and circumscribe about it any quadrilateral $ABCD$. Find by measurement the sum of AB and DC, and also of AD and BC. What do you notice ?

7. Draw a quadrilateral $ABCD$ in which $AB = 7$ cm., $BC = 9$ cm., $CD = 12$ cm., $DA = 10$ cm. Draw a circle to touch three of the sides. Does it touch the fourth side ? Considering the result of Question 6, what do you think is the reason of this ?

8. Draw two circles of radii 5 cm. and 2 cm. with centres A and B respectively, where $AB = 10·5$ cm. Mark a point P on AB such that $AP = 6·25$ cm. At P erect a perpendicular PM to AB of length 8 cm. Draw tangents from M to the circles and measure their lengths. Also draw tangents to the circles from any other point on PM and measure their lengths.

9. Draw two circles of radii $2\frac{1}{2}$ in. and 1 in. with centres A and B respectively 4 in. apart. With centre A draw a circle with radius equal to the difference of the radii of the given circles. From B draw a tangent BP to this circle. Produce AP to meet the outer circle at Q. Draw BR parallel to PQ to meet the circle centre B at R. Join QR.

Prove that QR is a tangent to both circles.

(A tangent to two circles which intersects the line joining their centres only if produced is a *direct* common tangent.)

10. Find the length of the direct common tangents to two circles, radii 8 cm. and 3 cm. with centres 13 cm. apart.

11. Draw two circles as in Question 9. With centre A and a radius equal to the sum of the radii of the given circles, draw a circle. Draw a tangent BP to this circle. Join AP to meet the circle centre A in Q. Draw BR parallel to PQ to meet the circle centre B at R. Join QR.

Prove that QR is a tangent to both circles.

(This is a *transverse* common tangent since it intersects AB between A and B.)

12. Find the length of the straight portions of a tight crossed belt passing round two pulleys, radii 5 cm. and 4 cm. respectively with centres 15 cm. apart.

13. Show how to draw a line meeting two circles so that the chord intercepted by each shall be of a given length.

14. Draw a circle passing through two given points with its centre on a given straight line.

15. Draw a circle passing through a given point and touching a given straight line at a given point.

16. Draw a segment of a circle on a chord of 3 in. such that the angle subtended by any point on the arc at the extremities of the chord is $75°$.

17. Draw a triangle and a circle. Inscribe in the circle a triangle similar to the triangle drawn.

18. I is the incentre of a triangle BAC. By producing AI, prove that $\widehat{BIC} = \widehat{A} + \dfrac{\widehat{B}+\widehat{C}}{2} = 90° + \dfrac{A}{2}$.

Deduce the locus of the incentre of a triangle with fixed base and constant vertical angle.

MENSURATION

CHAPTER XV

Many of the results in this section will, for the present, be assumed.

APPROXIMATIONS TO AREAS OF IRREGULAR FIGURES

Areas by Counting Squares

The figure is drawn on squared paper to some suitable scale so that the area represented by each square unit is known. The number of squares enclosed is then counted. In the case of squares intersected by the boundary of the curve, parts of squares greater than half a square which are enclosed are counted as whole squares and those less than a half are neglected.

Mid-ordinate Rule

Suppose the area represented in Fig. 126 is required where AB is a straight line and AC and BD are perpendicular to

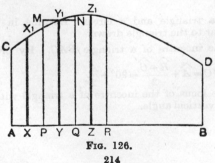

FIG. 126.

AB. AB is divided into a number of equal parts by the points $P, Q, R \ldots$.   At the mid-points $X, Y, Z \ldots$ of the parts, ordinates (i.e. perpendiculars to AB) are erected.   The area above PQ is assumed to be approximately equal to that of the rectangle $PMNQ$, i.e. $PQ.YY_1$.   In this way the total area is approximately :

$$AP.XX_1 + PQ.YY_1 + QR.ZZ_1 + \ldots$$

$$= \frac{AB}{n}(XX_1 + YY_1 + ZZ_1 + \ldots), \text{ if there are } n \text{ equal parts}$$
in AB

$$= AB\frac{(XX_1 + YY_1 + ZZ_1 + \ldots)}{n}$$

$$= AB \times (\text{average of the ordinates}).$$

Trapezoidal Rule

Suppose the area represented in Fig. 127 is required. Divide AB into n equal parts and erect ordinates y_1, y_2, y_3, ... y_{n+1} at the points of division.   An area such as PQQ_1P_1 is assumed to be approximately the area of the trapezium PQQ_1P_1 obtained by joining P_1Q_1.

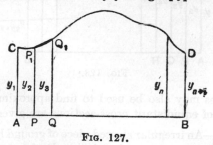

Fig. 127.

Since $AP = PQ = QR = \ldots$,

$$\text{total area} = AP\left(\frac{y_1 + y_2}{2} + \frac{y_2 + y_3}{2} + \ldots + \frac{y_n + y_{n+1}}{2}\right)$$

$$= AP\{\tfrac{1}{2}(y_1 + y_{n+1}) + y_2 + y_3 + \ldots + y_n\}$$

$$= AP \text{ (half the sum of first and last ordinates + the}$$
sum of the other ordinates).

Simpson's Rule

Suppose the area represented in Fig. 128 is required.

Divide AB into an *even* number, $2n$, of equal parts.   Let the ordinates drawn at the points of division as shown be y_1, y_2, y_3, ... y_{2n+1} respectively.   Then area approximately

$$= \frac{AP}{3}\{y_1 + y_{2n+1} + 2(y_3 + y_5 + \ldots.) + 4(y_2 + y_4 + \ldots.)\}.$$

or $\dfrac{AP}{3}$ (sum of first and last ordinates + twice the sum of the other odd ordinates + four times the sum of the even ordinates).

This rule will in general give a more accurate result than either the mid-ordinate or trapezoidal rule.

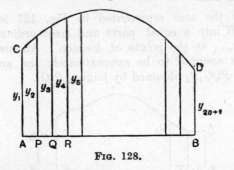

Fig. 128.

These rules may also be used to find approximate volumes when areas of equidistant cross-sections are given.

Example.—An irregular shaped piece of ground has a straight side.   Off-sets are measured at intervals of 1 yard along this side and the results given in the table.   Find the approximate area of the ground by using Simpson's rule.

Distance in yards from one end of straight side ..	0	1	2	3	4	5	6	7	8	9	10	11	12
Length of off-set in yards.. ..	0·6	1·4	2·7	4·4	6	7·5	9·1	10·7	9·9	7·6	4·3	2·1	1·2

Area $= \frac{1}{3}\{0\cdot6 + 1\cdot2 + 2(2\cdot7 + 6 + 9\cdot1 + 9\cdot9 + 4\cdot3)$
$\qquad\qquad + 4(1\cdot4 + 4\cdot4 + 7\cdot5 + 10\cdot7 + 7\cdot6 + 2\cdot1)\}$ sq. yd.

$= \frac{1}{3}(1\cdot8 + 2 \times 32\cdot0 + 4 \times 33\cdot7)$ sq. yd.

$= \frac{1}{3}(1\cdot8 + 64 + 134\cdot8)$ sq. yd.

$= \frac{1}{3} \times 200\cdot6$ sq. yd.

$= 67$ sq. yd.

The rules also apply when the area is closed, as in Fig. 129, the ordinates being measured as shown.

Example.—A straight line is drawn on a cross-section of a tree trunk and lines are drawn at right angles to this at intervals of 6 inches. The lengths of these lines, termi-

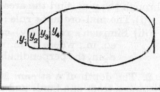

Fig. 129.

nated by the trunk, are given in the table.   Find the area of the cross-section.

Distance in inches from end of straight line	0	6	12	18	24	30	36	42	48	54	60
Length in inches of perpendicular lines	0	17·1	33·2	48·4	55·3	47·2	37·4	26·0	18·5	8·2	0

By Simpson's rule, approximate area

$= \frac{6}{3}\{0 + 0 + 2(33\cdot2 + 55\cdot3 + 37\cdot4 + 18\cdot5)$
$\qquad\qquad + 4(17\cdot1 + 48\cdot4 + 47\cdot2 + 26\cdot0 + 8\cdot2)\}$ sq. in.

$$= \frac{2 \times 876\cdot4}{144} \text{ sq. ft.}$$

33·2	17·1
55·3	48·4
37·4	47·2
18·5	26·0
	8·2
144·4	146·9
2	4
288·8	587·6
	288·8
	876·4

$\begin{array}{r} 219\cdot1 \\ 72 \\ 18 \end{array}$

$= 12$ sq. ft.

Exercise XXXVIII

NOTE.—If different scales are taken on the axes in drawing a graph, account must be taken of this in evaluating an area.

1. Fix two pins vertically through a sheet of graph paper on a drawing board. Tie a loop at each end of a piece of thread and put one loop over each pin. Draw the curve (an ellipse) which you obtain by keeping the thread taut with a pencil.

Taking not fewer than 10 equal divisions on the diameter through the pins, find the area of the ellipse by :

(i) The mid-ordinate rule ; (ii) the trapezoidal rule ;

(iii) Simpson's rule ; (iv) calculation from the formula $\frac{11}{14}d_1d_2$ sq. in., where d_1 in. is the diameter through the pins and d_2 in. the perpendicular diameter.

2. The depth of a stream 20 yd. wide is measured at different distances from one bank and the results given in the table :

Distance in yd.	0	2	4	6	8	10	12	14	16	18	20
Depth in ft. ..	1	3·2	3·7	4·7	5	5·5	6	4·7	3	1	1

Find the area of the cross-section of the stream.

If the water is flowing at 3 m.p.h., what is the number of gallons per minute ?   [1 cu. ft. = $6\frac{1}{4}$ gal.]

3. The widths of an irregular-shaped piece of land at 4-feet intervals are given in the table. Find the approximate area of the land in square yards.

Width in ft. ..	2	$7\frac{1}{4}$	14	19	$24\frac{1}{2}$	31	$39\frac{1}{4}$	43	$37\frac{1}{2}$	29	19	$9\frac{1}{2}$	$3\frac{1}{2}$
Distance from end of base line in ft.	0	4	8	12	16	20	24	28	32	36	40	44	48

4. A volume of 250 c.c. of gas under a pressure of 16 gm. per sq. cm. expands to 500 c.c. when the pressure is 8 gm. per sq. cm. The table gives the volume as the pressure is reduced.

Pressure in gm. per sq. cm.	16	15	14	13	12	11	10	9	8
Volume in c.c.	250	267	286	308	333	364	400	444	500

If these values be shown on a graph with ordinates representing pressure, the area enclosed by the curve, the extreme ordinates and the volume-axis represents the work done in cm. gm. Hence find the work done.

5. The velocity of a car at various times from starting is given in the table :

Time in sec... ..	0	5	10	20	30	40	45	50	55	60
Vel. in ft. per sec. ..	0	7	13	22	30	35	37	39	40	40

Draw a graph (with ordinates representing velocities) showing the relation between velocity and time. Assuming that the area enclosed by the curve, the time-axis and the extreme ordinate represents the distance gone, find the distance travelled in a minute.

6. During excavations the areas of cross-sections at equal intervals of 3 feet were as follows :

0, 11·5, 18·5, 20·5, 20, 18·5, 16, 13, 10, 6, 0 sq. ft.

Draw a graph (with ordinates representing areas) showing the relation between area and distance from one side. Hence find the volume excavated, assuming that the area enclosed by the curve and the x-axis represents volume.

7. The diameters of cross-sections of a barrel at various distances from one end are given in the table.

Distance from end in ft. ..	0	$\frac{1}{2}$	1	$1\frac{1}{2}$	2	$2\frac{1}{2}$	3	$3\frac{1}{2}$	4
Diameter in ft.	2	2·44	2·75	2·94	3	2·94	2·75	2·44	2

Find the area of a section through the axis of the barrel.

Calculate the areas of the cross-sections assuming that the area of a circle of diameter d in. is $\frac{\pi}{4}d^2$ sq. in., where $\pi = 3\cdot142$.

Draw a graph (with ordinates representing areas) showing the relation between area of section and distance from one end. Hence find the volume of the barrel, assuming that the area enclosed by the curve, the extreme ordinates and the x-axis represent the volume.

Circle

The ratio $\dfrac{\text{circumference of circle}}{\text{diameter of circle}}$ is the same for all circles and is represented by the Greek letter π (pronounced pi).

An approximate value of π may be found by wrapping a sheet of paper round a cylinder and, with a pin, pricking through the overlapping parts. The paper is then laid out flat and the distance between the pin-pricks measured ; this is the circumference of the cylinder. The diameter may be measured by placing the cylinder between two blocks with parallel plane faces and measuring the distance between them.

Fig. 130 shows an inscribed and a circumscribed polygon of a circle. It will be seen that as the number of the sides of the polygons is increased, the perimeters become more nearly the circumference of the circle, the perimeter of the inscribed polygon being less and of the circumscribed polygon greater than the circumference.

It is believed that Archimedes reached his conclusion that π lies between $3\frac{1}{7}$ and $3\frac{10}{71}$ by considering polygons of 96 sides.

Correct to four places of decimals, $\pi = 3\cdot1416$; an approximate value of π is $\frac{22}{7}$.

Since $\dfrac{\text{circumference of circle}}{\text{diameter of circle}} = \pi$, the *length of the circumference of a circle of radius r in. is $2\pi r$ in.*

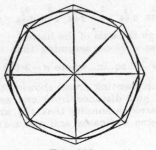

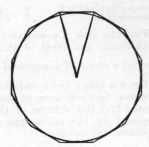

FIG. 130.   FIG. 131.

Area of circle

In Fig. 131, we see that as the number of sides of the circumscribed polygon becomes larger and larger, the perimeter of the polygon becomes more and more nearly the circumference of the circle and the area of the polygon more and more nearly the area of the circle. We state this by saying that the limiting value of the perimeter of the polygon is the circumference of the circle and the limiting value of the area of the polygon is the area of the circle.

The area of the polygon is clearly the sum of the areas of the triangles formed by joining the vertices to the centre of the circle. The height of each of these triangles is the radius of the circle. Suppose the polygon to have n sides each of length l inches and the radius of the circle to be r inches.

Since the area of a triangle $= \frac{1}{2}$ base $\times$ height, the area of each of n triangles forming the polygon is $\frac{1}{2}lr$ sq. in.

$$\therefore \text{ area of polygon} = \frac{nlr}{2} \text{ sq. in.}$$

As the number n of the sides becomes very large, the limiting value of the perimeter, nl inches, is the circumference of the circle, i.e. $2\pi r$ inches.

$$\text{Hence } \textit{area of circle} = \frac{2\pi r r}{2} \text{ sq. in.}$$

$$= \pi r^2 \text{ sq. in.}$$

Arc of circle

AB is an arc of a circle radius r inches, subtending an angle of x degrees at the centre C.

Since the circumference subtends an angle of 360 degrees at the centre,

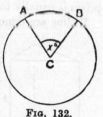

Fig. 132.

$$\frac{\text{length of arc}}{\text{length of circumference}} = \frac{x}{360}.$$

$$\therefore \frac{\text{length of arc}}{2\pi r \text{ inches}} = \frac{x}{360}.$$

Hence $\textit{length of arc} = \dfrac{x}{360} \times 2\pi r \textit{ in.}$

Area of sector of circle

$$\frac{\text{Area of sector } CAB}{\text{area of circle}} = \frac{x}{360},$$

$$\therefore \frac{\text{area of sector}}{\pi r^2 \text{ sq. in.}} = \frac{x}{360}.$$

Hence $\textit{area of sector} = \dfrac{x}{360} \times \pi r^2 \textit{ sq. in.} = \dfrac{arc \times radius}{2}.$

Sphere

For a sphere of radius r in.—

(i) *The area of the surface is $4\pi r^2$ sq. in.*;

(ii) *the area of the surface between two parallel planes h in. apart is $2\pi rh$ sq. in.*;

(iii) *the volume of the sphere is $\frac{4}{3}\pi r^3$ cu. in.*

Prism

A prism is a solid whose base and top are parallel congruent polygons joined by faces which are parallelograms.

When the faces are perpendicular to the base, the faces are rectangles and the solid is said to be a right prism ; the word prism is usually taken to mean a right prism.

Prisms are denoted by the shape of the base, thus Fig. 133

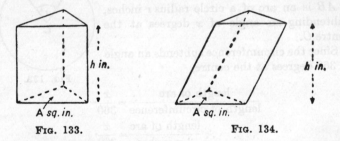

FIG. 133.   FIG. 134.

represents a triangular prism. A square prism is one in which the base is a square.

Suppose the area of the base to be A sq. in. If a slice of thickness 1 in. be taken, its volume will be A cu. in. If the prism be of height h in., h of these slices will form the prism. Its volume is therefore Ah cu. in.

Hence *volume of prism =*

(area of base) × (perpendicular distance between parallel ends).

The result still holds when the faces are not perpendicular to the base as in Fig. 134.

Volume = Ah cu. in.

Cylinder

If the curved surface of a cylinder be made of paper, this may be unfolded and laid flat to form a rectangle as shown in Fig. 135. The circumference of the base will become one side of the rectangle and the height the other.

Hence *area of curved surface of cylinder* of radius r in. and height h in. $= 2\pi rh$ sq. in.

Dividing the cylinder into slices of thickness 1 in., as in the

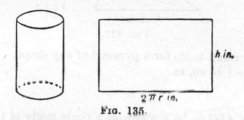

$2\pi r$ in.

Fig. 135.

..... of the prism, will show that the volume = (area of base) × (height).

Hence *volume of cylinder* $= \pi r^2 h$ cu. in.

Pyramid

Suppose V to be the centre of a cube of side a in. with base $ABCD$. $VABCD$ is a square pyramid.

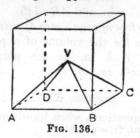

Fig. 136.

The cube will consist of 6 equal pyramids formed by joining each face to V.

8

$$\therefore \text{ volume of each pyramid} = \frac{a^3}{6} \text{ cu. in.}$$

$$= \frac{1}{3} \cdot a^2 \cdot \frac{a}{2} \text{ cu in.}$$

Volume of pyramid $= \frac{1}{3}$(*area of base*) × (*perpendicular height*).

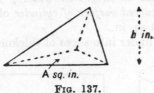

A *sq. in.*

FIG. 137.

The last result holds for a pyramid of any shape.
$Volume = \frac{1}{3}Ah$ cu. in.

Cone

Suppose ABC to be a sector of a circle made of thin sheet metal. If this be uniformly bent until the radii AB and AC

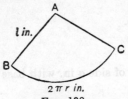

$2\,\pi\,r$ *in.*

FIG. 138.

meet, it will form the curved surface of a cone. The arc BC will become the circumference of the base of the cone and a radius AB of the arc will become the slant height of the cone.

If r in. is the base radius and l in. the slant height of the cone, $BC = 2\pi r$ in. and $AB = l$ in.

Area of curved surface of cone = area of sector $ABC = \pi rl$ sq. in.
The result above for the volume of a pyramid applies to the cone. Hence if h in. be the perpendicular height, *volume of cone* $= \frac{1}{3}\pi r^2 h$ *cu. in.*

Exercise XXXIX

In the following questions, when logarithms are used, assume that $\pi = 3 \cdot 142$. (1 cu. ft. $= 6\frac{1}{4}$ gal.)

1. Find the weight of a closed box made of steel $\frac{1}{2}$ in. thick if the external dimensions are 1 ft. 8 in., 1 ft. 6 in. and 1 ft. 4 in., and steel weighs 483 lb. per cu. ft.

2. The average diameter of a closely coiled helical spring of 20 turns is $1\frac{1}{4}$ in. Find the length of wire, correct to the nearest foot, necessary to make the spring, allowing 4 in. for hooks.

3. A piece of wire 8 in. long is bent into an arc of a circle subtending 20° at the centre. What is the radius of the circle ?

4. The diameter of the driving wheel of an engine is 6 ft. Find the number of revolutions it makes per minute when travelling at 40 m.p.h.

5. A piece of sheet iron 6 ft. wide is made into corrugated iron. Find the new width if the section is now a series of semicircles.

6. A crossed belt passes round two pulleys of radii 4 in. and 2 in. respectively. If the straight portions are at right angles, find the length of the belt.

7. A cable consists of three wires each 0·04 in. in diameter. What is the greatest weight that can be hung from the cable if the breaking load is 20 tons per sq. in. ?

8. A dining table is in the shape of a rectangle with semicircular ends. If its width is 5 ft. and its greatest length 12 ft., find its surface area.

9. A hollow pipe has external diameter 9 in. and internal diameter 7 in. Find what load it can carry at 3 tons per sq. in.

10. What is the external diameter of a circular pipe of 15 sq. in. cross-section if the internal diameter is 8 in. ?

11. Two equal circular holes are punched in a metal plate 8 in. by 6 in. If a quarter of the metal is removed, find the diameter of each hole.

12. A kite is in the form of a sector of a circle of radius 2 feet subtending an angle of 65° at the centre. What is its area ?

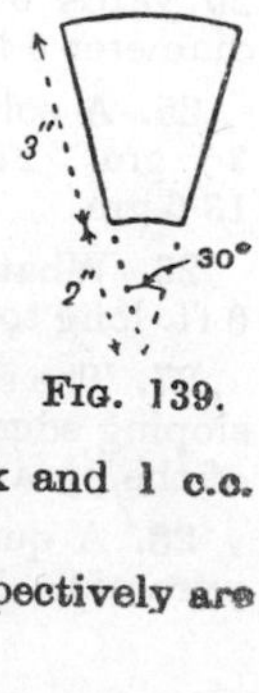

13. There are four holes in a disc ventilator each of the shape shown in Fig. 139. What area is available for the inlet of air ?

14. Find to the nearest $\frac{1}{2}$ oz. the weight of 10,000 lead shot of diameter ·06 in., assuming that 1 cu. ft. of lead weighs 710 lb.

FIG. 139.

15. Find the weight of a hollow copper sphere of external radius 1·5 cm. if the copper is 2 mm. thick and 1 c.c. of copper weighs 8·94 gm.

16. Three spheres of radii 3 in., 4 in., and 5 in. respectively are melted down and cast into a single sphere. Find the radius of this sphere if 10% of the original metal is wasted.

17. A hemispherical bowl with an internal diameter of 18 in. is filled to a depth of 16 in. with water. Find the area of the surface of the water and the area of the wetted surface of the bowl.

18. The section of a railway cutting 14 ft. deep is a trapezium. At the bottom it is 17 ft. wide and at the top 27 ft. Find to the nearest ton the weight of earth removed in cutting 30 yd. if 1 cu. ft. of earth weighs 110 lb.

19. The water in a swimming bath 100 ft. long and 24 ft. wide is 6 ft. deep at one end and 3 ft. deep at the other. How many gallons of water does it contain ?

20. A wooden lean-to store shed is built against a wall. It is 8 ft. high at the back and 5 ft. high in front. The width from back to front is 11 ft. and it is 14 ft. long. Find the number of sq. ft. of wood required if there is a window 3 ft. by 2 ft., and also the number of cu. ft. of store space.

21. A revolving drum is in the form of a hexagonal prism of length 8 ft. If each side of the hexagon is $1\frac{1}{2}$ ft., find the volume of the drum.

22. Find the rate in ft. per sec. at which water is flowing through a pipe of 2 in. diameter if it delivers 4000 gallons of water per hour.

23. A steel rivet is in the shape of a cylinder surmounted by a hemisphere. The diameter of the cylinder is $\frac{1}{4}$ in. and of the head 1 in. ; the greatest length of the rivet is 2 in. Find the weight of 100 rivets if steel weighs ·285 lb. per cu. in.

24. Find in cwt. correct to one decimal place, the weight of 20 yards of iron piping, external diameter 7 in. and internal diameter 6 in., assuming that 1 cu. ft. of iron weighs 449 lb.

25. A column of mercury 2·9 cm. long in a glass tube weighs 3·1 gm. Find the bore of the tube if 1 c.c. of mercury weighs 13·6 gm.

26. What would be the diameter of a cylindrical petrol tank 6 ft. long to hold 250 gallons ?

27. The side of the base of a square pyramid is 10 in. and each sloping edge is 13 in. Find the area of each face and the volume of the pyramid.

28. A quarry wagon is in the shape of a frustum of a square pyramid. The side of the top is 3 ft., of the bottom 2 ft., and it is

3 ft. deep. What weight of limestone will it hold if the limestone occupies two-thirds of the volume of the wagon and weighs 156 lb. per cu. ft. ?

29. A steel drill for plaster is a cylinder 6 in. long and ·2 in. diameter, surmounted by a cone whose height is equal to the diameter of its base. What is its weight if the steel weighs ·285 lb. per cu. in. ?

30. Find the base radius of a cone of copper of height 6 cm. weighing 1·5 Kg., given that 1 c.c. of copper weighs 8·94 gm.

31. A sector of radius 5 in. and of angle 120° is cut from sheet metal which is then bent to form a cone. Find its base radius, height and volume.

32. What area of sheet tin is required to form the conical part of a funnel, 6 in. diameter at top and 6 in. deep ? Assume the complete cone is made.

33. A measuring jug is in the shape of a frustum of a hollow cone. The internal diameter at the bottom is 3 in. and at the top 4 in. and it is 6 in. deep. Show that it may be graduated up to 1½ pt., given that 1 pt. = 34·66 cu. in.

34. A parchment lamp shade is a frustum of a hollow cone. The diameter of the ends are 4 in. and 8 in. respectively and the slant distance between them is 6 in. What is the area of the parchment, neglecting overlap ?

TRIGONOMETRY

CHAPTER XVI

TRIGONOMETRY

If you want to show a friend how to go from one place to another, you draw a rough map to show him the roads and turnings, which he will have to take, and you probably mark on it any special landmarks such as churches, inns, etc., which will help him to find his way. To make an accurate map a surveyor starts with a line AB of some given length, say 500 yd., and measures the angles, which the lines from A and

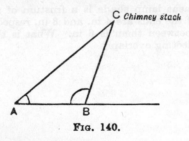

FIG. 140.

B to some landmark C, perhaps a factory chimney, make with AB. Knowing the length of AB and the angles $\widehat{ABC}$ and $\widehat{ACB}$ he can draw the triangle ABC to scale and from his drawing find the distances of C from A and B. But a scale drawing is not accurate enough for survey work and so some method of calculating the lengths of AC and BC had to be discovered.

Trigonometry, which means literally *the measurement of triangles*, is the branch of mathematics which deals with calculating the unknown sides and angles of a triangle when the other sides and angles are given.

One of the first things civilised man wanted to know was how far and in what direction the neighbouring towns were. For this reason he needed maps of the earth and he also needed maps showing the positions of the stars in the heavens so that he could use the stars to guide him by night. Through these needs he was led to discover the elements of trigonometry as we know it to-day.

The first people to make calculations based on trigonometry were the Greek teachers of the University of Alexandria in the period from 300 B.C. to A.D. 150. The results of their work were collected by Ptolemy and published in a book called the Almagest in A.D. 150.

There was no great advance from the work of the Greeks until the Middle Ages, when the extension of trigonometry to angles greater than 180° gave rise to mathematical expressions, which repeat their values periodically just as the bob of a clock pendulum passes through the vertical at equal periods of time.

These expressions, although they had their origin in the measurement of triangles, are now used in measuring the size of an alternating current and the displacement of any vibrating point, such as a point on a violin string. Thus, trigonometry, in addition to its applications in surveying and astronomy now has applications, in almost every branch of science and engineering, many of which have little relation to triangles.

Measurement of angles

We have seen in Chapter X that in geometrical work angles are measured in degrees, minutes, and seconds. The same units are used in all applications of trigonometry to triangles, but in other applications it is often more convenient to use another unit of angle. It is the angle subtended at the centre of a circle by an arc equal in length to the radius and it is called a *radian*. It is the angle $\widehat{AOB}$ in Fig. 141.

In a circle radius r ft. half the circumference has a length πr ft. and this arc subtends 180° at the centre. Hence an arc of length r ft. subtends $(180°/\pi)$ at the centre. But, by the definition above, this arc subtends 1 radian at the centre.

$$\therefore 1 \text{ radian} = \frac{180°}{\pi},$$

or 1 radian $\simeq$ 57·296 degrees $\simeq$ 57° 17·7′.

Conversely—

$$1 \text{ degree} = \frac{\pi}{180} \text{ radian},$$

or 1 degree $\simeq$ 0·01745 radian.

180 degrees equals π radians, i.e. a little more than 3 radians.

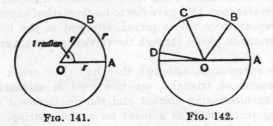

FIG. 141.   FIG. 142.

Fig. 142 shows 3 radians marked off from 180° each of the arcs AB, BC, CD having the same length as the radius r.

2·5 radians is sometimes written 2·5°, but the unit is often omitted, an angle of 2·5 radians being called an angle of 2·5.

Exercise XL

1. Show that 30°, 45°, 60° and 90° are $\frac{1}{6}\pi$, $\frac{1}{4}\pi$, $\frac{1}{3}\pi$ and $\frac{1}{2}\pi$ radians.

2. Express 15° in radians to 3 decimal places.

3. Express 100° in radians to 3 decimal places.

4. Express 0·8 radian in degrees and minutes to the nearest minute.

5. Express 1·52° in degrees and minutes to the nearest minute.

6. Express 42° 54′ in radians to 3 decimal places.

7. If an arc subtends α radians at the centre of a circle of radius r ft., show that its length is rα ft.

8. If a wheel has 20 spokes, what is the angle between adjacent spokes in radians ?

9. Express 120°, 135° and 150° as fractions of π radians.

10. If a wheel makes n revs. per minute, how many radians does it turn through per sec. ?

11. Show that, if the arc AB of a circle radius r ft. subtends α radians at the centre O, the area of the sector AOB is ½r²α sq. ft.

12. How many radians does a chord equal in length to the radius of a circle subtend at the centre ?

13. If the rim of a wheel of radius a ft. has a speed v ft./sec., how many radians does a spoke turn through per sec. ?

14. If a rod 1 ft. long is bent into an arc of a circle of radius ·7 ft., express the angle which it subtends at the centre in degrees and also in radians.

The sine of an angle

In Fig. 143 *OX* and *OK* are two lines intersecting at an angle of 25°. *A*, *B*, *C* are points on *OK* at intervals of 1 in. and

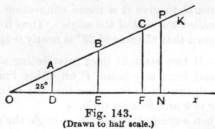

Fig. 143.
(Drawn to half scale.)

AD, *BE*, *CF* are lines drawn from *A*, *B*, *C* perpendicular to *OX*, and therefore parallel to each other. By measurement it is found that

$$DA \simeq 0·42 \text{ in.}, \qquad EB \simeq 0·84 \text{ in.} \simeq 2DA,$$
$$FC \simeq 1·27 \text{ in.} \simeq 3DA.$$

Therefore

$$\frac{DA}{OA} \simeq \frac{0\cdot42}{1} = 0\cdot42, \qquad \frac{EB}{OB} = \frac{2DA}{2OA} = \frac{DA}{OA}, \qquad \frac{FC}{OC} = \frac{3DA}{3OA} = \frac{DA}{OA},$$

and so each of the three ratios DA/OA, EB/OB, FC/OC is equal to $0\cdot42$.

In the same way, if P is any point whatever on OK, and PN is drawn perpendicular to OX, it will be found by measuring NP and OP that

$$\frac{NP}{OP} \simeq 0\cdot42 = \frac{DA}{OA}.$$

In the figure, OP is $3\cdot4$ in., and $NP \simeq 1\cdot43$ in., making

$$\frac{NP}{OP} = \frac{1\cdot43}{3\cdot4} = \frac{0\cdot715}{17} = 0\cdot42.$$

Hence, as nearly as we can show by measurement, the ratio NP/OP is the same whatever the position of P on an arm of the angle XOK, and, if the student makes similar measurements with other angles, he will find that the ratio NP/OP is independent of the position of P in every case, but it will of course be a different ratio for different angles. It can be shown by theoretical geometry that this result, which we have arrived at by measurement, is exactly true.

Since the value of this ratio depends only on the size of the angle it is natural to give it a name connecting it with the angle. It is called the *sine* of the angle. Thus from Fig. 143 it has been shown that the sine of 25° is nearly 0·42.

Definition.—If two straight lines intersecting at O contain the angle θ and from any point P on either line a perpendicular PN is drawn on to the other line, the ratio NP/OP is called the sine of θ and written $\sin \theta$.

NOTE.—When a symbol is used for an angle the unit is often omitted, θ degrees being written θ.

Suppose now that a man climbing a hill can find by means of some instrument that the inclination of the hill to the horizontal is 25°, how far will he have risen vertically when he has walked 220 yd. up the hill ?

Let *OP* represent the distance he has walked and *PN* be perpendicular to the horizontal plane through *O*. Then we

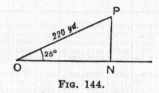

FIG. 144.

require the length of *NP*, and by the definition of the sine of an angle

$$\frac{NP}{OP} = \sin 25°.$$

We have already found, from Fig. 143, that sin 25° $\simeq$ 0·42, and we know *OP* = 220.

$$\therefore \frac{NP}{220} \simeq 0·42. \quad \therefore NP \simeq 93.$$

Hence the man has risen about 93 yd.

Clearly, if we did not already know sin 25°, it would be easier to draw Fig. 144 to scale and measure *NP*, but the values of sin θ have been calculated and tabulated (by methods beyond the scope of this book) to a large number of decimal places for every minute of angle from 0° to 90° and these values can be found in any book of mathematical tables under the heading " natural sines." The fact that the values of sin θ can be found quickly from a book of tables, and at the same time far more accurately than can be done by drawing, is the reason why this ratio is so useful. When we use tables of sines it is not necessary to draw a figure to scale. A rough sketch is sufficient to show us how to make use of the sine ratio.

How to read a table of sines

On p. 234 is reproduced the part of a table of natural sines from 0° to 30° :

Natural sines

	0'	6'	12'	18'	24'	30'	36'	42'	48'	54'	1'	2'	3'	4'	5'
0°	·0000	0017	0035	0052	0070	0087	0105	0122	0140	0157	3	6	9	12	15
1	·0175	0192	0209	0227	0244	0262	0279	0297	0314	0332	3	6	9	12	15
2	·0349	0366	0384	0401	0419	0436	0454	0471	0488	0506	3	6	9	12	15
3	·0523	0541	0558	0576	0593	0610	0628	0645	0663	0680	3	6	9	12	15
4	·0698	0715	0732	0750	0767	0785	0802	0819	0837	0854	3	6	9	12	14
5	·0872	0889	0906	0924	0941	0958	0976	0993	1011	1028	3	6	9	12	14
6	·1045	1063	1080	1097	1115	1132	1149	1167	1184	1201	3	6	9	12	14
7	·1219	1236	1253	1271	1288	1305	1323	1340	1357	1374	3	6	9	12	14
8	·1392	1409	1426	1444	1461	1478	1495	1513	1530	1547	3	6	9	12	14
9	·1564	1582	1599	1616	1633	1650	1668	1685	1702	1719	3	6	9	11	14
10	·1736	1754	1771	1788	1805	1822	1840	1857	1874	1891	3	6	9	11	14
11	·1908	1925	1942	1959	1977	1994	2011	2028	2045	2062	3	6	9	11	14
12	·2079	2096	2113	2130	2147	2164	2181	2198	2215	2233	3	6	9	11	14
13	·2250	2267	2284	2300	2317	2334	2351	2368	2385	2402	3	6	8	11	14
14	·2419	2436	2453	2470	2487	2504	2521	2538	2554	2571	3	6	8	11	14
15	·2588	2605	2622	2639	2656	2672	2689	2706	2723	2740	3	6	8	11	14
16	·2756	2773	2790	2807	2823	2840	2857	2874	2890	2907	3	6	8	11	14
17	·2924	2940	2957	2974	2990	3007	3024	3040	3057	3074	3	6	8	11	14
18	·3090	3107	3123	3140	3156	3173	3190	3206	3223	3239	3	6	8	11	14
19	·3256	3272	3289	3305	3322	3338	3355	3371	3387	3404	3	5	8	11	14
20	·3420	3437	3453	3469	3486	3502	3518	3535	3551	3567	3	5	8	11	14
21	·3584	3600	3616	3633	3649	3665	3681	3697	3714	3730	3	5	8	11	14
22	·3746	3762	3778	3795	3811	3827	3843	3859	3875	3891	3	5	8	11	13
23	·3907	3923	3939	3955	3971	3987	4003	4019	4035	4051	3	5	8	11	13
24	·4067	4083	4099	4115	4131	4147	4163	4179	4195	4210	3	5	8	11	13
25	·4226	4242	4258	4274	4289	4305	4321	4337	4352	4368	3	5	8	11	13
26	·4384	4399	4415	4431	4446	4462	4478	4493	4509	4524	3	5	8	10	13
27	·4540	4555	4571	4586	4602	4617	4633	4648	4664	4679	3	5	8	10	13
28	·4695	4710	4726	4741	4756	4772	4787	4802	4818	4833	3	5	8	10	13
29	·4848	4863	4879	4894	4909	4924	4939	4955	4970	4985	3	5	8	10	13
30	·5000														

The left hand column gives the number of degrees and the numbers along the top give the number of minutes of angle at intervals of six minutes.

Look at the row beginning 25°. The number 0·4226 in the column under 0' is sin 25°. You will remember that from Fig. 143 we found that sin 25° ≃ 0·42 ; this is the value of sin 25° to two places of decimals. In the next column under the heading of 6' we find the number 4242, which stands for 0·4242, the decimal point being shown in the first column only ; 0·4242 is the sine of 25° 6'. In the same way, reading across the row beginning 25°, we find sin 25° 12' = 0·4258, sin 25° 18' = 0·4274, etc.

If an angle is one like 25° 38', in which the number of minutes is not a multiple of 6', we first find the sine of the multiple of 6', which is just smaller than the given angle, in this case 25° 36'. The tables of numbers on the right hand side, called "mean differences," give us the correction to make in order to find the value of sin 25° 38'. Since 25° 38' is 2' more than 25° 36', we find the number in the 25° row underneath the heading of 2' in the table of mean differences; this number is 5, which stands for 0·0005. This means that 0·0005 has to be added to sin 25° 36' to find the value of sin 25° 38'. Thus

$$\text{Sin } 25° 38' = \sin 25° 36' + \text{difference for } 2'.$$
$$= 0·4321 + 0·0005 = 0·4326.$$

To find an angle whose sine is a given number we use the reverse process. Suppose we know sin θ = 0·8955. Looking for numbers near 8955 in the tables we find sin 63° 30' = 0·8949 and sin 63° 36' = 0·8957. Hence θ must lie between 63° 30' and 63° 36'. Now sin θ is 0·0006 more than sin 63° 30' and from the table of differences we find that in the 63° row the number 6 comes in the mean difference column headed 5'. Therefore θ is 5' more than 63° 30', which is 63° 35'.

Example.—Sin 29° 22' = sin 29° 18' + difference for 4'.
$$= 0·4894 + 0·0010 = 0·4904.$$

Example.—Sin (0·65 radian) = sin (0·65 × 57·296°)
$$= \sin 37·242° = \sin 37° 15'$$
$$= \sin 37° 12' + \text{difference}$$
$$\text{for } 3'$$
$$= 0·6046 + 0·0007 = 0·6053.$$

Example.—Find θ, if sin θ = 0·7151.
$$0·7145 = \sin 45° 36'.$$
$$0·7151 - 0·7145 = 0·0006 = \text{difference for } 3'.$$
$$\therefore 0·7151 = \sin (45° 36' + 3') = \sin 45° 39'.$$
$$\therefore \theta = 45° 39'.$$

Example.—The string of a kite is 150 ft. long and it makes 65° with the horizontal. Assuming the string to be straight, find the height of the kite above the lower end of the string.

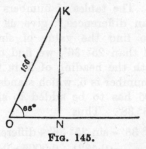

FIG. 145.

In the figure, K is the kite, O the lower end of the string, and KN the perpendicular from K into the horizontal plane through O. Then $K\widehat{O}N = 65°$ and the length of KN is required.

$$\frac{KN}{OK} = \sin K\widehat{O}N.$$

$$\therefore \frac{KN}{150} = \sin 65°.$$

$\therefore KN = 150 \sin 65° = 150 \times 0.9063 \risingdotseq 136.$

Hence the kite is nearly 136 ft. above the lower end of the string.

Example.—A mountain railway rises 123 ft. for every 250 yd. along the track. Find the angle which the track makes with the horizontal.

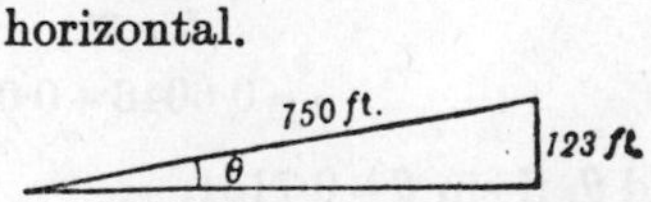

750 ft.   123 ft

θ

FIG. 146.

If the angle required is θ,
$$\text{Sin } \theta = \tfrac{123}{750} = \tfrac{41}{250} = 0.164.$$
From the table of sines, sin 9° 24′ = 0.1633, and the difference

of this from 0·164 is 0·0007 ; the nearest difference in the mean difference columns is 0·0006, which is the difference for 2'.

∴ $\theta = 9° 24' + 2' = 9° 26'$.

Tables of logarithms of sines

These are tables of the logarithms of the numbers found in the sine tables. For instance, on the same line as 44° in the column headed "degrees", we find the number $\bar{1}·8418$. This is the logarithm of the sine of 44° and we write it log sin 44°. From the table of sines, sin 44° = 0·6947, and from the table of logarithms log 0·6947 = $\bar{1}·8418$. Thus the table of logarithms of sines enables us to find log sin 44° by looking at one page of the tables instead of two. The table is read in practically the same way as the table of natural sines. For example :

log sin 20° 38' = log sin 20° 36' + difference for 2'.
= $\bar{1}·5463 + 0·0007 = \bar{1}·5470$.

The following examples show how the table of log sines is used in practical calculations.

Example.—A wheel centre O has spokes 3 ft. 4½ in. It is turning at a rate of 17½ revs. per min. If a spoke starts from a position OA, find the perpendicular distance of its end from OA after ½ sec., to the nearest $\frac{1}{16}$ in.

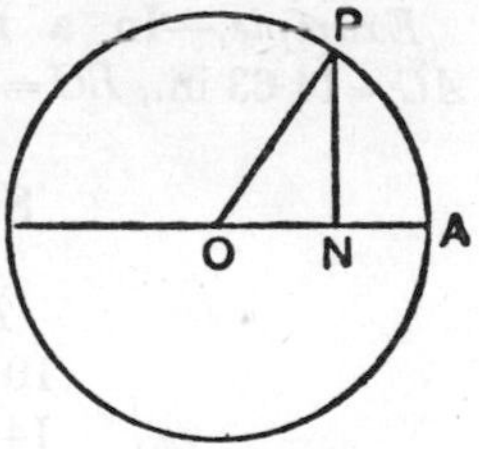

In one minute the wheel turns through 360 × 17½ degrees and hence in ½ sec. it turns through

FIG. 147.

$$\frac{360 \times 17·5}{120} \text{ degrees} = 52° 30'.$$

If the end of the spoke is then at P and PN is perpendicular to OA,

$$\frac{PN}{OP} = \sin 52° 30' \text{ and } \therefore PN = OP \sin 52° 30'.$$

But $OP = 3$ ft $4\frac{1}{2}$ in. $= 40.5$ in.

$\therefore PN = 40.5 \sin 52° 30'$.

The calculation of PN by logarithms is set out in the same way as in calculating any other product by logarithms.

Number	Logarithm
40·5	$\bar{1}$·6075
sin 52° 30′	$\bar{1}$·8995
32·14	$\bar{1}$·5070

$\therefore PN = 32.14 = 32.1$ to the nearest $\frac{1}{10}$ in.

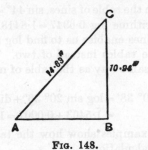

FIG. 148.

Example.—In a right-angled triangle ABC, $\widehat{ABC} = 90°$. $AC = 14.63$ in., $BC = 10.94$ in.   Find the angle BAC.

$$\text{Sin } \widehat{BAC} = \frac{BC}{AC} = \frac{10.94}{14.63}.$$

Number	Logarithm
10·94	1·0391
14·63	1·1653
sin 48° 24′.	$\bar{1}$·8738

$\therefore \widehat{BAC} = 48° 24'$.

Exercise XLI

1. Draw two lines OK and OL at an angle of 40°.   Mark points A, B, C, D on OK at 1 in., 2 in., 3 in., and 4 in. respectively from O.   From these points draw AE, BF, CG, DH perpendicular

to OL and measure their lengths. Calculate the values of the ratios $\frac{AE}{OA}, \frac{BF}{OB}, \frac{CG}{OC}$ and $\frac{DH}{OD}$, and verify that they are equal to the degree of accuracy obtainable by drawing. Compare their value with the value of sin 40° shown in the tables.

2. Using the figure of question 1, take a point P on OK at 2·6 in. from O and draw PQ perpendicular to OL. Calculate the length of PQ and afterwards measure it, and compare the two values obtained.

3. Find from the table of sines the values of sin 4°, sin 47°, sin 78°.

4. A coal seam slopes down from a point A at an angle of 43° with the horizontal, to a point B. If AB is 800 yd., how far is B below A ?

5. The bob A of a conical pendulum (or governor) is revolving round the vertical through O, the fixed end of the pendulum. If OA is 8 cm. and makes an angle of 10° with the vertical, find the radius of the circle described by A.

If A makes 3 rev. per sec., find its speed in cm. per sec.

6. The angle between the legs of a pair of dividers is 54°, and the legs are each 5 in. long. Draw the line, which bisects the angle between the legs, and hence find the distance between the points.

7. A chord AB of a circle of radius 9 in. subtends 140° at the centre. Draw the perpendicular from the centre on to the chord and hence find the length of the chord.

8. If a regular eight-sided figure (octagon) is inscribed in a circle show that each side subtends 45° at the centre. If the radius of the circle is 6 in., find the length of a side. Draw a figure to scale, measure the length of a side of the octagon and compare the two answers.

9. A trapdoor 2 ft. by 3 ft. is hinged along one of its longer edges, which is horizontal. If its weight, which is 20 lb. wt., acts at its centre, find the moment of its weight about the hinges when the door makes 35° with the vertical.

10. Find from the table of sines : sin 78° 24′, sin 16° 19′, sin 41° 52′.

11. Find from the tables of sines : sin 14° 50′, sin 81° 2′, sin 58° 39′.

12. In a triangle ABC, $A\widehat{B}C = 90°$, $AC = 12$ in. and $B\widehat{A}C = 40° 23'$. Find the length of BC.

13. A road slopes at $10° 14'$ with the horizontal. How far does it rise in 300 yd. ?

14. Find the angle θ if (a) sin $\theta = 0\cdot4736$, (b) sin $\theta = 0\cdot7149$.

15. Find the angle θ if (a) sin $\theta = 0\cdot9957$, (b) sin $\theta = 0\cdot1670$.

16. In a triangle PQR, $P\widehat{Q}R = 90°$, $PR = 8$ in. and $QR = 4\cdot5$ in. Find $R\widehat{P}Q$.

17. The jib of a crane is 15 ft. long and the tie-rod, which is horizontal, is 7 ft. long. Find the angle which the jib makes with the vertical.

18. Gradients in roads are given by (vertical rise)/(distance along road). A road sign gives a gradient of 1 in $5\frac{1}{2}$. Find the angle of inclination of the road to the horizontal. How far does a motor car rise while travelling 500 yd. along the road ?

19. A square picture of side 16 in. is inclined at $6°$ to the wall. How far is its upper edge from the wall ? The picture is hung by a cord 2 ft. long, which is attached to two points at the same level, each $\frac{1}{4}$ in. from a side of the picture. What is the angle between the two halves of the cord at the nail ?

20. Find from the table of logarithms of sines : log sin $23° 27'$, log sin $82° 43'$, log sin $43° 16'$.

21. Find from the table of logarithms of sines : log sin $5° 32'$, log sin $62° 58'$, log sin $19° 13'$.

22. Find θ if (a) log sin $\theta = \bar{1}\cdot4255$, (b) log sin $\theta = \bar{1}\cdot9708$.

23. Find θ if (a) log sin $\theta = \bar{1}\cdot9787$, (b) log sin $\theta = \bar{1}\cdot7063$.

Use logarithms in answering the following questions :

24. By using a theodolite it is found that the line joining two points 247 ft. apart is inclined at an angle $9° 37'$ to the horizontal. Find the height of one point above the other.

25. In a right-angled triangle the hypotenuse is $18\cdot62$ cm. and one of the other sides is $9\cdot84$ cm. Find the angle opposite the latter side.

26. In a survey it is found that the line joining two points A and B makes $54° 21'$ with a line AL. If AB is 1247 yd., find the shortest distance from B to the line AL.

27. *The sine bar.* A device called a " sine bar " is used to set out angles with great precision. It consists of a steel strip with a peg at O, which can be clamped at any height to a vertical support, $PQRS$. This stick has two hardened studs, or "buttons" of exactly the same diameter, their centres A and B being at a precise distance apart, usually 10 in. To set a line EF in a piece of work at any required angle, say 42° 30′ with an edge CD, the edge is placed on the base and the studs A and B are raised by means of block gauges to such heights that $BK/AB=\sin 42° 30′$.

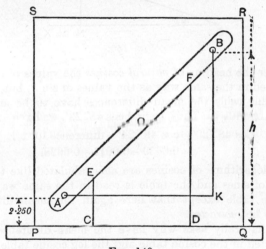

Fig. 149.

If the lowest point of the stud A is set at a height 2·250 in. above the base, what must be the height h *in.* of the lowest point of the stud B ?

28. If, using a sine bar as in the above question, it is found that the lowest points of the studs are at heights 1·431 and 8·187 in. respectively, find the angle between FE and CD.

Cosine of an angle

If two lines OX, OK intersecting at O contain an angle θ and from any point P on one line PN is drawn perpendicular to the other line, it will be found by taking P in various positions that the ratio $\dfrac{ON}{OP}$ is the same for all positions of P. This ratio is called the *cosine* of θ and written cos θ.

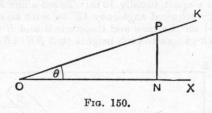

Fig. 150.

Under the heading of *natural cosines* the values of cos θ are tabulated in the same way as the values of sin θ, but in using the cosine table the mean differences have to be *subtracted* instead of added. Thus, to find cos 48° 29′, we have

Cos 48° 29′ = cos 48° 24′ − difference for 5′.
= 0·6639 − 0·0011 = 0·6628.

The logarithms of cosines are also tabulated like the logarithms of sines and the table is read in the same way as the log sine table except that here again the mean differences have to be *subtracted*.

One naturally asks why have the mean differences to be subtracted in the cosine table and the log cosine table.

A glance along the row through 48° will show that the cosine of an angle decreases as the angle increases and consequently cos 48° 29′ must be less than cos 48° 24′.

Example.—Find cos 70° 40′ from the table of natural cosines.

cos 70° 40′ = cos 70° 36′ − difference for 4′
= 0·3322 − 0·0014 (= 0·3308).

Example. — Find θ, if cos θ = 0·6643.

0·6639 = cos 48° 24′ ;

∴ 0·6643 − 0·6639 = 0·0004 = difference for 2′.

∴ θ = 48° 24′ − 2′ = 48° 22′.

Example.—The foot of a ladder 15 ft. long is placed at 3 ft. from the wall. Find the angle which the ladder makes with the horizontal.

If the angle is θ,

$$\text{Cos } \theta = \tfrac{3}{15} = \tfrac{1}{5} = 0\cdot2.$$

$$0\cdot1994 = \cos 78^\circ\ 30'.$$

$$0\cdot2 - 0\cdot1994 = 0\cdot0006 = \text{difference for } 2'.$$

$$\therefore\ \theta = 78^\circ\ 30' - 2' = 78^\circ\ 28'.$$

Fig. 151.

Exercise XLII

1. Draw two lines OK and OL at an angle of 34°. Mark points A, B, C, D on OK at 1 in., 2 in., 3 in. and 4 in. respectively from O. From these points draw Aa, Bb, Cc, Dd perpendicular to OL. Measure Oa, Ob, Oc, Od and calculate the values of the ratios $\dfrac{Oa}{OA}$, $\dfrac{Ob}{OB}$, $\dfrac{Oc}{OC}$, $\dfrac{Od}{OD}$. Verify that your answers are equal to the degree of accuracy obtainable by drawing and compare them with the value of cos 34° in the table of natural cosines.

2. In a triangle PQR the angle PQR is 58° and the angle PRQ is 90°. If PQ is 3 in., find the length of QR, given that cos 58° $= 0\cdot5299$.

3. If ABC is a triangle in which $\widehat{ABC}$ is 90° and $\widehat{BAC}$ is θ, write down the ratio which is equal to cos θ. Is this ratio larger or smaller than 1 ?

4. Find cos 54° 36', cos 20° 14', cos 79° 28' from a table of natural cosines.

5. Find cos 84° 3', cos 8° 53', cos 14° 41' from a table of natural cosines.

6. A point P starts from O and moves along a line OK at 3 ft./sec. and PN is perpendicular to a line OL which makes 27° 42' with OK. How far will N have moved after 2 sec. ?

7. A ship sails 10 miles in a direction making 47° with due north. How far will it then be north of its starting point ?

8. Find θ if (a) cos $\theta = 0\cdot9092$, (b) cos $\theta = 0\cdot1891$.

9. Find θ if (a) cos $\theta = \cdot2624$, (b) cos $\theta = \cdot7098$.

10. The slant height of a cone is 18 cm. and the diameter of the base is 12 cm. Find the cosine of the angle, which a slant height makes with the diameter of the base in the same vertical plane. Hence find the angle between the slant height and the diameter. Measure the slant height and base diameter of a solid cone and calculate the angle between them in the same way.

11. Find log cos 49°, log cos 18° 54', log cos 72° 17' from a table of logarithms of cosines.

12. The ball O of a governor is attached to two points on a rod by arms OA, OB, each 16·5 cm. long. Find the angle which the arms make with AB when AB is (a) 21·3 cm., (b) 28 cm.

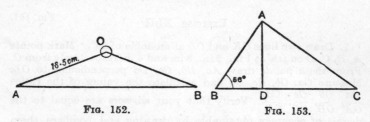

FIG. 152. FIG. 153.

13. The distance between two points on a hill measured up the hill is 1242 yd.; the distance measured from the map, i.e. the horizontal distance, is 1196 yd. Find the angle which the hill makes with the horizontal.

14. A stay for a wireless mast is 145 ft. long and its lower end is 29·5 ft. from the base of the mast. Find the angle which it makes with the horizontal.

15. In a right-angled triangle ABC (Fig. 153) the angle A is 90° and AD is perpendicular to BC. If $\widehat{ABC}$ is 56° and BC is 4 in., find the lengths of (a) AB, (b) BD.

16. In a triangle PQR the angle PQR is 90°. If QR is p in., PR is q in. and $\widehat{PRQ}$ is α, show that $p = q \cos \alpha$.

17. Find the cosines of (a) $\frac{1}{2}$ radian, (b) 1·2 radians.

18. An alternating current is $100 \cos (100\pi t$ radians) ampères after t secs. Find its magnitude, after $\frac{1}{400}$ sec. and after $\frac{1}{300}$ sec.

19. Find the values of θ if (a) cos (θ radians) = 0·6, (b) cos (θ radians) = 0·125.

How to remember the sine and cosine ratios

In a right-angled triangle ONP, in which the angle ONP is 90° and the angle PON is θ, the longest side OP, which is opposite to the right angle, is called the hypotenuse. We will

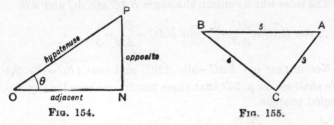

FIG. 154. FIG. 155.

call the side NP the side opposite to θ and the side ON the side adjacent to θ. Using the words " opposite " and " adjacent " for these sides

$$\text{Sin } \theta = \frac{\text{opposite}}{\text{hypotenuse}}, \quad \cos \theta = \frac{\text{adjacent}}{\text{hypotenuse}}.$$

Since the hypotenuse is the longest side of a right-angled triangle, neither the sine nor the cosine of an angle is ever greater than one.

Another way of remembering these ratios is to notice that they both have the hypotenuse in the denominator and that the cosine is the ratio of two sides, which contain the angle θ. The same two letters, *co*, begin the words *co*sine and *co*ntain.

Either of the above methods will be found useful in determining which pair of sides to take for the sine and cosine when the right-angled triangle is drawn in different positions. The student should draw right-angled triangles in various positions, and practise reading off the sine and cosine of each of the acute angles as in the following examples.

Example.—In the right-angled triangle ABC in Fig. 155 the shorter sides are 3 and 4 units. Find the sine and cosine of each of the acute angles of the triangle.

By Pythagoras' theorem the hypotenuse AB is $\sqrt{3^2+4^2}$, i.e. 5 units. The sides which contain the angle ABC are BC and AB.

$$\therefore \cos A\widehat{B}C = \frac{BC}{AB} = \frac{4}{5}, \quad \sin A\widehat{B}C = \frac{AC}{AB} = \frac{3}{5}.$$

The sides which contain the angle BAC are AC and AB.

$$\therefore \cos B\widehat{A}C = \frac{AC}{AB} = \frac{3}{5}, \quad \sin B\widehat{A}C = \frac{BC}{AB} = \frac{4}{5}.$$

Notice that $\cos B\widehat{A}C = \sin A\widehat{B}C$, and $\cos A\widehat{B}C = \sin B\widehat{A}C$. We shall see on p. 247 that these results are true for any right-angled triangle.

Example.—AB is a horizontal line $\frac{1}{2}$ in. long and a circle centre A and radius 2 in. cuts the downward vertical through B in C.

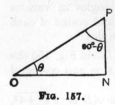

If $A\widehat{C}B = \theta$, find $\sin \theta$ and $\cos \theta$.

By Pythagoras' theorem.

$$BC^2 = 2^2 - (\tfrac{1}{2})^2 = \tfrac{15}{4}.$$

$$\therefore BC = \tfrac{1}{2}\sqrt{15}.$$

$$\therefore \text{Sin } \theta = \frac{\text{opposite}}{\text{hypotenuse}} = \frac{\frac{1}{2}}{2} = \frac{1}{4}.$$

and $\cos \theta = \dfrac{\text{adjacent}}{\text{hypotenuse}} = \dfrac{\frac{1}{2}\sqrt{15}}{2} = \dfrac{\sqrt{15}}{4} \simeq 0.9683.$ Fig. 156.

Ratios of complementary angles

If the sum of two angles is a right angle, each angle is the complement of the other. Hence the complement of θ is $90° - \theta$.

If the angle $P\widehat{O}N$ in a right-angled triangle PON is θ, then the angle OPN is $(90° - \theta)$.

Fig. 157.

$$\therefore \sin(90° - \theta) = \frac{\text{side opposite } \widehat{OPN}}{\text{hypotenuse}} = \frac{ON}{OP} = \cos\theta,$$

and $\cos(90° - \theta) = \dfrac{\text{side adjacent to } \widehat{OPN}}{\text{hypotenuse}} = \dfrac{NP}{OP} = \sin\theta.$

Thus the cosine of an angle θ is the sine of the complement of θ. This was the origin of the use of the prefix co in the name cosine.

These results mean that we can always use a table of sines to find cosines and vice versa. Thus

Cos 34° 21′ = sin (90° − 34° 21′) = sin 55° 39′ = 0·8256 from the table of sines.

Exercise XLIII

Write down the sine and cosine of the angle marked in each of the right-angled triangles in Fig. 158 :

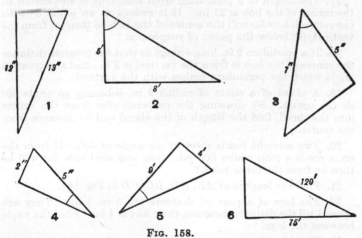

Fig. 158.

Fill in the brackets in the following equations :

7. Sin 54° = cos ( ).   8. Cos 21° = sin ( ).

9. Cos 43° 14′ = sin ( ).   10. Sin 19° 53′ = cos ( ).

11. Sin $(45 - x)° = \cos ($).   **12.** Cos $30° = \sin ($).

13. Find cos 37° and cos 48° 25' from a table of sines.

14. For what value of θ is sin $\theta = \cos \theta$?

15. Find the lengths of AB, AC, AD, BD, CD in Fig. 159.

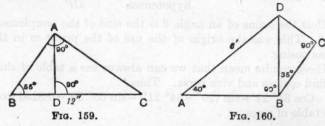

FIG. 159.   FIG. 160.

16. An aeroplane flying at 200 m.p.h. climbs at an angle $2\frac{1}{2}°$ with the horizontal. How many feet will it have climbed in 3 minutes ?

17. The length of a pendulum from the point of suspension to the centre of the bob is 21 in. If it swings to an angle 8° with the vertical, how far will the centre of the bob be then (a) from the vertical, (b) below the point of suspension ?

18. If a pendulum 2 ft. long swings so that the greatest distance the centre of the bob is from the vertical is 5 in., find the greatest angle which the pendulum makes with the vertical.

19. A chord of a circle of radius 9 in. subtends an angle 80° at the centre. By drawing the perpendicular from the centre into the chord, find the length of the chord and its distance from the centre.

20. Two straight roads meet at an angle of 50°. If from the cross roads a man walks 600 yd. along one road how far will he then be from the other road ?

21. Find the lengths of AB, BD, BC, CD in Fig. 160.

22. The legs of a pair of dividers are 5 in. long. They are opened till the distance between their feet is 4 in. Find the angle between the legs.

23. The sides of a rhombus are 8 in. long and one of the angles of the rhombus is 62°. Find the lengths of the diagonals.

24. A diagonal of a rectangle is 15 in. long and one side is 11 in. long. Find the length of the other side and the angle between the diagonals of the rectangle.

25. The figure shows the shape of an aerodrome. Find the distance from *B* to *D*, and by drawing a perpendicular from *C* on to *BD*, find the angle $C\widehat{D}B$. Find also the angles $C\widehat{D}A$, $C\widehat{B}A$, $B\widehat{C}D$.

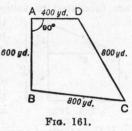

FIG. 161.

26. A spoke of a wheel of length $1\frac{1}{2}$ ft. starts from a horizontal position. When the wheel has rotated $\frac{1}{2}$ radian (the centre remaining fixed) how far has the end of the spoke moved (*a*) vertically, (*b*) horizontally?

27. Find the angle in radians subtended at the centre of a circle radius 6 in. by a chord *AB*, (*a*) when the chord *AB* is 10 in. long, (*b*) when the arc *AB* is 10 in. long.

28. A current *i* ampères and a voltage *V* volts are given by $i = 15 \sin 20t$ and $V = 4 \cos 20t$, where the angle is in radians. Find the values of *i* and *V* when *t* is 0·04.

Tangent of an angle

In Fig. 162, which is a copy of Fig. 154 on p. 245, the ratio $\dfrac{NP}{ON}$ is called the tangent of θ and written $\tan \theta$.

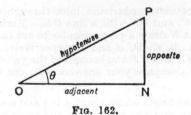

FIG. 162.

Hence

$$\tan \theta = \frac{NP}{ON} = \frac{\text{opposite}}{\text{adjacent}}.$$

Since

$$\frac{NP}{OP} = \sin \theta \text{ and } \frac{ON}{OP} = \cos \theta$$

$$\tan \theta = \frac{OP \sin \theta}{OP \cos \theta} = \frac{\sin \theta}{\cos \theta}.$$

The values of tan θ for every minute of angle from 0° to 90° are tabulated in tables of *natural tangents*; there are also

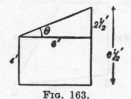

tables of logarithms of tangents and in both of these sets of tables the mean differences have to be added.

Example.—A hut 6 ft. wide has a sloping roof; one side is 4 ft. high and the other side is 6½ ft. high. Find the angle of slope of the roof.

FIG. 163.

If the required angle is θ,

$$\tan \theta = \frac{2\frac{1}{2}}{6} = \frac{5}{12} = 0 \cdot 4167.$$

From the table of natural tangents tan 22° 36′ is 0·4163, which is 0·0004 less than tan θ, and the differences for 1′ and 2′ are 0·0003 and 0·0006 respectively. Hence, to the nearest minute

$$\theta = 22° 36′ + 1′ = 22° 37′.$$

Exercise XLIV

1. With a protractor construct lines through O making 20°, 30°, 40°, 50°, 60°, and 70° with a line OX. Mark off $ON = 3$ in. along OX and at N draw a perpendicular to cut the other arms of the angles in A, B, C, D, E and F respectively. Measure NA, NB, NC, ND, NE and NF and hence find the value of the tangent of each angle. Compare your answers with the values given in the tables.

2. Construct an angle whose tangent is ¾ and measure the angle in degrees. Also find the angle from the table of tangents and compare the two answers.

3. If the shadow of a vertical stick 2 ft. high is 3 ft. long, what length is the shadow of a chimney 50 ft. high?

4. On squared paper plot the point (2, 3) and find the angle the line joining it to the origin makes with the axis OX.

5. A post casts a shadow 20 ft. long when the sun's rays make 55° with the horizontal. Find the length of the post.

6. The sides of a roof make 25° with the horizontal. If the span is 28 ft., find the height of the ridge of the roof above the level of the top of the walls.

FIG. 164.

7. From a table of tangents find tan 40° 51′, tan 12° 17′, tan 75° 11′.

8. Find θ if (a) tan $\theta = 2 \cdot 103$, (b) tan $\theta = 0 \cdot 1889$.

9. Find from tables the values of log tan 18° 17′, log tan 64° 21′, log tan 72° 55′.

10. The coefficient of friction μ between two surfaces and the angle of friction λ are related by the equation $\mu = \tan \lambda$. Find μ when $\lambda = 15°$ and find λ when $\mu = 0 \cdot 28$.

11. The angle of a wedge is 20°. Find, to the nearest $\frac{1}{100}$th in., the width of the opening it makes when it is driven in $\frac{3}{8}$ in. (Fig. 165.)

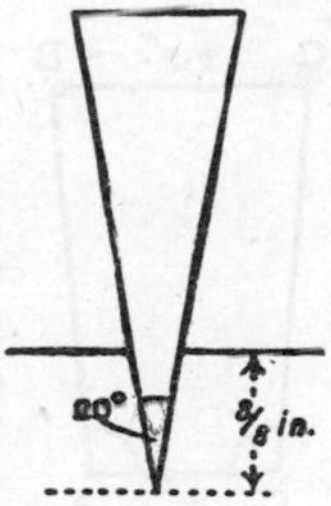

12. If the height of a cone is 8 in. and the vertical angle is 66°, find the diameter of the base. Deduce the volume of the cone.

13. A railway cutting is to be 36 ft. wide at the bottom and 45 ft. deep, and the sides are to slope at 40° to the horizontal. Find the width of the cutting at the top. How many cu. ft. of earth will have to be removed to make a cutting of this cross section 100 yd. long ?

FIG. 165.

14. The equal base angles of an isosceles triangle are 50° and the base is 6 in. Find the height and area of the triangle.

15. The diameter of a screw is 2 in. and the pitch-angle is 5° 30′. If tan (pitch-angle) $= \dfrac{\text{pitch}}{\text{circumference of screw}}$, find the pitch of the screw. How far will the screw move forward in 10 turns ?

16. If each step of some stairs is $6\frac{1}{2}$ in. high and $8\frac{1}{4}$ in. wide, find the angle of slope of the banister rail.

17. A rectangular field is 50 yd. by 40 yd. A path runs across it from one corner to the opposite corner. Find the angles which it makes with the sides of the field.

18. The span of a roof is 20 ft. and it rises 4 ft. 3 in. in the middle. Find the angle which each side makes with the horizontal.

19. A bell tent is 8 ft. high and the diameter of the base is 15 ft. Find the angle which the slant side of the tent makes with the horizontal.

20. On a map with a scale 2 in. to the mile the distance between two points A and B is $\frac{7}{8}$ in. A is on the 100-ft. and B on the 200-ft. contour line. Find the angle AB makes with the horizontal.

21. If the diameter of the base of a cone is 6 in. and its height is 9 in., find its vertical angle.

22. A railway cutting is 100 ft. wide at the top, and 40 ft. at the bottom. If it is 45 ft. deep, what is the inclination of the sides, which are equal, to the horizontal ?

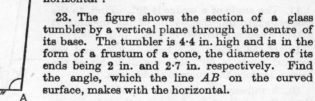

23. The figure shows the section of a glass tumbler by a vertical plane through the centre of its base. The tumbler is 4·4 in. high and is in the form of a frustum of a cone, the diameters of its ends being 2 in. and 2·7 in. respectively. Find the angle, which the line AB on the curved surface, makes with the horizontal.

Fig. 166.

24. A flagstaff is stayed by a wire fastened to a point 30 ft. above the ground and to a point in the ground 8 ft. from the base of the flagstaff. Find the angle the wire makes with the horizontal.

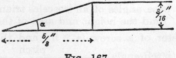

Fig. 167.

25 The figure shows a section of a chisel perpendicular to its edge. If the chisel tapers for a distance of $\frac{5}{8}$ in. and its greatest thickness is $\frac{3}{16}$ in., find the angle α between the two faces at its edge.

Harder examples on the use of the sine, cosine and tangent ratios

Example.—The figure shows a section of a cam perpendicular to its axis of rotation, which has its centre at O. The straight edge AB touches the circles with centres at O and C, which have radii $1''$ and $\frac{1}{4}''$ respectively. Find the angle between AB and OC. The cam follower makes point contact with the cam and its point moves along a straight line OK. Find the angle COK when the point of the follower is at P, the middle point of AB.

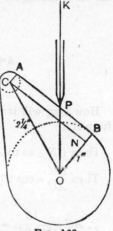

FIG. 168

Since AB is a tangent, CA and OB are perpendicular to it.

Draw CN parallel to AB to cut OB in N. Then $O\widehat{N}C$ is 90° and $O\widehat{C}N$ is the angle between AB and OC.

$$ON = OB - BN = OB - AC = \tfrac{3}{4} \text{ in.}$$

$$\therefore \sin O\widehat{C}N = \frac{ON}{OC} = \frac{\tfrac{3}{4}}{2\tfrac{1}{4}} = \tfrac{1}{3}.$$

$$\therefore O\widehat{C}N = 19° 28'.$$

Also by Pythagoras' theorem

$$CN^2 = OC^2 - ON^2 = (2\tfrac{1}{4})^2 - (\tfrac{3}{4})^2 = \tfrac{9}{2}.$$

$$\therefore CN = \frac{3}{\sqrt{2}} \text{ and } PB = \tfrac{1}{2}AB = \tfrac{1}{2}CN = \frac{3}{2\sqrt{2}}$$

$$\therefore \tan P\widehat{O}B = \frac{PB}{OB} = \frac{3}{2\sqrt{2}} = \tfrac{3}{4}\sqrt{2} = \tfrac{3}{4}(1\cdot4141) = 1\cdot0606.$$

$$\therefore P\widehat{O}B = 46° 41'.$$

$$\therefore C\widehat{O}K = C\widehat{O}N - P\widehat{O}B = (90° - 19° 28') - 46° 41' = 23° 51'.$$

Example.—It is 30 sea miles from *A* to *B* as the crow flies.

A ship sails from *A* to *B* at 12 knots by the course *ACB* shown in the figure (1 knot = 1 sea mile per hour).

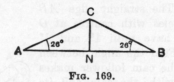

FIG. 169.

How long will it take and what will be its greatest distance from *AB* ?

Draw *CN* ⊥ as to *AB*.

Then $\dfrac{AN}{AC} = \cos 26°$.   ∴ $\dfrac{15}{AC} = \cos 26°$.   ∴ $15 = AC \cos 26°$.

	No.	Log.
∴ $AC = \dfrac{15}{\cos 26°} = 16\cdot69$.	15	1·1761
	cos 26°	$\bar{1}$·9537
	16·69	1·2224

∴ $AC + CB = 2AC = 33\cdot38$.

∴ the time taken will be $\dfrac{33\cdot38}{12}$ hr. = 2 hr. 47 min.

The greatest distance from *AB* is *CN*.
CN/*AN* = tan 26°.

	No.	Log.
∴ *CN* = 15 tan 26°	15	1·1761
	tan 26°	$\bar{1}$·6882
	7·316	0·8643

∴ greatest distance ≏ 7·32 sea miles.

Exercise XLV

1. In each of the following figures write down the given ratios :

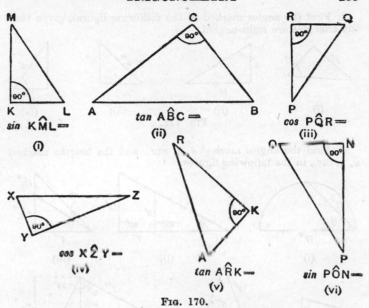

$sin\ K\hat{M}L=$

(i)

$tan\ A\hat{B}C=$

(ii)

$cos\ P\hat{Q}R=$

(iii)

$cos\ X\hat{Z}Y=$

(iv)

$tan\ A\hat{R}K=$

(v)

$sin\ P\hat{O}N=$

(vi)

Fig. 170.

2. Fill in the brackets in the following equations.

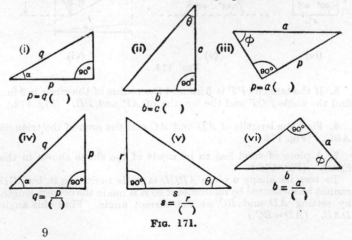

(i) $p=q(\ \ )$

(ii) $b=c(\ \ )$

(iii) $p=a(\ \ )$

(iv) $q=\dfrac{p}{(\ \ )}$

(v) $s=\dfrac{r}{(\ \ )}$

(vi) $b=\dfrac{a}{(\ \ )}$

Fig. 171.

9

3. Find the angles marked in the following figures, given that the triangles are right-angled.

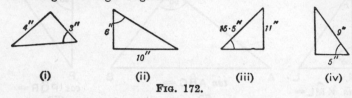

(i)   (ii)   (iii)   (iv)

FIG. 172.

4. Find the angles marked θ, ϕ, etc., and the lengths marked x, y, etc., in the following figures.

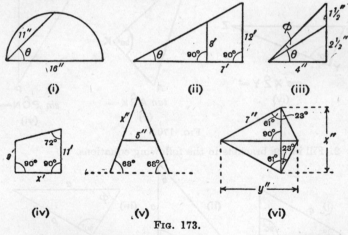

(i)   (ii)   (iii)

(iv)   (v)   (vi)

FIG. 173.

5. If the tangent PT is 5 in. and the radius of the circle is 2 in., find the angle POT and the lengths of AP and PB. (Fig. 174.)

6. Find the lengths of AD and AC and the area of the triangle ABC. (Fig. 175.)

7. A piece of steel has to be made of the shape shown in the figure. (Fig. 176.)

To test its shape a piece $ABCD$ is made to fit into it, but CD cannot be measured by micrometer so it is made the correct length by setting AD and BC at the correct angle. Find this angle DAB. ($AD = BC$.)

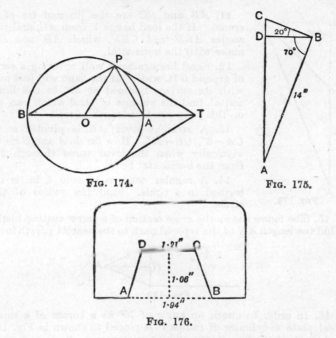

FIG. 174.

FIG. 175.

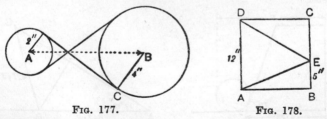

FIG. 176.

8. The vertical angle of a cone is 80° and the diameter of its base is 16 in. What is its height ?

FIG. 177.   FIG. 178.

9. The figure (Fig. 177) shows a crossed belt round two pulleys, centres A and B.

If AB is 10 in., find the angle between the two straight parts of the belt by drawing AN perpendicular to BC produced.

10. ABCD is a square. Find the angle AED.

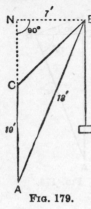

FIG. 179.

11. AB and BC are the jib and tie of a crane. If the load hangs 7′ from AC, find the angles ABN and CBN, which AB and BC make with the horizontal.

12. Sand lies against a wall covering a strip of ground 6 ft. wide. If the sand will just rest with its surface inclined at 37° to the horizontal, find the volume of sand which can lie on this strip per foot length of wall.

13. A straight lever AB is pivoted at C. $CA = 6″$, $CB = 15″$. How far do A and B move vertically when the lever turns through 27° from the horizontal ?

14. A regular octagon of side 4 in. is inscribed in a circle. Find the radius of the circle.

15. The figure shows the cross section of a screw cutting blade. Find the length AN of the tapered part, to the nearest $\frac{1}{1000}$th inch.

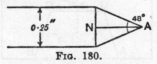

FIG. 180.

16. In order to check an angle of 70° at a corner of a small steel plate a cylinder of radius 1″ is placed as shown in Fig. 181 and the distance d in. measured by a micrometer.

If the angle is correct, what should be the reading of the micrometer ?

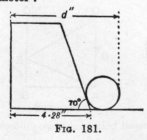

FIG. 181.

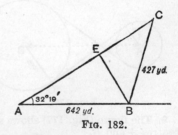

FIG. 182.

17. In a survey it is found that $B\widehat{A}C$ is 32° 19′, AB is 642 yd., and BC is 427 yd. If BE is perpendicular to AC, find the lengths of BE, AE, EC, AC and the angle $B\widehat{C}E$.

18. In a friction experiment it is found that an effort of 8 lb. wt. up the plane AB will just pull up a load of 15 lb. wt. when B is 10″ above A. In mechanics it is shown that

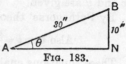

FIG. 183.

effort/load $= \mu \cos \theta + \sin \theta$,

where μ is the co-efficient of friction, and θ is the angle of slope of the plane. Calculate μ from this equation, using the ratio of θ given by the triangle ABN.

CHAPTER XVII

RATIOS OF ACUTE ANGLES

Position of a point in a plane—Polar co-ordinates

The position of a point P in a plane, for instance, the position of a light in a harbour, of a post in a playing field, of a hole or a pin in a piece of machinery, etc., may be fixed conveniently in two different ways.

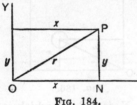

FIG. 184.

1. By measuring its distances x and y from two perpendicular lines in the plane OY and OX. These are the rectangular co-ordinates of P with respect to the axes OX and OY (see p. 101).

2. By measuring its distance r from a fixed point O and the angle θ which OP makes with a fixed straight line OX. r and θ are called the polar co-ordinates of P.

From Fig. 184 we find

$$\frac{x}{r} = \cos \theta \quad \text{and} \quad \frac{y}{r} = \sin \theta.$$

$$\therefore x = r \cos \theta, \, y = r \sin \theta.$$

These equations enable us to find x and y when we know r and θ.

Again using Fig. 184, we can find the values of r and θ when x and y are given.

By Pythagoras' theorem, $r^2 = x^2 + y^2$;

$$\text{Also } \tan\theta = \frac{y}{x}.$$

These equations enable us to find r and θ when x and y are given.

Example.—A light is to be placed in a harbour 70 yd. due E. and 110 yd. due N. of a point O. How far must it be from O and in what direction ?

If the light is r yd. from O in a direction making θ with a line due E., (Fig. 185).

$$r^2 = 70^2 + 110^2 = 4900 + 12100 = 17000.$$
$$\therefore r = \sqrt{17000} \backsimeq 130 \cdot 4.$$
$$\text{Also } \tan\theta = \frac{110}{70} = 1\cdot 5714, \therefore \theta = 57° 30'.$$

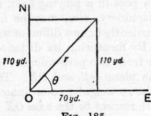

FIG. 185.

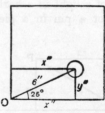

FIG. 186.

Since the angle between r and due N. is $90° - \theta$, which is $32° 28'$, we say that the bearing of the light from O must be $130 \cdot 4$ yd. in a direction $32° 28'$ East of North.

Example.—A hole is to be made in a square piece of metal of side 8 in. so that the centre of the hole is 6 in. from one corner O in a direction making an angle $25°$ with a side of the square. Find the least distances of the centre of the hole from the sides of the square through O. If the hole is to have a diameter of $\frac{1}{4}$ in., what must be the nearest distances of the edge of the hole from each of the four sides of the square to the nearest $\frac{1}{1000}$th of an inch ?

6 in. and 25° are the polar co-ordinates of the centre P.

Let the distances of P from the sides through O be x in. and y in. Then

$$x = 6 \cos 25° = 6 \times 0·9063 = 5·4378 = 5·438 \text{ to } \tfrac{1}{1000}\text{th in.}$$
$$y = 6 \sin 25° = 6 \times 0·4226 = 2·5356 = 2·536 \text{ to } \tfrac{1}{1000}\text{th in.}$$

Since the radius of the hole is $\tfrac{1}{8}$ in. $= 0·125$ in., the distances of the edge of the hole from the sides through O are

$$5·438 - 0·125 = 5·313 \text{ in. and } 2·536 - 0·125 = 2·411 \text{ in.,}$$

and the distances from the other sides are

$$8 - 5·438 - 0·125 = 2·437 \text{ in. and } 8 - 2·536 - 0·125 = 5·339 \text{ in.}$$

Vectors

Suppose a body is pulled by a force of 10 lb. wt. to the right and upwards in a direction, which makes 50° with the horizontal. From any point A on the paper we can draw a line AK to represent the horizontal, and then draw a line AB at 50° with AK and length 2 in. say, to show the direction of the force and also its magnitude to a scale of 5 lb. wt. to 1 in. It is advisable to put an arrow head on AB pointing from A to B to show that the force acts from A towards B and not from B towards A. This line with the arrow head represents the force in magnitude and direction.

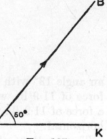

Fig. 187.

Any physical quantity, which can be represented in this way by a line of a certain length drawn in a certain direction, is called a *vector*. Velocity, acceleration and force are vectors. Quantities, which have magnitude only and no direction, such as work, kinetic energy, the volume of a body, and a sum of money are *scalars*.

Resultant of two vectors

Suppose a body is acted on by two forces, one of 8 lb. wt. which acts in a direction 40° below the horizontal, and another of 6 lb. wt., which acts in a direction 25° above the horizontal. These forces are represented by the lines AB, AD in Fig. 188, using a scale of 5 lb. wt. to 1 in. and the parallelogram $ABCD$ is completed.

It is shown by experiments in mechanics that these two forces have the same effect on a body as a single force, represented by AC. This force is called their *resultant* and the forces 8 lb. wt. and 6 lb. wt. are called its *components*. From Fig. 188 we find by measurement that AC is 2·37 in. and makes

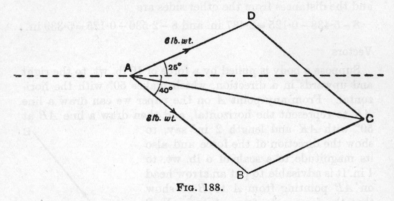

FIG. 188.

an angle 13° with the horizontal. Since 2·37 in. represents a force of 11·9 lb. wt., the resultant of the two given forces is a force of 11·9 lb. wt., which acts in a direction 13° below the horizontal.

The resultant of any pair of vectors is found by the same method. In the above example for instance the forces of 8 and 6 lb. wt. could be replaced by velocities of 8 and 6 ft./sec. respectively and their resultant would be a velocity of 11·9 ft./sec. in a direction 13° below the horizontal.

Example.—On the deck of a ship moving at 20 m.p.h. a man runs at 8 m.p.h. in a direction making an angle 80° with the direction of motion of the ship. Find graphically the magnitude and direction of his resultant velocity.

Draw a line AB $2\frac{1}{2}$ in. long to represent the velocity of the ship, using a scale 8 m.p.h. to 1 in., and then draw a line AD 1 in. long at 80° with AB to represent the velocity of the man on the deck. Complete the parallelogram $ABCD$.

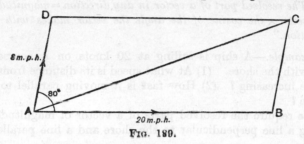

Fig. 189.

Then by measurement AC is 2·85 in., which represents 22·8 m.p.h. and $C\hat{A}B$ is 20°. Therefore the man's resultant velocity is 22·8 m.p.h. in a direction making 20° with the direction of motion of the ship.

Resolved part of a vector

Let OP be a vector and PN, PM be the perpendiculars from P on to two perpendicular lines OX and OY, as in Fig. 190. Then OP is the resultant of the two perpendicular vectors ON and OM. In this particular case where the components are at right angles they are called the resolved parts of OP. ON is the resolved part of OP along OX and OM is the resolved part along OY.

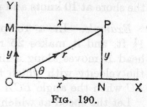

Fig. 190.

Suppose the length of OP is r units and that it makes an angle θ with OX, and that the magnitudes of the resolved parts are x and y units. Then we have seen on page 259 that

$$x = r \cos \theta, \text{ and } y = r \sin \theta.$$

Since $\sin \theta = \cos (90° - \theta)$, $y = r \cos (90° - \theta)$.

9*

But the angle POY is $(90° - \theta)$ and so both the resolved parts x and y are found by multiplying r, the length of the vector, by the cosines of the angles which OP makes with OX and OY respectively. Therefore we have the rule—

"*The resolved part of a vector in any direction = magnitude of the vector × the cosine of the angle the vector makes with that direction.*"

Example.—A ship is sailing at 20 knots on a course at 30° with the shore. (1) At what speed is its distance from the shore increasing ? (2) How fast is it moving parallel to the shore ?

We require the resolved parts of a vector of magnitude 20 along a line perpendicular to the shore and a line parallel to

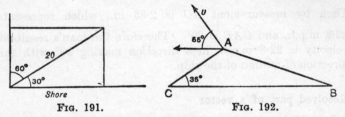

FIG. 191.   FIG. 192.

the shore. These are $20 \cos 60° = 20 \times 0.5 = 10$, and $20 \cos 30° = 20 \times 0.8660 = 17.32$. Hence the ship is moving away from the shore at 10 knots and parallel to the shore at 17.32 knots.

Example.—In a reciprocating engine the crank CA is $1\frac{1}{2}$ ft. and it makes 25 revolutions per minute. The piston head B moves along a line through the crank axis C. Find the velocity with which the crank head is moving parallel to BC when the angle BCA is 35°. (Fig. 192.)

Let the speed at which A is moving in its circle be v ft./sec. A describes the circumference of a circle radius $1\frac{1}{2}$ ft., which is $2\pi \times 1\frac{1}{2}$ ft., in $\frac{60}{25}$ sec.

$$\therefore v = 2\pi \times 1\frac{1}{2} \div \frac{60}{25} = \frac{3\pi \times 5}{12} = \frac{5\pi}{4} = 3.926.$$

v is perpendicular to OA and therefore makes an angle

$90° - 35°$, which is $55°$, with a line parallel to BC. Therefore the resolved part of v parallel to BC is

$$v \cos 55° = 3.926 \times 0.5736 = 2.25.$$
$$\therefore \text{velocity} = 2.25 \text{ ft./sec.}$$

Example.—A tug is pulling a liner by a hawser inclined at an angle of $25°$ with the length of the liner. If the tension of the hawser is 4 tons wt., what is the force exerted on the liner in the direction of its length ?

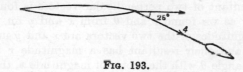

Fig. 193.

The force is the resolved part of 4 tons wt. along the length of the liner and this is $4 \cos 25°$ or 3.6 tons wt.

Example.—4 cwt. is being lifted by two ropes both inclined at $28°$ to the vertical. Find their tensions.

Let the tensions be each T cwt. Each T cwt. is the resultant of the resolved parts $T \cos 62°$ cwt. horizontally and

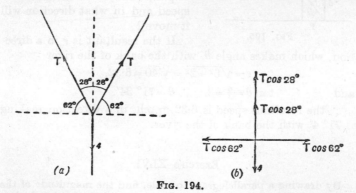

Fig. 194.

$T \cos 28°$ cwt. vertically. Replacing the T's by these resolved parts we get Fig. 194 (*b*). The two forces $T \cos 62°$ cwt. balance, and so the 4 cwt. is supported by the vertical resolved parts, which together amount to $2T \cos 28°$ cwt.

$$\therefore 2T \cos 28° = 4.$$

$$\therefore T = \frac{4}{2 \cos 28°} = \frac{2}{0.8829} = 2.27.$$

∴ the tension is 2·27 cwt.

Resultant of two perpendicular vectors

The resultant of two perpendicular vectors is found in the same way as we found r and θ from x and y on page 260. If the magnitudes of the two vectors are x and y units, as in Fig. 184, and their resultant has a magnitude r units and makes an angle θ with the vector of magnitude x, then

$$r^2 = x^2 + y^2, \quad \tan \theta = \frac{y}{x}.$$

Example.—If a motor boat, which can move at 6 m.p.h. in still water, is steered perpendicular to the bank of a river in which there is a current of 2 m.p.h., what will be its resultant speed and in what direction will it move ?

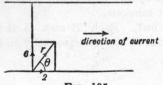

direction of current

FIG. 195.

If the resultant is r in a direction, which makes angle θ, with the bank of the river

$$r = \sqrt{6^2 + 2^2} = \sqrt{40} = 6.32,$$

and $\qquad \tan \theta = \frac{6}{2} = 3. \quad \therefore \theta = 71° 34'.$

∴ the resultant speed is 6·32 m.p.h. in a direction making 71° 4′ with the bank of the river.

Exercise XLVI

By drawing a parallelogram to scale, find the magnitude of the resultant of the following pairs of vectors and the angle which it makes with the direction of the first vector :

1. Perpendicular forces 7 and 10 lb. wt.

2. Forces 2 and 3 ton wt. inclined at 50°.

3. Velocities 15 m.p.h. and 28 m.p.h. inclined at 70°.

4. Velocities 20 ft./sec. and 18 ft./sec. inclined at 135°.

5. Forces 8 lb. wt. and 8 lb. wt. inclined at 100°.

Answer the questions 6—9 by drawing parallelograms to scale :

6. If the resultant of two perpendicular forces is 10 lb. wt. at an angle of 30° with one of the forces, find the forces.

7. If the resultant of two forces 8 lb. wt. and P lb. wt. inclined at an angle of 70° is a force of 15 lb. wt., find P.

8. A boat can sail at 15 knots in still water. When it sails perpendicular to a current its resultant speed is 17 knots. Find the speed of the current.

9. A load of 4 ton wt. is supported by two chains at 30° and 45° to the vertical. Find their tensions.

Answer the following questions by calculation.

10. Draw two lines OX, OY at right angles, and draw a line OP 3 in. long between OX and OY making 38° with OX. Calculate the distances of P from OX and OY ; also measure them and compare the results of calculation and measurement.

11. If a man pulls the handle of a garden roller with a force of 50 lb. wt. and the handle makes 30° with the horizontal, what force is he exerting on the roller horizontally ?

12. B is 4 miles N.E. of A ; how far is it east of A ?

13. The longest side of a 60° set-square is 10 in. Find the lengths of the other two sides.

14. The polar co-ordinates of a point are $r = 12·3$, $\theta = 27° \; 32'$; find its x, y co-ordinates.

15. A sailing boat is sailing at 8 knots in a direction 40° west of north. Find the rate at which it is moving northward. If it is $\frac{1}{2}$ a sea mile south of a certain line drawn east and west, find how long it will take to cross the line.

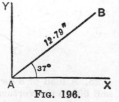

Fig. 196.

16. In making a hole in a jig plate the centre B is given by radial measurements from A and angular measurements from AX, as shown in the figure. Find the rectangular co-ordinates of B with respect to AX and AY to nearest $\frac{1}{10}''$.

17. A man pulls a body along a horizontal plane by a rope at 20° to the horizontal. If he pulls the rope with a force of 2 cwt., with what force is he pulling the body (1) horizontally, (2) vertically ?

18. Find the resolved part of a vector 20 units long along a line making 35° with the vector.

19. A body of $\frac{1}{2}$ ton wt. rests on a rough plane inclined at 10° to the horizontal. What are the resolved parts of the weight of the body down the plane and perpendicular to the plane ?

20. A ship steers due north at 20 knots in a current flowing due west at 5 knots. Find the resultant speed of the ship and the direction in which it moves.

21. Find the magnitude and direction of the resultant of two perpendicular vectors of 10 and 15 units respectively.

22. If two forces of 30 lb. wt. and 40 lb. wt. act on a body in perpendicular directions, what is the resultant force on the body and what is its direction ?

23. A body of 500 lb. wt. is supported by two chains each at 40° to the vertical. If the tension on a chain is T lb. wt., what are its resolved parts vertically and horizontally ? Replace each tension by its resolved parts and hence find T.

24. Three struts, AO, BO, CO, are pinned at O. A force 2 cwt. acts along the strut CO towards O. Resolve this force into two components parallel to OA and OB and hence find the forces exerted by the struts AO and BO at O.

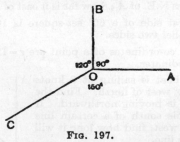

FIG. 197.

25. A load of 8 cwt. is supported by two ropes at angles of 30° and 60° to the vertical. Find the tensions in the ropes by finding the resolved parts of the load parallel to the ropes.

26. If a stone is thrown horizontally from the edge of a cliff at 50 ft./sec. its velocity after one second is the resultant of this velocity and a vertical velocity of 32 ft./sec., and its velocity after two seconds is the resultant of the same horizontal velocity and a vertical velocity of 64 ft./sec. Find in what direction and with what speed it is moving (a) after 1 sec., (b) after 2 sec.

27. Holes are to be set out in a steel plate with their centres A and B in the positions shown in the figure. Find the distances of A and B from the perpendicular lines OX and OY and hence find the length of AB. If studs of diameters 0·24 in. are placed in each hole, what will be the distance from the outside of one stud to the outside of the other, as measured by a micrometer ?

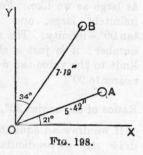

FIG. 198.

Variation of the ratios as the angle increases from 0° to 90°. Ratios of 0° and 90°

Let a radius vector OP of a circle radius r units make an angle θ with a fixed radius OA and let PN be perpendicular to OA. Let ON = x units and PN = y units. Then $\sin \theta = \frac{y}{r}$ and since y increases as θ increases, while r remains fixed, sin θ increases as θ increases from 0° to 90°. Since y is 0 when θ is 0 and y is 1 when θ is 90°, sin 0° = 0 and sin 90° = 1.

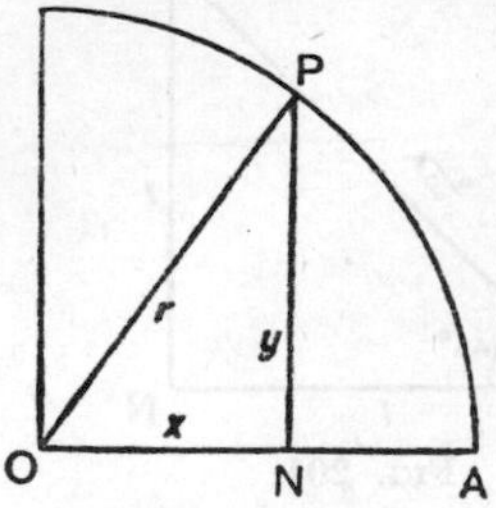

FIG. 199. In the same way since $\cos \theta = \frac{x}{r}$ and x decreases from r to 0 as θ increases, cos θ decreases as θ increases from 0° to 90°, and cos 0° = 1, cos 90° = 0.

Tan $\theta = \frac{y}{x}$ and in this ratio both numerator and denominator vary. As θ increases y increases and x decreases, and so tan θ increases as θ increases, beginning with the value 0 at θ = 0. By making θ near enough to 90° we can make x as small as we like while y is nearly r, and so we can make tan θ as large as we like. For this reason we say that tan 90° is infinitely large, and write shortly tan $90° = \infty$, read tan 90° = infinity. The symbol ∞ does not stand for a definite number; it is just a short way of stating that there is no limit to the value tan θ can have when θ is made nearer and nearer to 90°.

Ratios of the angles 30°, 60° and 45°

If we draw an equilateral triangle ABC of side 2 units and draw AD perpendicular to the side BC, $BD = 1$, and by Pythagoras' theorem $AD = \sqrt{2^2 - 1^2} = \sqrt{3}$.

But the acute angles in the triangle ABD are 60° and 30°.

$$\therefore \text{Sin } 60° = \frac{\sqrt{3}}{2}, \quad \cos 60° = \frac{1}{2}, \quad \tan 60° = \sqrt{3}.$$

$$\text{Sin } 30° = \frac{1}{2}, \quad \cos 30° = \frac{\sqrt{3}}{2}, \quad \tan 30° = \frac{1}{\sqrt{3}}.$$

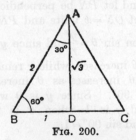

FIG. 200.

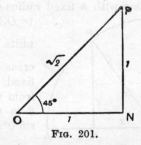

FIG. 201.

If we draw a right-angled isosceles triangle OPN in which the shorter sides are each 1 unit, the hypotenuse is, by Pythagoras' theorem, $\sqrt{2}$ units. Each acute angle is 45°.

$$\therefore \text{Sin } 45° = \frac{1}{\sqrt{2}}, \quad \cos 45° = \frac{1}{\sqrt{2}}, \quad \tan 45° = 1.$$

The student should convert these ratios to decimals and compare his values with the values in the tables. The advantage of remembering these ratios is that the angles 30°, 45°, 60° are common in many applications of trigonometry to engineering.

Graphs of sin θ and cos θ

Let OP be a radius vector of a circle centre O and radius 1 unit, which makes an angle θ with a fixed radius OA. Take a point O' on OA produced and at O' draw a line $O'Y$ perpendicular to OA. Mark off a scale of values of θ from 0° to

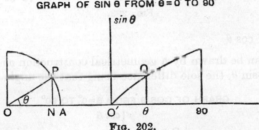

GRAPH OF SIN θ FROM $\theta = 0°$ TO 90°

Fig. 202.

90° on OA produced, starting with 0° at O', and mark off a vertical scale on $O'Y$, taking as unit on this scale the radius of the circle. Draw PN perpendicular to OA and through P draw a line parallel to OA and mark on it the point Q, which has co-ordinate θ on the angle scale.

Since $\dfrac{NP}{1} = \sin \theta, \therefore NP = \sin \theta.$

$\therefore$ the ordinate of Q is $\sin \theta$.

Hence points plotted in the same way as Q lie on the graph of $\sin \theta$. If we take positions of P at intervals of, say, 10° from 0° to 90°, plot the corresponding positions of Q and join them by a smooth curve, we get the graph of $\sin \theta$ shown in Fig. 203. We could, of course, have found the values of $\sin 10°$, $\sin 20°$, etc., from the tables instead of by the above geometrical method and plotted them against θ in the usual way.

GRAPH OF Y = SIN θ FROM θ = 0° TO θ = 90°

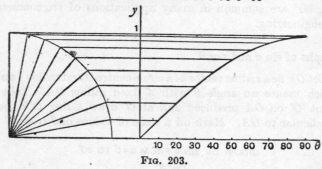

FIG. 203.

Graph of cos θ

This can be drawn by a geometrical construction as was the graph of sin θ, the sole difference being that the angle θ has to

GRAPH OF COS θ FROM θ = 0° TO 90°

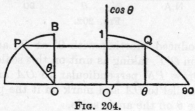

FIG. 204.

be measured from a vertical radius OB instead of from a horizontal one OA.

We leave it to the student to show that the ordinate of Q in Fig. 204 is cos θ and to draw the graph for himself by the construction shown in the figure. Instead we will plot the graph of cos θ using tables of cosines and taking values of 0 at intervals of 15°.

θ . .	0	15	30	45	60	75	90
Cos θ .	1	0·966	0·866	0·707	0·5	0·259	0

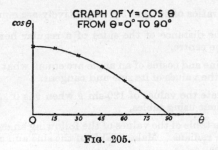

GRAPH OF Y=COS θ
FROM θ=0° TO 90°

Fig. 205.

Exercise XLVII

1. Write down the values of sin 60°, cos 45°, tan 0°.

2. Write down the values of cos 0°, tan 30°, tan 45°.

3. Find the lengths of AB and BD, given that C is 6 in. from AB. (Fig. 206.)

4. If AB is vertical, find the height of C above A and $\widehat{BAC}$. (Fig. 207.)

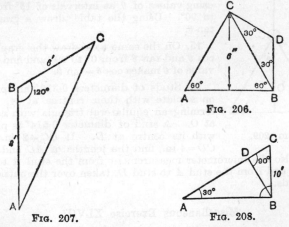

Fig. 206.

Fig. 207.   Fig. 208.

5. Find the resultant of two forces each 8 lb. wt. at an angle of 60°.

6. If $\widehat{ABC}$ is 90°, find the lengths of AC and BD. (Fig. 208).

7. Which ratios of 60° and 30° respectively are equal to $\dfrac{\sqrt{3}}{2}$?

8. Find the distance of the sides of a regular hexagon of side 4 in. from the centre.

9. If the sine and cosine of an angle are equal, what is the angle ? Write down the values of its sine and tangent.

10. Calculate the values of 120 sin θ when θ is 0°, 30°, 45°, 60° and 90° without using tables.

11. Make a table of the values of the following angles in degrees : $\frac{1}{6}\pi, \frac{1}{4}\pi, \frac{1}{3}\pi, \frac{1}{2}\pi$ radians. Make a table of the sine and cosine of each of these angles.

12. Make a table of the values of sin θ at intervals of $11\frac{1}{4}°$ from 0° to 90°. Plot the points given by the table on a graph and join them by a smooth curve. From this curve read off the value of sin 50° and compare it with the value given in the tables.

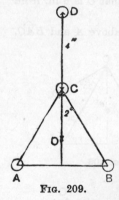

FIG. 209.

13. Draw a graph of cos θ from 0° to 90° using a rotating vector of a circle of unit radius.

14. Make a table of the values of tan θ using values of θ at intervals of 15° from 0° to 90°. Using the table, draw a graph of tan θ.

15. On the same axes draw the graphs of cos θ and tan θ from 0° to 90° and find what value of θ makes cos $\theta = \tan \theta$.

16. Studs of diameters 0·316″ are placed on a plate with their centres at A, B, C forming an equilateral triangle with centre at O. A stud of diameter 0·514″ is placed with its centre at D. If $OC = 2$ in. and $CD = 4$ in., find the lengths of AC and AD. Find also the micrometer measurement from the stud A to the stud C and from the stud A to stud D, taken over the outside of the studs.

Miscellaneous Exercise XLVIII

1. Find the value of θ if (a) cos $\theta = \cos 21° \ 15'$, (b) cos $\theta = \sin 43° \ 49'$.

2. Show by a figure that the sine of a small angle is nearly 'equal to its radian measure, and by using a table of sines show that they are equal to within 1 % for angles smaller than 14°.

3. A plank 10 ft. long has one end raised by a prop 5 ft. long. Find the angle the plank makes with the horizontal (a) when the prop is vertical, (b) when it is perpendicular to the plank. In the latter case find the height of the upper end of the plank above the ground.

4. The current in a tangent galvanometer is given by the formula $I = \dfrac{5\,Hr \tan \theta}{\pi n}$. If $H = 0.1853$, $r = 12$, and $n = 4$, calculate the values of I when $\theta = 35° 15'$ and the value of θ when $I = 0.26$.

5. The dip of a magnet is given by $\tan \alpha = \dfrac{H_1}{H_2}$, where H_1 and H_2 gauss are the vertical and horizontal components of the earth's magnetic force. If $H_2 = 0.1853$ and $\alpha = 66° 52'$, find H_1.

6. The force P lb. wt. required to pull a body weight W lb. wt. along a rough horizontal plane is given by $P = \dfrac{W \sin \lambda}{\cos (\theta - \lambda)}$, where λ is the angle of friction between the body and the plane and θ is the angle which P makes with the plane. Find P when $W = 150$, $\lambda = 5°$ and $\theta = 25°$.

7. The potential difference V volts established across a circuit is given by $V = 223 \cos 18000t$, where t seconds is the time and the angle is in degrees. Calculate the value of V when t is 0.002, 0.003, 0.004 and 0.005. Also find the value of t when V is 160.

8. From the tables decide which ratio of θ is the greater, $\tan \theta$ or $\sin \theta$? Is this true for all values of θ from 0° to 90°? Give a geometrical proof of your answer.

9. Which of the ratios $\sin \theta$, $\cos \theta$ and $\tan \theta$ involves only the two shorter sides of the right-angled triangle?

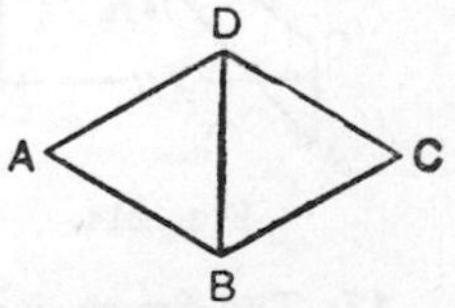

10. Without looking at the tables prove that $\sin 70°$ is greater than $\sin 50°$. Of what general statement is this an example?

11. Find θ if $\tan \theta = \tan 15° + \tan 25°$.

Fig. 210.

12. In the figure ABD and BCD are equilateral triangles. If AB is 4 in., calculate the distance of A from C. Also if AC is 10 in., find the length of AB.

13. The base of a tank is a square of side 4 ft., and it contains water to a depth of 3 ft. It is then tilted through an angle of 20° about one edge, as shown in the figure. Find (a) the length of AP, (b) the depth AB of the water at A.

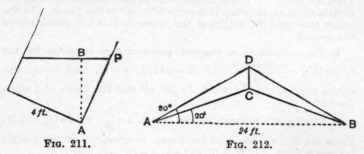

FIG. 211.

FIG. 212.

14. Find the lengths of AC, CD, AD in the framework shown.

15. The cross-section of a groove in a metal plate is an arc of a

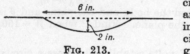

FIG. 213.

circle. The groove is 6 in. wide and its maximum depth is 2 in. Find the radius of the circle and the angle which the groove subtends at the centre.

16. In a crane ABC the jib AB is 14 ft., the tie BC is 12 ft., and the load D hangs at 9 ft. from the vertical line AC. Find the angles AB and CB make with the vertical.

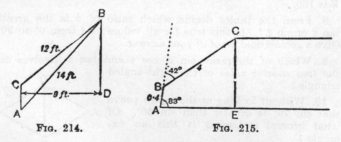

FIG. 214.

FIG. 215.

17. The figure shows the cross-section of a cutting tool. AB has to be 0·4 mm. and BC 4 mm. Find CE, the thickness of the tool at C.

18. A plane surface is to be set at an angle θ with the direction

of travel of a machine by making it touch two discs which touch each other, as in the figure. Show that $\sin \frac{1}{2}\theta = \dfrac{R-r}{R+r}$.

From this formula calculate the value of R required if $r = 2$ and θ is to be 18°. Give R to three sig. fig.

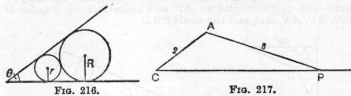

FIG. 216.   FIG. 217.

19. In a reciprocating engine the crank CA is 2 ft. and the connecting rod AP is 8 ft. The piston head P moves along a line through C.

Find (a) the angle APC when CA is perpendicular to the direction of motion of the piston (this is the largest value of $\widehat{APC}$); (b) the angle APC when the crank is perpendicular to the connecting rod.

20. A ship sails 7 miles due north and then 12 miles 70° east of north. Find its distance from its starting point.

21. A ship sails 7 miles 18° east of north and then 12 miles 88° east of north. Find its distance from its starting point. [This gives the same figure as the previous question turned through 18° towards the east.]

22. The mechanism shown in the figure turns about A and D. Draw a figure in which CD is perpendicular to AD and calculate the angles CAD and CAB. Hence find the angles BAD and ABC.

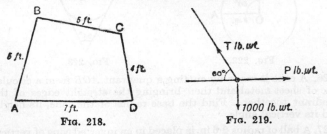

FIG. 218.   FIG. 219.

23. The figure shows a mass of 1000 lb. wt. at B supported by a rope AB at 60° with the horizontal and by a horizontal force

P lb. wt. If the tension of the rope is T lb. wt., what are its resolved parts vertically and horizontally ? By making these resolved parts balance the downward force of 1000 lb. wt. and the horizontal force of P lb. wt., find T and P.

24. The figure shows the girders of a certain crane. BD is $3\frac{1}{2}$ ft. Draw DN perpendicular to AB and hence find the lengths of DN, BN, AN, AD, and the angle BAD.

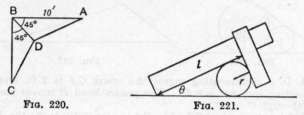

FIG. 220.   FIG. 221.

25. To set up a line at a slope θ in a machine, a disc of radius r mm. is laid on the table and a T-square placed over it so that both the blade and stock touch the disc, and the tip of the blade rests on the table. Show that, if l mm. is the length of the blade from the stock to the table,

$$l = r + r/(\tan \tfrac{1}{2}\theta).$$

If $r = 8$ and the blade can slide on the stock, find, as accurately as you can by using four figure tables, the values of l required to make θ (a) $10°$, (b) $50°$.

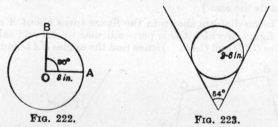

FIG. 222.   FIG. 223.

26. A cone is made by cutting a quadrant AOB from a circular disc of sheet metal and then bringing the straight edges of the quadrant together. Find the base radius of the cone, its height and its vertical angle.

27. A ball of radius $2\cdot6$ in. is placed in an inverted cone of vertical angle $54°$. Find the distance of the lowest point of the ball from the vertex of the cone.

28. A metal plate is in the form of a triangle which has two sides 12 in. and 9 in. and the included angle 70°. Find the distance of the corner opposite the 12 in. side from this side, and use it to calculate the area of the triangle. If the plate is $\frac{1}{4}$ in. thick and weighs 3·36 lb. wt., find its density.

29. In making a certain machine it is necessary to divide a complete revolution of 360° into n equal parts. This is done by placing n discs of known radius r cm. in contact with each other and with the outside of a circular disc of radius R cm. Show that this disc must be ground down till its radius R cm. is given $R = \left(r / \sin \dfrac{180°}{n} \right) - r$. Calculate R cm. to the nearest $\frac{1}{10}$ mm., when r is 2 and n is (a) 9, (b) 20.

CHAPTER XVIII

RATIOS OF ANGLES OF ANY MAGNITUDE

Angles of any magnitude

Two perpendicular lines in a plane $X'OX$ and $Y'OY$ divide the plane into four quadrants. If a radius vector OP starts

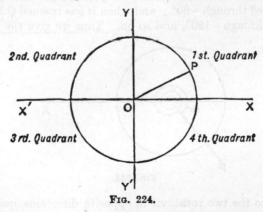

2nd. Quadrant   1st. Quadrant

3rd. Quadrant   4th. Quadrant

FIG. 224.

from OX and rotates round O anti-clockwise, it will pass first through the quadrant XOY, then through the quadrant YOX' and so on. For this reason XOY is called the first quadrant,

YOX' the second quadrant, $X'OY'$ the third quadrant and $Y'OX$ the fourth quadrant.

The angle $X\widehat{O}P$ will increase from 0° to 90° as OP revolves from OX to OY, from 180° as OP revolves from OY to OX' and if OP continues to rotate it will have turned through 180° and 90°, i.e. 270°, when it reaches OY', and through 360° when it reaches OX again. If it continues to rotate still more, it can rotate through any angle whatever. It can, for instance, rotate through 950°. This means rotating through two complete revolutions, which make 720°, and then through 230°. This will bring OP to the position in the third quadrant shown in Fig. 225, in which it makes an angle 230°–180°, i.e. 50°, with the horizontal.

Negative angles

When OP rotates anti-clockwise the angle it turns through is considered positive, but when it rotates *clockwise*, starting from the direction OX, the angle it turns through is considered *negative*. When it has reached the position OY' in Fig. 224 it has turned through – 90° ; and when it has reached OX' it has turned through – 180°, and so on. Thus we give the signs +

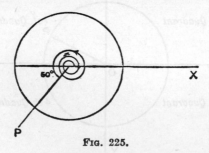

Fig. 225.

and – to the two rotations in opposite directions just as we do for measurements in opposite directions along a line when we are making a scale of directed numbers. There is, however, a difference because although the position of a point on a line is fixed by one number on the scale the position of a radius vector can be determined by several different angles. For instance, the position of OP in Fig. 225 is given by the angles $+230°$, $-130°$, $+230° + 360° = 590°$, $-130° - 360° = -490°$, etc.

Extensions of the definitions of sin θ, cos θ, and tan θ to all values of θ

Suppose a radius vector of length r units starts from the position OA and rotates through an angle $θ$ to the position OP, $θ$ being reckoned positive anti-clockwise and negative clockwise. Let the co-ordinates of P with respect to an axis OX along OA and a perpendicular axis OY be x and y units. Then we have seen that, when $θ$ is an acute angle,

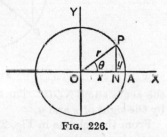

Fig. 226.

$$\cos θ = \frac{x}{r}, \sin θ = \frac{y}{r}, \text{ and } \tan θ = \frac{y}{x}.$$

In order to extend these definitions to positive and negative values of $θ$ of any magnitude, we suppose that r is always positive and x, y are the co-ordinates of P, whatever the size of the angle $θ$.

Example.—Find the sine, cosine and tangent of 220°.

$\widehat{NOP} = 220° - 180° = 40°$, and, since P is to the left of OY and below OX, x and y are both negative, that is $x = -ON$ and $y = -NP$. (Fig. 227.)

$$\therefore \sin 220° = \frac{y}{r} = -\frac{NP}{OP} = -\sin 40° = -0.6428.$$

$$\cos 220° = \frac{x}{r} = -\frac{ON}{OP} = -\cos 40° = -0.7660.$$

$$\tan 220° = \frac{y}{x} = \frac{-NP}{-ON} = +\frac{NP}{ON} = +\tan 40° = +0.8391.$$

It is clear that, since x and y are always numerically equal to ON and NP, the numerical values of the ratios are those of

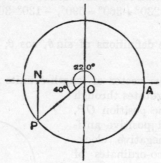

FIG. 227.

the acute angle NOP. The signs of the ratios are determined by the signs of x and y.

From the scheme in Fig. 228 we see that, when the radius vector OP is in the first quadrant, $\sin\theta$, $\cos\theta$, and $\tan\theta$ are all positive, while when OP is in the second quadrant $\sin\theta$ is positive and the other ratios are negative. Similarly $\tan\theta$ is the only positive ratio in the third quadrant and $\cos\theta$ the only positive ratio in the fourth quadrant.

$x-ve$ $y+ve$	$x+ve$ $y+ve$
$x-ve$ $y-ve$	$x+ve$ $y-ve$

(a)

Sin	All
Tan	Cos.

(b)

FIG. 228.

The signs of the ratios may be remembered by Fig. 228 (b). The words in the quadrants show which ratios are positive in each quadrant, the others being negative.

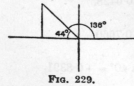

FIG. 229.

Example.—Find $\sin 136°$. $\sin 136°$ is numerically equal to $\sin 44°$, and it is positive, since $\sin\theta$ is positive when θ is in the second quadrant.

$\therefore \sin 136° = +\sin 44° = 0.6947$.

Example.—Find tan $(-40°\ 23')$. Tan $(-40°\ 23')$ is numerically equal to tan $40°\ 23'$ and it is negative, since tan θ is negative when θ is in the fourth quadrant.

$\therefore$ tan $(-40°\ 23') = -$ tan $40°\ 23' = -0·8506$.

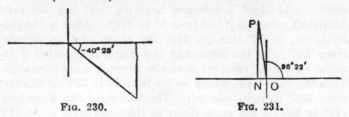

FIG. 230.   FIG. 231.

Example.—Cos (8 radians).

8 radians $= (8 \times 57·296)° = 458·368° = 458°\ 22'$.

Also $458°\ 22' = 360° + 98°\ 22'$ and so the radius vector OP is in the position shown in Fig. 231.

$\therefore$ $\widehat{NOP} = 180° - 98°\ 22' = 81°\ 38'$.

Since the radius vector is in the second quadrant the cosine is negative.

$\therefore$ cos (8 radians) $= -$ cos $\widehat{NOP} = -$ cos $81°\ 38' = -0·1455$.

Graph of sin θ for all values of θ

We can draw the graph of sin θ for all values of θ by merely extending the method on page 271 to include a rotation of the radius vector through an angle of any size.

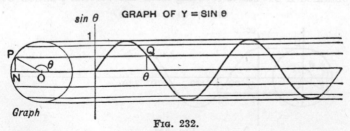

GRAPH OF Y = SIN θ

FIG. 232.

If $r = 1$, then for all values of θ, sin $\theta = y$ and so, just as in Fig. 202, the construction makes the ordinate of Q equal to sin θ for every position of P, but now negative values of the ordinate have to be included. As θ increases from 0° to 90°, the graph of Q is the curve shown in Fig. 202 ; as θ increases from 90° to 180°, we get the same values of y but in the reverse order ; after 180° y becomes negative, but has the same numerical values as it has from 0° to 180°. After a complete revolution of OP through 360° the graph of Q is repeated every 360°. In the same way the graph is repeated if the radius vector OP revolves clockwise through a negative angle. Thus the wave form, which we get from 0° to 360°, is repeated every 360° to right and left. The trough of the wave from 180° to 360° is the same shape as the crest from 0° to 180° but upside down, and the crest is symmetrical about the vertical line through 90°.

GRAPH OF Y = SIN θ

Fig. 233.

Since the wave repeats itself every 360° this is called the *period* of sin θ. Fig. 233 shows the graph of sin θ for several periods.

Graph of cos θ

In the same way as for an acute angle, the graph of cos θ is obtained if OP starts rotating from the vertical position OB

GRAPH OF Y = COS θ

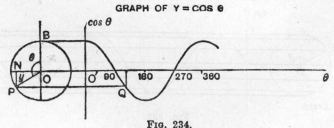

Fig. 234.

instead of from the horizontal as it does for the graph of sin θ. The construction is shown in Fig. 234 ; for the position of OP shown in the figure, $\theta = 120°$. The student should draw the graph of cos θ by taking values of θ at every 15° from 0° to 360°.

Clearly, if we draw the graph of sin θ and then move the origin and the vertical axis 90° to the right, we obtain the graph of cos θ. Thus cos θ really gives the same wave form as sin θ and its period is also 360°.

From the graphs it is easy to see at a glance approximately what values of θ make sin θ or cos θ have a given value. For instance, if we wish to find the angles which make sin $\theta = -\frac{1}{3}$, we have only to draw a horizontal line at $\frac{1}{3}$ unit

GRAPH TO SHOW THE VALUES OF θ WHICH MAKE SIN θ = $-\frac{1}{3}$

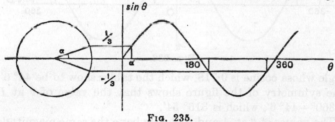

FIG. 235.

below the horizontal axis. Then the symmetry of the unit circle on the left shows that the two smallest positive values of θ differ from 180° and 360° respectively by the acute angle, whose sine is $\frac{1}{3}$; this angle is indicated by the letter a in the figure.

From the tables this angle a is 19° 28'.

Therefore the smallest positive value of θ is 180° + 19° 28', that is, 199° 28', and the next positive value is 360° − 19° 28' that is, 340° 32'. If the graph is continued to right and left, it is clear that the horizontal line at height $-\frac{1}{3}$ unit will cut it an infinite number of times and the value of θ at any one of these will differ from one of the above two values by a multiple of the period 360°. Hence placing the above values in the middle and making a table to right and left by adding and subtracting multiples of 360° we get the following table of values of the angle whose sine is $-\frac{1}{3}$. The table may be extended to right and left as far as we wish.

$\longleftarrow -380°\ 28',\ -160°\ 32',\ -20°\ 28',\ 199°\ 28',\ 340°\ 32',\ 559°\ 28',\ 700°\ 32'\longrightarrow$

Example.—If cos $\theta = 0.718$, find the values which θ can have between $-360°$ and $+360°$.

The figure shows the graph of cos θ from $-360°$ to $+360°$, with a horizontal line drawn at a height of 0·718 cutting the graph at A, B, C and D. The value of θ at C is the acute

GRAPH TO SHOW THE VALUES OF θ WHICH MAKE COS θ = 0·718

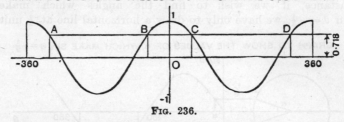

FIG. 236.

angle whose cosine is 0·718, which the tables show to be 44° 6′. The symmetry of the figure shows that the value of θ at D is $360° - 44°\ 6'$, which is 315° 54′.

The values of θ at A and B clearly have the same magnitude as those at C and D, but opposite sign. Hence the four values required are $-315°\ 54',\ -44°\ 6',\ +44°\ 6',\ +315°\ 54'$.

Graph of a sin θ

If in the construction in Fig. 232 we use a circle of radius

GRAPH OF Y = 2 SIN θ

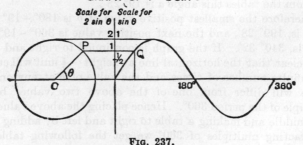

FIG. 237.

2 units, $PN = 2 \sin \theta$ and hence the ordinate of Q is $2 \sin \theta$. Therefore the graph obtained by plotting a number of positions of Q is the graph of $y = 2 \sin \theta$. This amounts to the same thing as drawing the graph of $y = \sin \theta$ and then making a new scale on the vertical axis so that 1 becomes 2, $\frac{1}{2}$ becomes 1, and every number on the old scale is doubled.

Graph of sin $p \theta$

The following table gives the values of 2θ and $\sin 2\theta$ for values of θ at intervals of $15°$ from $\theta = 0°$ to $180°$.

θ . .	0	15	30	45	60	75	90	105	120	135	150	165	180
2θ .	0	30	60	90	120	150	180	210	240	270	300	330	360
Sin 2θ	0	0·5	0·87	1	0·87	0·5	0	−0·5	−0·87	−1	−0·87	−0·5	0

This table shows that, if we draw the graph of $y = \sin 2\theta$ the ordinates at $\theta = 15°$, $30°$, $45°$, etc., are the same as the ordinates of the graph of $y = \sin \theta$ at $\theta = 2 \times 15°$, $2 \times 30°$, $2 \times 45°$, etc.

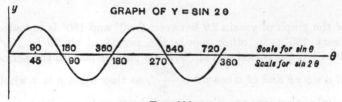

FIG. 238.

Thus with different scales on the horizontal axis the same curve can be the graphs of $y = \sin 2\theta$ and $y = \sin \theta$; each number on the scale for $y = \sin \theta$ being double the corresponding number on the scale for $y = \sin 2\theta$.

The curve in Fig. 238 is the graph of $y = \sin 2\theta$ using the scale below the horizontal axis and of $y = \sin \theta$ using the scale above the horizontal axis.

Graphs of $a \sin p \theta$ and $a \cos p \theta$

The results of the last two paragraphs show that with different scales on both axes the same curve can be regarded

10

as the graph of $y = a \sin p\theta$ and as the graph of $y = \sin \theta$. Similarly the same curve can be the graph of $y = a \cos p\theta$ and $y = \cos \theta$. Fig. 239 shows the graph of $y = 3 \sin 60\theta$.

Periods of $a \sin p\theta$ and $a \cos p\theta$

In Figs. 238 and 239 the distances along the horizontal axis from the beginning of a wave to the end of the same wave are $\dfrac{360°}{2} = 180°$, and $\dfrac{360°}{60} = 6°$ respectively. Thus the part

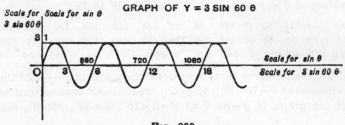

GRAPH OF Y = 3 SIN 60 θ

Scale for *3 sin 60 θ* Scale for *sin θ*

Scale for *sin θ*
Scale for *3 sin 60 θ*

Fig. 239.

of the graph of $y = \sin 2\theta$ between $\theta = 0°$ and $180°$ is repeated every $180°$; in other words the period of $\sin 2\theta$ is $180°$. Similarly the period of $3 \sin 60\theta$ is $6°$, and in general the period of $a \sin p\theta$ and of $a \cos p\theta$ is $\dfrac{360°}{p}$, so that when p is a whole number there are exactly p periods between $0°$ and $360°$.

Amplitude of $a \sin p\theta$ and $a \cos p\theta$

The figures we have drawn show that the values of these expressions increase to $+a$ and decrease to $-a$ periodically as θ

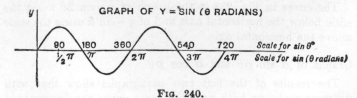

GRAPH OF Y = SIN (θ RADIANS)

Scale for *sin θ°*
Scale for *sin (θ radians)*

Fig. 240.

increases. We say that their values oscillate between $-a$ and $+a$, and a is called the *amplitude* of the oscillation.

Graphs of $y = a$ sin (θ radians) and $y = a$ cos (θ radians)

If the graph of $y = \sin\theta$ is drawn by means of a rotating vector, as in Fig. 232, but with the angle measured in radians, the only difference is that there will be a different scale on the horizontal axes $\frac{1}{2}\pi$, π, $\frac{3}{2}\pi$, 2π radians replacing 90°, 180°, 270°

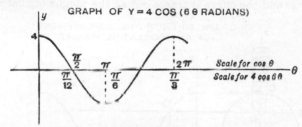

GRAPH OF Y = 4 COS (6 θ RADIANS)

FIG. 241.

and 360° respectively, as in Fig. 240. Thus the period of $y = \sin$ (θ radians) and also of $y = \cos$ (θ radians) is 2π radians.

Similarly the period of $y = a$ sin ($p\theta$ radians) and of $y = a$ cos ($p\theta$ radians) is $\dfrac{2\pi}{p}$ radians. Fig. 241 shows one wave of the graph of $y = 4\cos$ (6θ radians).

Distance-time graph for a weight oscillating at the end of a spring

Suppose a weight N at the end of a spring oscillates up and down through a length $CD = 6''$ in a total time of 2 sec. from C to D and back to C. Let the horizontal line through N cut the circle on CD as diameter at P, then it is shown in mechanics that as the weight oscillates up and down the point P moves at a uniform speed round the circle.

Since the weight goes from C to D and back in 2 sec., P goes once round the circle in 2 sec. and the radius vector OP from the centre O turns through 2π radians in 2 sec., that is,

π rad. per sec. Therefore if the weight takes t sec. to go from C to N, the radius vector will have turned through (πt) radians from OC to OP, and hence $\widehat{COP} = \pi t$ radians.

But $\dfrac{ON}{OP} = \cos \widehat{COP}$. $\therefore ON = 3 \cos (\pi t \text{ radians})$.

Now if we plot a time scale horizontally from a point O' on the same level as O and produce PN horizontally to Q, which is t units to the right of O', the ordinate of Q will be $3 \cos \pi t$ and the curve it traces out as the weight oscillates up

**GRAPH TO SHOW THE DISPLACEMENT
OF AN OSCILLATING WEIGHT**

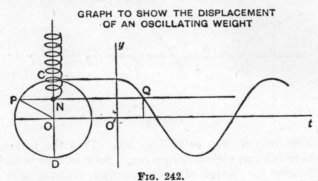

Fig. 242.

and down will be the graph of $y = 3 \cos \pi t$. The ordinate of this graph at any time gives the distance of the weight from O, the centre of its oscillation, at that time. The graph of $y = 3 \cos \pi t$ is called a distance-time or space-time graph of the motion of the weight.

It should be noticed here that when the weight is oscillating no actual angle occurs, the angle πt that has been used is introduced by the mathematical device of drawing the circle on CD as diameter and supposing that P moves round it as N oscillates up and down.

Mechanical and electrical oscillations

In the same way as in the motion of a weight at the end of a spring it often happens that the displacement of a body making mechanical oscillations, such as the vertical oscillations of a motor car on its springs, can be expressed in terms of the time t by expressions like $2 \sin 3t$, $20 \cos 50t$, $a \sin pt$. In these expressions radian measure is generally used for the angle because the radian measure happens to be easier to use in the mechanics of the problem.

In the same way in electricity the number of units of current (generally ampères) in an alternating current can be expressed in terms of the time by expressions like $2 \cos 4t$, $15 \sin 100\pi t$, $I \cos \omega t$ (where I and ω are constants). The current used in the grid system in England makes 50 cycles per second, that is, 50 complete oscillations per second. If this current is i ampères, where $i = I \cos \omega t$, t seconds being the time and the angle being in radians, the period of one oscillation is $\frac{2\pi}{\omega}$ sec.

$$\therefore 50 \times \frac{2\pi}{\omega} = 1.$$
$$\therefore \omega = 100\pi.$$

If also the maximum value of the current is 15 ampères, I must be 15.

$$\therefore i = 15 \cos (100\pi t).$$

This is a typical expression for an alternating current.

Exercise XLIX

(In questions 1–38, the angles are measured in degrees.)

1. Draw a circle of radius 2 in., centre O, and a diameter $A'OA$. Draw radius vectors OP, OQ, OR making angles 110°, 225°, 300° with OA, measured counter-clockwise. Draw PL, QM, RN perpendicular to $A'OA$, and measure their lengths. Hence write down the approximate values of the sines of 110°, 225° and 300°.

2. What acute angles have ratios numerically equal to the ratios of 150° and − 20° respectively?

3. Find the values of the sine, cosine and tangent of 150° and − 20° respectively.

4. Find the values of the sine, cosine and tangent of 210° and 310° respectively.

5. What is (a) the maximum value of sin θ, (b) the minimum value of sin θ, (c) the least numerical value of sin θ as θ varies ?

6. Of what expression is this wave form the graph ?

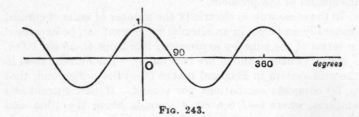

Fig. 243.

Find the values of:

7. Sin 110° 34'.   8. Sin 215° 14'.   9. Cos 243° 27'.

10. Cos 310° 4'.   11. Tan 157° 41'.   12. Tan 218° 31'.

13. Sin (− 21°).   14. Cos (− 142°).   15. Tan (− 68° 20').

Find the two values of θ between 0° and 360° which make :

16. Sin θ = 0·4237.   17. Cos θ = 0·5169.

18. Tan θ = 1·1423.   19. Sin θ = − 0·5.

20. Cos θ = − 0·7196.   21. Tan θ = − 2.

22. Sin θ = 0·9175.   23. Cos θ = − 0·9175.

24. Tan θ = 2·25.

25. Draw a graph of y = sin θ from θ = 0° to 360°, using a rotating vector as in Fig. 232. From your graph read off sin 238°, sin 310°, and the angles between 0° and 360° whose sine is − 0·4.

26. Make a table of the values of tan θ for the following values of θ : 0°, 22½°, 45°, 67½°, 112½°, 135°, 157½°, 180°. Draw a graph to show how tan θ varies as θ increases from 0° to 67½° and from 112½° to 180°. By looking at a table of tangents, find how tan θ varies as θ increases from 67½° to 112½° and indicate this roughly on your graph.

27. If the graph of y = sin θ is drawn and the scale on the θ axis is altered so that 360° becomes 120°, show that when the new scale is used for θ, the curve is the graph of y = sin 3θ.

28. Make a table of values of cos 2θ for values of θ from 0° to 360° at intervals of 15°, and hence draw the graph of $y = \cos 2\theta$. From your graph find the values of θ which make cos $2\theta = 0 \cdot 6$.

29. What is the period of the expression 2 sin 3θ ? Tabulate its values at intervals of 10° throughout a whole period, starting with 0°, and hence draw a graph showing its values throughout this period.

30. Write down the periods of each of the following expressions : cos θ, sin 5θ, sin $\frac{1}{2}\theta$, cos 180θ.

31. Find the values of n if sin $n\theta$ has a period (a) 720°, (b) 120°, (c) $\frac{1}{4}$°, (d) 5000°.

32. In a triangle ABC, the angles at B and C are 40° and 35° respectively. Find from the tables the sine, cosine and tangent of each of the three angles of the triangle.

33. Draw the graph of $y = \tan \theta$ from $\theta = 120°$ to $\theta = 180°$ and from it find the value of tan 155° and the value of θ between 120° and 180° which makes tan $\theta = -\frac{3}{5}$. Check your answers from a table of tangents.

34. Draw roughly 4 waves of the graph of $y = \sin \theta$ from $\theta = 0°$ to 1440° and alter the scales on the axes so that it becomes the graph of (a) $y = \frac{1}{2}\sin \theta$, (b) $y = 2 \sin 3\theta$, (c) $y = \sin 20\theta$.

35. Draw roughly two waves of the graph of $y = \cos \theta$ from $\theta = -360°$ to $\theta = +360°$ and alter the scales on the axes so that it becomes the graph of (a) $y = \frac{1}{4}\cos 3\theta$, (b) $y = \cos 720\theta$.

36. How many periods sin 2θ and sin 3θ are there in one period of sin θ ?

37. In a triangle ABC, AD is drawn perpendicular to BC. Show that $AD = AB \sin \widehat{ABC}$ when $\widehat{ABC}$ is either an acute angle or an obtuse angle.

38. Make a table of the values of sin $\theta + \cos \theta$ from $\theta = 0°$ to $\theta = 180°$ and hence draw a graph of $y = \sin \theta + \cos \theta$. From the graph find (a) the greatest value of y, (b) the values of θ when $y = 0$ and $y = 0 \cdot 5$ respectively.

In questions 39–67 the angles are measured in radians.
Find the values of the following ratios :

39. Sin 2.

40. Cos 1·9.

41. Tan 4·2.

42. Cos (– 1).

43. Tan (– 2·5).

44. Sin 5·6.

45. Sin $\dfrac{2\pi}{3}$.

46. Cos $\dfrac{3\pi}{4}$.

47. Tan $\dfrac{2\pi}{3}$.

48. Sin $\dfrac{7\pi}{6}$.

49. Cos $\left(-\dfrac{\pi}{3} \right)$.

50. Cos $\dfrac{11\pi}{12}$.

Find the two values of θ between 0 and 2π which make :

51. Sin $\theta = -0.5$.   **52.** Cos $\theta = 0.8$.   **53.** Tan $\theta = -1.4$.

54. Cos $\theta = -0.36$. **55.** Sin $\theta = 0.6$.   **56.** Tan $\theta = 5/3$.

57. If sin $\theta = -\frac{1}{2}$, express the two values of θ between 0 and 2π as fractions of π.

58. Draw the graph of $y = \sin$ (θ radians) from $\theta = 0$ to 2π, taking values of θ at intervals of $\pi/12$. Use a scale for θ of π radians to 3 in. From your graph read off the value of sin (2 radians). [2 radians is represented on the θ scale by $\frac{2}{\pi} \times 3$ in. $= 1.91$ in.]

59. If a voltage V is given by $V = 220 \sin 400t$ after t secs., the angle being measured in radians, find V when $t = 0.001$, 0.002, 0.003, and find the two smallest values of t, which make $V = 110$.

60. A current i ampères is given by $i = I \sin 2\pi n t$, where t seconds is the time and I and n are fixed numbers. Show that the graph of i has n complete waves from $t = 0$ to $t = 1$; in other words, show that the expression makes n oscillations or cycles per second.

61. Draw the graph of $y = \cos$ (θ radians) from 0 to π. If the scale on the θ axis is changed so that π becomes $\frac{1}{2}\pi$, show that the curve is then the graph of $y = \cos$ (2θ radians).

62. A weight hanging from a spring oscillates up and down so that after t sec. it is x in. below its equilibrium position, where x is given by $x = 4 \cos (40\pi t)$ and the angle is in radians. Show that one complete oscillation from the lowest position back to the lowest position takes $\frac{1}{20}$th sec. Draw a graph showing the variation of x for one complete oscillation.

63. An alternating current is $5 \sin 40t$ ampères after t sec., the angle being measured in radians. Draw its graph from $t = 0$ to $t = \frac{1}{20}$, using values of t at intervals of 0.005 sec. How many complete oscillations does it make per sec. ?

64. Make a table of the values of cos (2θ radians) for values of θ at intervals of $\frac{\pi}{12}$ from $\theta = 0$ to $\theta = \pi$ and use the table to plot a graph. Extend this graph from $\theta = \pi$ to 2π by making use of the same table.

65. The current of the grid system makes 50 cycles or oscillations per second. What sine expression has a graph with 50 complete waves per second ? If the maximum value of the alternating current in a wave is 20 ampères, what sine expression will give the value of the current after t seconds ?

66. The frequency of an oscillation, or alternating current, is the number of oscillations or cycles per second. If the time is

t seconds and the angle is in radians, find the frequency of the following : (a) sin $20\pi t$, (b) cos $4t$, (c) sin $\frac{1}{3}t$.

67. The pitch of a musical note is the frequency of the sound oscillation, that is, the number of oscillations per sec. If the displacement of the particles of air in a sound wave is (a sin pt) centimetres after t seconds, find the value of p for the note middle C, which has a pitch of 261.

Relationship between the sine and cosine of an angle

We have already seen that in Fig. 184,

$$x^2 + y^2 = r^2.$$

Dividing by r^2

$$\frac{x^2}{r^2} + \frac{y^2}{r^2} = 1$$

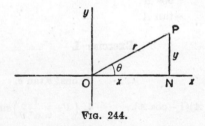

Fig. 244.

But $\dfrac{x^2}{r^2} = \left(\dfrac{x}{r}\right)^2 = (\cos \theta)^2$, which is written $\cos^2 \theta$,

and $\dfrac{y^2}{r^2} = \left(\dfrac{y}{r}\right)^2 = (\sin \theta)^2 = \sin^2 \theta.$

$$\therefore \cos^2 \theta + \sin^2 \theta = 1.$$

This identical relationship between the sine and cosine enables us to simplify an expression containing sines and cosines. For example, to simplify

$$(1 + \cos \theta)^2 + (1 + \sin \theta)^2 - 3$$

we expand the brackets by the formula for $(a + b)^2$. Then

expression $= 1 + 2 \cos \theta + \cos^2 \theta + 1 + 2 \sin \theta + \sin^2 \theta - 3.$

$\qquad = \cos^2 \theta + \sin^2 \theta - 1 + 2 \cos \theta + 2 \sin \theta.$

$\qquad = 2 \cos \theta + 2 \sin \theta,$

since $\cos^2 \theta + \sin^2 \theta = 1.$

10*

To simplify expressions containing the tangent of an angle as well as the sine and cosine we may put $\tan \theta = \sin \theta / \cos \theta$ first.

Example.—Simplify $\sin A \cos A (1 + \tan^2 A)$.

Writing $\tan A = \sin A / \cos A$,

$$\text{expression} = \sin A \cos A \left(1 + \frac{\sin^2 A}{\cos^2 A}\right)$$

$$= \sin A \cos A \left(\frac{\cos^2 A + \sin^2 A}{\cos^2 A}\right)$$

$$= \frac{\sin A \cos A}{\cos^2 A} \qquad (\text{since } \cos^2 A + \sin^2 A = 1)$$

$$= \frac{\sin A}{\cos A}$$

$$= \tan A.$$

Exercise L

Simplify :

1. $\dfrac{\sin \theta}{\tan \theta}$.

2. $\cos^2 \theta \tan \theta$.

3. $(1 + \cos A)(1 - \cos A)$.

4. $\left(1 + \dfrac{1}{\tan^2 \theta}\right) \sin^2 \theta$.

5. $(1 - \sin^2 \alpha) \tan^2 \alpha$.

6. $2 \sin \phi - \cos \phi \tan \phi$.

7. $\dfrac{\tan B (\cos B + \cos^2 B)}{\sin B}$.

8. $(1 + \sin \theta)^2 - 2 \sin \theta (1 + \sin \theta)$.

9. $\dfrac{\cos^2 \theta}{1 - \sin \theta}$.

10. $\dfrac{\tan A + \sin A}{1 + \cos A}$.

Prove that :

11. $\cos^2 \theta - \sin^2 \theta = 1 - 2 \sin^2 \theta$.

12. $(\cos x + \sin x)^2 + (\cos x - \sin x)^2 = 2$.

13. $\sin^4 \alpha + \sin^2 \alpha \cos^2 \alpha = \sin^2 \alpha$.

14. $\dfrac{1}{\cos^2 A} - 1 = \tan^2 A$.

15. $\tan B + \dfrac{1}{\tan B} = \dfrac{1}{\sin B \cos B}$.

16. $(\sin A + \cos A)^2 = 1 + 2 \sin A \cos A$.

ANSWERS

EXERCISE I (Page 5.)

1. $\frac{17}{500}, \frac{1}{2}, \frac{1}{4}, \frac{3}{4}, \frac{1}{8}, \frac{3}{8}, \frac{1}{16}, 2\frac{1}{20}, 20\frac{1}{40}, 3\frac{41}{2000}, 5\frac{9}{2000}$.
2. (i) 11, 110, 0·036, 0·020 ; (ii) 10·9, 109, 0·0364, 0·0204 (5).
3. 1·09, 0·09, 4·60, 0·01.
4. 90·34.   5. 46·83.   6. 2·936.
7. 9307 cm.   8. 15·9202 Km.   9. 2,033,770 cm.
10. 3·88 mm.   11. 17·87 cm.   12. 3·89 ft.

EXERCISE II (Page 11.)

1. 0·0280 in.   2. 0·000361.   3. 22·4.
4. 71, 87, 14.   5. £39,615, £43,214.   6. 14·0 kilowatts.
7. 50·4 h.p.   8. 1·03 Kg. per sq. cm.
9. 32·2 ft. per sec.   10. 0·914.   11. 2·54 cm.
12. 10·76.   13. 61.   14. 140 yd. 2 in.
15. 13,000 tons per sq. in.

EXERCISE III (Page 17.)

1. $3^2 \times 5 \times 7$, $3^3 \times 7^2$, 63, $3^3 \times 5 \times 7^2$.
2. $2^3 \times 5$, $2^2 \times 5^2$, $2 \times 3 \times 5$, 10, $2^3 \times 3 \times 5^2$.
3. $3^2 \times 7 \times 11$, $3^3 \times 11$, $3^2 \times 11 \times 13$, 99, $3^3 \times 7 \times 11 \times 13$.
4. $2^2 \times 11 \times 13$, $2^2 \times 5 \times 11 \times 13$, $2 \times 11^2 \times 13$, 286, $2^2 \times 5 \times 11^2 \times 13$.
5. $2^3 \times 3^2 \times 7^2$, $2^2 \times 3^3 \times 7$, $2^4 \times 3^2 \times 7$, $2^2 \times 3^2 \times 7^3$, 252, $2^4 \times 3^3 \times 7^2$.
6. $5^2 \times 7^2$, 35.   7. $2^3 \times 3^2$, 48.   8. $2^4 \times 3^2 \times 13^2$, 156.
9. $3^2 \times 5^4 \times 11^2$, 825.   10. $5^3 \times 7^3$, 35.   11. $2^9 \times 3^3$, 24.
12. $3^6 \times 5^3$, 45.   13. 4, 3.   14. 12 min.
15. 20 yd.   16. 0.   17. 41.
18. 31.   19. $6\frac{2}{11}$.   20. 1.
21. $2\frac{13}{18}$.   22. 0·015625.   23. 0·008.
24. 0·015873̇.   25. 0·0093458.   26. 5·72̇.
27. 0·714285̇.   28. 1·85.   29. 0·250.
30. 18 ft.   31. $1\frac{13}{47}$ ohms.   32. $\frac{1}{6}$, 6 min.
33. $1\frac{1}{7}$ min.   34. £1463 8s. 4d., £1829 5s. 4d., £1707 6s. 4d.

EXERCISE IV (Page 20.)

1. 73.   2. 52·6.   3. 39·04.
4. 14·87.   5. 10·09.   6. 0·186.
7. 0·0257.   8. 0·911.   9. 16·6.
10. 73·3.   11. 17·7.   12. 2·76.

13. 15·3.

14. 3·32.

15. 0·306.

16. 0·0911.

17. 1·00.

18. 0·0316.

19. 0·0379.

20. 0·0221.

21. 6·4 cm.

22. 2510 yd.

23. 4927 lb. per sq. in.

24. 0·06 ohms.

25. 0·88 in.

26. 1·8 sec.

27. 6·8 cm.

28. 3·40.

29. $22\frac{1}{2}$.

30. 1 ft. 9 in.

EXERCISE V (Page 25.)

1. 176, 1250 yd.

2. 12·7 yd.

3. 61·5.

4. 29·32.

5. £42.

6. $92\frac{4}{9}$ lb., 39 lb. copper, 21 lb. zinc, 65 per cent. copper, 35 per cent zinc.

7. 60 per cent.

8. 3200 acres.

9. 1s. 1d. per gal.

10. $2\frac{1}{4}$ hr.

11. £66 13s. 4d., £66 13s. 4d., £100, £66, 13s. 4d.

12. $3\frac{1}{2}$.

13. $1\frac{9}{16}$ per cent.

14. 34·39 per cent.

15. $23\frac{1}{4}$ per cent, £26, £20.

16. 0·38 per cent., 398 yd. 1 ft. 5 in.

17. 1·60 per cent.

18. 4·96 per cent.

19. 0·74 per cent.

20. B, 3·9 per cent, £3 17s. 0d.

21. £560, £500.

EXERCISE VI (Page 31.)

1. (a) xy sq. ft., (b) $3ab$ sq. ft., (c) $6ac$ sq. ft., (d) $\frac{pq}{10}$ sq. cm.

2. $3n$ pence.

3. (i) $\frac{x}{3}$ sh., (ii) $\frac{dx}{12}$ sh.

4. $6s$ ft., (i) $\frac{s}{10}$ ft. per min., (ii) $\frac{s}{600}$ ft. per sec.

5. (i) $3t$ sec., (ii) $\frac{5t}{s}$ min., (i) $\frac{s}{t}$ ft. per sec., (ii) $\frac{15s}{22t}$ ml. per hr.

6. (i) nc in., (ii) $\frac{nc}{12}$ ft.

7. $45t$ ml.

8. 3·3 kilowatts.

9. 0·43 amp.

10. 3·63 Kg.

11. 135.

12. 5·0.

EXERCISE VII (Page 34.)

1. $(p+2)$ lb.

2. (i) $\frac{£3q-3p}{5}$, (ii) $\frac{(q-p)\,100}{p}$ per cent.

3. $(6l-b)$ yd.

4. $\left(x+\frac{y}{3}\right)$ sh.

5. (i) $(k-4)$ gal., (ii) $\left(k-\frac{n}{25}\right)$ gal., $25k$ ml.

6. $\left(l-\frac{wx}{20}\right)$ cm.

7. $(pa+9b)$ sh.

8. $\left(\frac{1}{a}+\frac{1}{b}\right)$ hr.

9. $C=\frac{6a+(n-6)s}{20}$, 2·7.

10. $S=10+5t$.

11. $\left(1+\dfrac{m}{4}\right)$ pence.   **12.** $(y-x)$ lb., $\dfrac{x+y}{2}$ lb., $\dfrac{y-x}{n}$ lb.

13. $\left(26+\dfrac{n}{12}\right)$ sh., $C=26+\dfrac{x}{12}$.   **14.** $\left(\dfrac{11}{6}p-x\right)$ sh.

EXERCISE VIII (Page 37.)

1. $3a$.
2. $5p$.
3. $4f$.
4. $5b^2$.
5. $6xy$.
6. $18x-11$.
7. $32y+5$.
8. $23c+2$.
9. 13.

10. $3yz+5$.
11. $\dfrac{3p}{8}$.
12. $\dfrac{C}{15}$.

13. $\dfrac{15l}{8}$.
14. $\dfrac{67cd}{14}$.
15. $72\,ab$ sq. in.

16. £325a.
17. $3 \cdot 71a^2$ sq. cm.
18. $\dfrac{3s}{2}$ sh.

EXERCISE IX (Page 40.)

1. $x=4$.
2. $t=3$.
3. $z=2$.
4. $s=2\frac{1}{4}$.
5. $y=2\frac{1}{4}$.
6. $p=1\frac{1}{3}$.
7. $l=2$.
8. $u=9$.
9. $r=6$.
10. $d=17 \cdot 6$.
11. $h=22\frac{1}{2}$.
12. $x=\frac{1}{2}$.
13. $y=4\frac{5}{13}$.
14. $q=0$.
15. $k=1$.
16. £4 10s. 0d., £3 10s. 0d.
17. 15, 12, 10 in.
18. £275.
19. 20 m.p.h., 50 m.p.h.
20. 65 m.p.h., 55 m.p.h.
21. 21 per cent.
22. $34\frac{8}{13}$ in.
23. 32°, 212° 131° F., 15° C.
24. $14 \cdot 18$.
25. $1 \cdot 74$.
26. $2 \cdot 73$.
27. 40 ft. per sec.

EXERCISE X (Page 45.)

1. -15.
2. -15.
3. -15.
4. -31.
5. 6.
6. 6.
7. -8.
8. -20.
9. 12.
10. 16.
11. -4.
12. 1.
13. $-15x$.
14. $-15x$.
15. $-18x$.
16. $-17x$.
17. $6x$.
18. $6x$.
19. $-8a$.
20. $-6a$.
21. $12x$.
22. $16y$.
23. $9z$.
24. $-3c$.
25. $-9a$.
26. $9y$.
27. $-3t$.
28. $-3a$.
29. $-7z$.
30. $-13z$.
31. $-10s$.
32. $-18s$.
33. -2.
34. -5.
35. -10.
36. 5.
37. $3x$.
38. $-3x$.
39. $-5x$.
40. $-4x$.
41. -2.
42. 14.
43. -14.
44. 2.
45. $3x$.
46. $-11y$.
47. $11t$.
48. $-3t$.
49. $-3°$.
50. $+36$ min., -13 min., -30 min., $+6$ min.
51. Stone rises for 2 sec. and then falls.
52. £$(300+15n)$, £225.
53. 18 ft. per sec., -14 ft. per sec.
54. Profit £600, loss £100.
55. 320 ft., -40 ft.
56. 12.33 p.m., 11.55 a.m.

EXERCISE XI (Page 49.)

1. -56.	**2.** -56.	**3.** 56.	**4.** 56.
5. 3.	**6.** $-\frac{5}{2}$.	**7.** -60.	**8.** 240.
9. -3.	**10.** -2.	**11.** 2.	**12.** 2.
13. 3.	**14.** $-\frac{1}{3}$.	**15.** 1.	**16.** -16.
17. -1.	**18.** 2.	**19.** $-xy$.	**20.** $-a^2b$.
21. $21s$.	**22.** $-12pt$.	**23.** $-6abc$.	**24.** $-8a^2b$.
25. $1\frac{3}{4}mnp$.	**26.** $2x$.	**27.** $2ab$.	**28.** $-4\dfrac{pq}{r}$.
29. $-\dfrac{2ab}{c}$.	**30.** $\dfrac{lmn}{4}$.		

EXERCISE XII (Page 53.)

1. $4a$.	**2.** $-10t$.	**3.** $-9p^2$.
4. $3xy$.	**5.** $2a^2b$.	**6.** $-8abc$.
7. $-9pq$.	**8.** 0.	**9.** $4a-3b$.
10. $-2a-3b-8c$.	**11.** $2ab+bc$.	**12.** $-4p^2-2p-5$.
13. $-3a-4b-5c$.	**14.** $2x^3+6xy^2$.	**15.** $-9a-10ab+9abc$.
16. $5z^3-5z+12$.	**17.** $4a$.	**18.** $-2a-b$.
19. $-9p^2$.	**20.** $6t^2-6t$.	**21.** $-2a+11b+4c$.
22. 0.	**23.** $-2xy+6x+3y$.	**24.** $-x^3-2x-3$.
25. $3m+n$.	**26.** $p-9q+10r$.	**27.** $-3a+3b-3c$.
28. $2p$.	**29.** $-a^2+ab+2a$.	**30.** $-14x^2$.
31. 0.	**32.** $-3p^2-q^2+3p-2q$.	

33. $l^2-2m^2+6n^3-5mn$.

34. $-b^2c+bc^2-c^2a+ca^2-a^2b+ab^2$.

35. $-2x^2-2$.	**36.** $-6p^2-5pq-4q^2$	**37.** $2x^2-10x-2$.
38. $-5x^2+2x-13$.	**39.** $-13a^2+17a+b$.	**40.** $2zx$.
41. $4u^3+2ab-7ac$.	**42.** $-20k^2m+k^2n$.	**43.** $3a+2b-4c$.
44. $-2p^2+9p-2$.	**45.** $-2b^2-2c^2$.	**46.** $2c$.
47. $-p-q+r$.	**48.** $5x^2+2x+10$.	**49.** $-3yz+2zx-5xy$.
50. $-2a+2b-2c$.	**51.** $3a^3-ab$.	**52.** $-lm$.
53. $25\cdot57a^2$ sq. in., $159\cdot8$ sq. in.		**54.** $a^2+ab+ac$ sq. in.
55. $(2l+n)t$ sq. in., $\frac{22}{90}$ sq. ft.		**56.** $8a^2$ sq. in.
57. $1797\frac{5}{7}$ sq. cm.	**58.** $33\frac{33}{50}$ sq. in.	

EXERCISE XIII (Page 57.)

1. x^2yz.	**2.** $20abc^2d$.	**3.** $42a^3b^3$.
4. $\frac{3}{2}p^3q^3$.	**5.** $6l^2m^2n^3$.	**6.** $2r^3s^2t^2$.
7. $-2al^2m+3blm^2$.	**8.** $-12x^3y^2+8x^2y-16xy^2$.	
9. $-a^3b+2ab^3$.	**10.** $2c$.	**11.** $2a$.
12. $\frac{3}{2}pq$.	**13.** $\frac{4}{3}st$.	**14.** $15e$.
15. $2y$.	**16.** $4a^2b^2c$.	**17.** $-p+2q$.
18. $-2a+5b+3c$.	**19.** $-2x^2+4x+3$.	**20.** $-5x-4y+1$.
21. $4a-2b+3c$.	**22.** $2l-\dfrac{m}{3}$.	**23.** $-\frac{2}{7}f+\frac{3}{7}g+h$.

24. $3x - 1\frac{1}{2}y + \frac{2}{3}z$. **25.** $a, 10ab$. **26.** $5pq, 15p^2q$.

27. $6xz, 36x^2yz$. **28.** $abc, 60a^2b^2c^3$. **29.** $2, 12xy^2$.

30. $5p, 10p^2q$. **31.** $2, 42r^2s^2$. **32.** $3bc, 18a^2b^2cd^2$.

33. $\dfrac{17a}{60}$. **34.** $-\dfrac{p}{q}$. **35.** $-\dfrac{9}{2x}$.

36. $\dfrac{5}{4y}$. **37.** $\dfrac{20v - 6u}{15uv}$. **38.** $\dfrac{9a^2 - 5b^2}{6ab}$.

39. $\dfrac{3a - 8b}{30b}$. **40.** $\dfrac{10ac - 3b}{5c}$. **41.** $\dfrac{-72p - 3q + 10}{36}$.

42. $\dfrac{2a^2 - 3b^2 - 4c^2}{abc}$. **43.** $\dfrac{-12x^2 - 3y^2 + 10z^2}{18xyz}$.

44. $\dfrac{3x + 5}{12}$. **45.** $\dfrac{3p - 6}{10}$. **46.** $\dfrac{-p^2 + 2pq - 2q^2}{6pq}$.

47. $\dfrac{7x - 11}{12}$. **48.** $\dfrac{12x - 11}{30}$. **49.** $\dfrac{3x^2 - 6x + 10}{12x}$.

50. $\dfrac{x + 1}{6}$. **51.** $\dfrac{4x - 1}{24}$. **52.** $\dfrac{x - 12}{30}$.

53. $\dfrac{-17}{36}$. **54.** $\dfrac{-5x + 12}{42}$. **55.** $\dfrac{-17x - 2}{60}$.

56. $\dfrac{45}{p}$ hr. **57.** $\dfrac{2ab}{a + b}$ ml. per hr. **58.** $\dfrac{17x}{12}, \dfrac{10}{17x}$ hr.

59. $\dfrac{5}{2x}, \dfrac{2ax}{5}$ sec. **60.** $100\left\{\dfrac{p + 2q}{a + 2b} - 1\right\}, 33\frac{13}{14}$ per cent.

61. $\dfrac{gr - g - r + 1}{gr}$. **62.** $\dfrac{11na}{200} + \dfrac{11c}{10}, \dfrac{1{,}000na}{11(na + 20c)}$ per cent.

EXERCISE XIV (Page 62.)

1. $x = -1$. **2.** $y = 3$. **3.** $r = 0$.

4. $p = -2\frac{1}{2}$. **5.** $a = 3\frac{2}{3}$. **6.** $x = 2\frac{1}{7}$.

7. $t = 1\frac{1}{3}$. **8.** $s = -5$. **9.** $a = 17$.

10. $b = -3$. **11.** $x = \frac{1}{3}$. **12.** $k = -\frac{1}{76}$.

13. $r = -3\frac{4}{5}$. **14.** $k = 7$. **15.** $l = 5\frac{5}{6}$.

16. $c = 12$. **17.** $d = -1\frac{3}{24}$. **18.** $f = -2 \cdot 24$.

19. $1\frac{11}{16}$ in. **20.** $10\frac{1}{2}$. **21.** $2 \cdot 14$.

22. 7. **23.** $1\frac{2}{3}$. **24.**

25. 80 men, 160 women. **26.** 75 ml. **27.** 40 steps, 40 sec.

28. $12s$. **29.** $\frac{1}{2}$ ml., $\frac{2}{3}$ ml.

30. $59 \cdot 73$ c.c. copper, $40 \cdot 27$ c.c. zinc.

EXERCISE XV (Page 66.)

1. $\dfrac{5}{l}$. **2.** $\frac{5}{8}k$. **3.** $C = \dfrac{5F - 160}{9}, 100$.

4. $R = \dfrac{V}{I}, V = IR$. **5.** $R_3 = \dfrac{R_1R_4}{R_2}, R_4 = \dfrac{R_2R_3}{R_1}, 18$.

6. $h = \dfrac{3l + c}{8}$. **7.** $5, h = \dfrac{s}{2\pi r} - r$. **8.** $a = \dfrac{bW}{W - 2EP}$.

9. $r = \dfrac{mu^2}{T + 5mg}$.

10. $b = \dfrac{(n-2)a}{n}$, $a = \dfrac{nb}{n-2}$.

11. $t = \dfrac{pv - 273k}{k}$.

12. $7\frac{1}{2}$, $s = \dfrac{rR}{r-R}$.

13. $k = \dfrac{(W+w)lr}{fw}$, $r = \dfrac{kfw}{(W+w)l}$.

14. $\dfrac{4}{3}$, $C = \dfrac{(I+M)r}{Ir+M}$, $r = \dfrac{Mc}{M+I-Ic}$.

15. $k = \dfrac{v(r-u)}{u(r-v)}$, $u = \dfrac{rv}{kr+v-kv}$, $v = \dfrac{kru}{r+ku-u}$.

EXERCISE XVI (Page 71.)

1. $x=1$, $y=2$.   **2.** $a=4$, $b=-2$.   **3.** $p=-2\frac{1}{2}$, $q=-1$.
4. $r=0$, $s=-1\frac{1}{2}$.   **5.** $l=-21\frac{1}{4}$, $m=-1\frac{1}{4}$.
6. $c=-3$, $d=4$.   **7.** $p=-5$, $q=8$.   **8.** $x=2\frac{1}{2}$, $y=-1\frac{1}{2}$.
9. $y=-5$, $z=1$.   **10.** $p=9$, $q=-5$.   **11.** $x=2$, $y=4$.
12. $a=\frac{2}{3}$, $b=\frac{1}{2}$.   **13.** $C=19\cdot4$, $k=0\cdot05$, $19\cdot95$ in., 12 lb.
14. 167° F.   **15** $9\cdot05$, $5\cdot26$.
16. $a=20$, $b=300$, $2\frac{3}{4}$ ml.   **17.** $R_0=15$, $a=0\cdot006$, 80° C.
18. 36.   **19.** 55.   **20.** 4.
21. $x=2\cdot2$, $y=3\cdot4$.   **22.** $x=2$, $y=3$.   **23.** $70s.$, $35s.$
24. 4 in., 6 in.

EXERCISE XVII (Page 80.)

5. $4s.$ $9d.$ **6.** 33 lb. per sq. in., 3 min. 20 sec.
7. $20\cdot7$ m.p.h., $10\cdot4$ knots.   **8.** $2\cdot4$ per cent., $24\cdot6^\circ$
9. $80\cdot8$ per cent.   **10.** $18\cdot5$ ohms.   **11.** $5\cdot6$ lb.
12. $1\cdot8$ foot-candles.   **13.** $87\cdot25$ per cent, 440 volts.
14. $18\cdot35$ lb., $2\frac{1}{8}$ in.   **15.** £11 $15s.$ $0d.$ **16.** $4\cdot09$.
17. 113 amp.   **18.** 435 h.p., 1960.   **19.** 3 yrs.

EXERCISE XVIII (Page 87.)

1. $P=0\cdot12W+4$.   **2.** $P=0\cdot05W+8$.   **3.** $W=7\cdot92\,P-211\cdot6$.
4. $n=0\cdot18t+11\cdot73$.   **5.** $p=1\cdot76t+1\cdot62$ **6.** $I=712\cdot5A+58\cdot75$
7. $N=7\cdot65V-23$.   **8.** $I=\dfrac{10}{R}$.   **9.** $pv=1,500$.

10. $\dfrac{1}{u}+\dfrac{1}{v}=\dfrac{1}{12}$.   **11.** $l=10\cdot92\sqrt{T}+1\cdot66$.

EXERCISE XIX (Page 92.)

1. $1\cdot54$, $4\cdot67$.   **2.** $0\cdot27$, $0\cdot55$.   **3.** $0\cdot41$, $0\cdot24$.
5. 3240, 5760.   **6.** $2\frac{1}{2}$ sec., $3\cdot54$ sec.   **9.** $7\cdot66$ sec.
10. $5\cdot88$; $0\cdot92$, $3\cdot46$; $6\cdot16$ cu. ft.   **17.** 1; $3\cdot73$; $0\cdot27$.

18. 1·1, 3·3, 4·5.   **19.** 25.
20. (a) 5·59 in., (b) 4·47 in.   **21.** 0·44, 5·77, 522 cu. in.
22. 0·56, 4·44, 5 sec.   **23.** 36·6 sec.   **25.** 0·037 in.

EXERCISE XX (Page 103.)

4. 2, $\frac{3}{4}$ ml.   **6.** 10°.   **8.** 2$\frac{1}{2}$ sec.
9. 3·33 ; rod in compression.   **10.** ±3·46.
11. 1·56, −2·56.   **12.** 16.   **13.** −1·14.
21. −0·28, 0·94 ; 7·6, 3·2.   **23.** −13° F.
25. $x=1$, $y=2$; $a=4$, $b=-2$; $p=-2\frac{1}{2}$, $q=-1$; $r=0$, $s=-1\frac{1}{2}$.
26. 21·2 ml., 9·41 a.m.   **27.** 48 ml. from Marylebone, 9.48 a.m.
28. Max. 2.   **29.** Max. 2, Min. −2. **30.** Max. 100.
31. Max. 4$\frac{1}{2}$.   **32.** Max. 8, Min. 0.
33. (a) 15·6 ft., (b) 72·8 ft.
34. (a) 6·16, 0·96 ; (b) 1, −4 ; (c) 0·56, −3·56 ; (d) 6·25.
35. ±3·72 ; 3·75 in.   **37.** 45.   **38.** $a=-0·4$, $b=2·2$.
39. $x+y+7=0$.   **40.** (1·29, 2·71), (2·71, 1·29)
41. (2, 5).   **42.** (2·30, −0·99), (−1·80, 1·74).

EXERCISE XXI (Page 111.)

1. 10^8.   **2.** 10^{12}.   **3.** 10^3.   **4.** 10^6.   **5.** 10^3.   **6.** 10^9.
7. 10^2.   **8.** 10^{-6}.   **9.** $10^{2\frac{1}{2}}$.   **10.** $10^{-2\frac{1}{2}}$. **11.** $10^{\frac{1}{2}}$. **12.** $10^{1\frac{1}{2}}$.
13. $10^{\frac{1}{2}}$.   **14.** 10^1.   **15.** 10^1.   **16.** 10^3.   **17.** 10^1.   **18.** 10^0.
19. $10^{-4\frac{1}{2}}$. **20.** $10^{-3\frac{1}{2}}$. **21.** a^8.   **22.** b^{12}.   **23.** 1.   **24.** $x^{2\frac{1}{2}}$.
25. p^2.   **26.** C^{-2}.   **27.** $y^{-2\frac{1}{2}}$. **28.** $y^{4\frac{1}{2}}$. **29.** $y^{\frac{1}{2}}$. **30.** a.
31. a.   **32.** a^3.   **33.** 3.   **34.** 2.   **35.** 4.   **36.** 1.
37. 3.   **38.** $16^{\frac{1}{2}}$.   **39.** $16^{\frac{1}{2}}$.   **40.** 16^3.   **41.** $16^{\frac{3}{4}}$.   **42.** $16^{\frac{3}{4}}$.
43. $10^{3·3}$.   **44.** $10^{2·7}$.   **45.** $10^{0·9}$.   **46.** 10.   **47.** $10^{1·5}$.   **48.** $10^{\frac{2}{3}}$.
49. $10^{·3}$.   **50.** $10^{1\frac{1}{3}}$.   **51.** $10^{\frac{2}{3}}$.   **52.** $10^{\frac{15}{6}}$.
53. $\sqrt{\dfrac{A}{4\pi}}$.   **54.** $\sqrt[3]{\dfrac{3v}{4\pi}}$.   **55.** $l=\dfrac{gt^2}{4\pi^2}$.   **56.** $b=\sqrt{a^2-\dfrac{A}{\pi}}$.
57. $\sqrt[3]{a^3-\dfrac{3v}{4\pi}}$. **58.** $\sqrt{\dfrac{a}{s+b}}$. **59.** $\sqrt{\dfrac{s^2}{\pi^2 r^2}-r^2}$. **60.** $\sqrt{\dfrac{ght^2}{4\pi^2}-h^2}$.

EXERCISE XXII (Page 117.)

1. (i) 2·83, 6·96, 13·00 ; (ii) 2·51, 3, 3·32, 3·86.
2. 0·3701, 1·699, 1·2319, 2·6321, 3·8034, 4·7621.
3. 1·939, 2·705, 28·36, 100·2, 2822, 61550.
4. 792·1.   **5.** 5093.   **6.** 1654.   **7.** 3·280.
8. 118·0.   **9.** 1·269.   **10.** 149·2.   **11.** 7·911.
12. 194·3.   **13.** 21·24.   **14.** 34900.   **15.** 1334.
16. 1·493.   **17.** 975400.   **18.** 1115.   **19.** 389·5.
20. 11·70.

EXERCISE XXIII (Page 120.)

1. 1·725. **2.** 67·80. **3.** 2·991. **4.** 4·641.
5. 14·09. **6.** 3·429. **7.** 0·3541. **8.** 5·263.
9. 18·08. **10.** 0·1728. **11.** 241·5 sq. in. **12.** 292·5 H.P.
13. 105 sq. ft., 101·1 cu. ft. **14.** 3·10 ft. **15.** 3·17 ohms.
16. 2100 cu. in. **17.** 124·3 lb. wt. **18.** 107·8 m.p.h.
19. 59·87 sq. in. **20.** 5·978 cm. **21.** 1·801 in.
22. 2422 cu. in. **23.** 18·84. **24.** 5·357 in.
25. 5·996 in. **26.** 0·364 m.

EXERCISE XXIV (Page 124.)

1. 17·18. **2.** 0·4317. **3.** 24·83. **4.** 1·817.
5. 0·9317. **6.** 4·697. **7.** 0·6561. **8.** 0·7698.
9. 0·6580. **10.** 0·2695. **11.** 2·809. **12.** 0·8030.
13. 187·1 lb. **14.** 89·06 in. lb. **15.** 3·009. **16.** 469·8 lb.
17. 0·1878 **18.** 0·5066 in. **19.** 21·48. **20.** 23·35.
21. 0·2701 cm. **22.** 0·9652 cm. **23.** 0·545 sec. **24.** 113·1.
25. 3·109.

EXERCISE XXV (Page 135.)

1. l^2+5l+6. **2.** a^2+3a+2. **3.** $x^2+16x+63$.
4. x^2+4x-5. **5.** $t^2-15t+44$. **6.** $6y^2-y-1$.
7. $p^2+pq-2q^2$. **8.** $6x^2+19xy-7y^2$. **9.** $8-2x-15x^2$.
10. $8-14t+3t^2$. **11.** $a^2+8a+12$. **12.** $6x^2+11x+4$.
13. $2l^2+lm-m^2$. **14.** $2-6y+4y^2$. **15.** p^3-4q^2.
16. $6t^3+t\mathrm{T}-\mathrm{T}^2$. **17.** $x^2+4xy+4y^2$. **18.** $4l^2-20lm+25m^2$.
19. $z^2-12z+36$. **20.** $1+6k+9k^2$. **21.** t^4+2t^2+1.
22. $x-4\sqrt{x}+4$. **23.** $4x^3-y^3$. **24.** a^3-49b^2.
25. $(x-4)$. **26.** $(2y-3x)$. **37.** $(a+b)$.
28. $(x-2l)$. **29.** $(\mathrm{R}+r)$. **30.** $(x+5)$.
31. $(x-2)$. **32.** $(k+1)$. **33.** $(\mathrm{T}-5)$.
34. $t(t+3)$. **35.** $l(l-m)$. **36.** $p^2(2p^2+q^2)$.
37. $x^2y(x-y)$. **38.** $3bc(2a-3c)$. **39.** $kl(4+5l^2)$.
40. $(x+1)(x+3)$. **41.** $(t+1)(t+6)$. **42.** $(l+2)(l+5)$.
43. $(p+3)(p+5)$. **44.** $(p+1)(p+15)$. **45.** $(x+3)(x+4)$.
46. $(p-1)(p-2)$. **47.** $(x-1)(x-10)$. **48.** $(x-2)(x-5)$.
49. $(y-2)(y-6)$. **50.** $(y-3)(y-4)$. **51.** $(k-4)(k-9)$.
52. $(x+1)(x-2)$. **53.** $(y+2)(y-5)$. **54.** $(t+1)(t-6)$.
55. $(t+2)(t-3)$. **56.** $(m+3)(m-4)$. **57.** $(m+2)(m-6)$.
58. l. **59.** $\dfrac{1}{t}$. **60.** $\dfrac{x}{x+1}$.
61. $\dfrac{l-m}{l+m}$. **62.** $\dfrac{x-1}{x+2}$. **63.** $\dfrac{y-4}{y+1}$.
64. $\dfrac{m-n}{m}$. **65.** $\dfrac{8}{k+3}$. **66.** $x=5$ or -1.

67. $x = -1$ or -5. **68.** $x = 5$ or -2. **69.** $t = 1$ or -11.
70. $l = 8$ or -2. **71.** $k = 2$ or -1. **72.** $m = \pm 3$.
73. $x = 5$ or 0. **74.** $x = -2$ or -5. **75.** 5 in., 3 in.
76. (i) 10 ; (ii) 20. **77.** 4. **78.** 1.
79. See Answers of 66, 67, 68, 69.
80. $-1 \pm \sqrt{15} = 2\cdot873$ or $-3\cdot873$. **81.** $2 \pm \sqrt{3} = 3\cdot732$ or $0\cdot268$.
82. $21 \pm \sqrt{591} = 45\cdot315$ or $-3\cdot315$.
83. $-14 \pm \sqrt{250} = 1\cdot810$ or $-29\cdot810$.
84. $20 - \sqrt{40} = 13\cdot68$. **85.** 115.
86. $9 \pm \sqrt{61} = 16\cdot810$ or $1\cdot180$. **87.** $\dfrac{r^2}{4h}$.

88. 1. **89.** $\dfrac{a^2 + b^2}{b^2}$. **90.** $\frac{1}{4}x^2$.

EXERCISE XXVI (Page 143.)

1. $5l = 7m$, 6. **2.** $\frac{6}{11}$, 4. **3.** $1\frac{1}{4}$ in., $\frac{1}{6}$ in., $\dfrac{n}{4}$ in.

4. $3h = 4b$, 4. **5.** $\frac{2}{5}$. **6.** $\dfrac{W_2 l}{W_1 + W_2}$ in., $\dfrac{W_1 l}{W + W_2}$ in.

7. 7 : 1, $\dfrac{n}{p-q}$. **8.** $(a-b)$ in., $(la + mb)$ in. **9.** $\frac{1}{14}$.

10. n^3, n^2. **11.** $\dfrac{kl - 1}{kl}$. **12.** $y = \frac{4}{5}x$.

13. $i = \frac{3}{46}V$, 6·52, 13·04, 16·30. **14.** $F = 0\cdot28W$, 28, 56, 84.

15. $x = \dfrac{W}{150}$, 0·137 in. **16.** $d = 0\cdot012W$.

17. $E = \frac{4}{2025}f^2$, 0·078, 0·126, 0·227. **18.** $pV = 8,000$, 53·3, 80, 160.

19. $v = 8\sqrt{s}$, 39·2, 50·6, 59·9. **20.** $V = \frac{85}{6}\sqrt{h}$.

21. $y = \frac{5}{4}x^3$, 4·31. **23.** $y = 4x^2$, 49.

24. $T = 0\cdot32\sqrt{l}$, 9·77.

EXERCISE XXVII (Page 150.)

23. Square pyramid 5, 5, 8 ; tetrahedron 4, 4, 6 ; house 7, 10, 15 ;
pencil 8, 12, 18 ; octahedron 8, 6, 12.

EXERCISE XXVIII (Page 157.)

1. Sum $= 180°$. **2.** $A\hat{C}D = \hat{A} + \hat{B}$.
3. 540°, 45°. **4.** $2\cdot12\frac{1}{2}$.
5. 279 yd., N. 36·8° E. **6.** 3·6 ml., S. 63·7° E.
7. 60°, 3 in., 3 in. **8.** 90°.

EXERCISE XXIX (Page 162.)

1. Coincident. **3.** $a + \beta + \gamma = 360°$.

EXERCISE XXX (Page 168.)

3. 49°. **4.** (i) No ; (ii) Yes. **5.** 110° ; Yes.
6. 90°, 45°, 45°. **7.** (i) $128\frac{4}{7}°$; (ii) 140°. **8.** 36°.
10. 34°, 53°, 93°. **11.** 80°. **12.** $A = B = C = 135°$, $D = E = 67\frac{1}{2}°$.

EXERCISE XXXI (Page 174.)

1–7. Sum=180°.

8. Impossible ; $BC > CA + AB$.

9. Impossible ; BC too short.

10. Possible.

11. Impossible ; Size unknown.

16. 4·9.

17. 72·1 ml., N. 61·1³ W.

18. 68 m.p.h., 140 m.p.h.

19. 69 yd.

20. 14 ft. 2 in.

21. 18 ft. 4 in.

22. 9·6°.

23. 32·8 ft.

EXERCISE XXXII (Page 183.)

9. 120° ; 1·39 in., 2·88 in.

11. Ratio=2 : 1.

12. Concurrent.

13. Touches sides.

14. Passes through ABC.

15. Concurrent.

16. Yes.

18. 45°, 60°.

26. All children are boys under eight. Untrue.

27. All Europeans are Englishmen. Untrue.

28. If one angle of a quadrilateral is known the other three angles are known. Untrue.

29. If the area of a rectangle is 12 sq. in. its sides are 3 in. and 4 in. Untrue.

30. If the four angles of a quadrilateral are equal it is a square. Untrue.

31. If a man earns two pounds a week he is a good engineer. Untrue.

32. All engines which can develop more than 10 horse-power are in new Rolls-Royce cars. Untrue.

33. All triangles with two equal angles are isosceles. True.

EXERCISE XXXIII (Page 190.)

1. 9·1 cm.

2. (i) 21 sq. cm. ; (ii) 3·5 cm. ; (iii) 4·58 cm.

3. 8·1 sq. in.

4. 22,650 sq. yd.

5. 77,440 sq. yd.

6. 6·08 cm.

7. 2·51 in. or 5·45 in.

8. 5·77 cm.

9. Yes.

10. 14·5 cm., 210 sq. cm.

11. $17\frac{3}{4}$ ft.

12. 82 ml.

13. 2·8 in.

14. 6·5 ft.

21. Obtuse.

22. Acute.

23. $6\frac{2}{3}$ cm

EXERCISE XXXIV (Page 197.)

1. Concentric circle of half radius.

2. Squares sides 2 in., 4 in.

3. (i) Two parallel lines ; (ii) Surface of cylinder.

4. Straight line parallel to ground.

5. Circle concentric with fixed circle.

6. Circle.

7. Two vertical tangents and two semi-circles.

8. Circle, line.

9. Parallel line.

10. Horizontal line midway between bars.
11. Circle.
12. A curve on a cylinder.
13. AB subtends angle of 60° at point.
16. An ellipse is obtained by reducing every half-chord perpendicular to a diameter of a circle in the same ratio.

EXERCISE XXXV (Page 203.)

6. 82°, 47°.   7. A 75°, C 105°, D 74°.
8. A 103°, B 108°, C 77°, D 72°.   9. B 90°, C 67$\frac{1}{2}$°, G 22$\frac{1}{2}$°.
14. Arcs of two circles, one on each side of line.
15. Arcs of two circles, one on each side of line.

EXERCISE XXXVI (Page 208.)

2. T 10°, A 135°, C 35°.   3. P 78°, Q 86°, R 16°.   4. C 112°, D 68°.

EXERCISE XXXVII (Page 212.)

2. $2AY=2AZ=$perimeter.   4. 5 in.
5. $\widehat{A}+\widehat{C}=180°$.   6. $AB+DC=AD+BC$.
7. Yes; $AB+DC=AD+BC$.   8. 8·8 cm.
10. 12 cm.   12. 12 cm.

18. Arc of circle any point of which subtends angle of $90°+\dfrac{A}{2}$ at base.

EXERCISE XXXVIII (Page 218.)

2. 227·6 sq. ft., 375,000.   3. 123 sq. yd.
4. 2,770 cm. gm.   5. 1,600 ft.
6. 407 cu. ft.   7. 10·7 sq. ft., 22·6 cu. ft.

EXERCISE XXXIX (Page 224.)

1. 256 lb.   2. 8 ft.   3. 22·9.
4. 186·7.   5. 3 ft. 10 in.   6. 40·3 in.
7. 0·0754 ton.   8. 54·6 sq. ft.   9. 75·4 tons.
10. 9·12 in.   11. 2·76 in.   12. 2·27 sq. ft.
13. 21·99 sq. in.   14. 7$\frac{1}{2}$ oz.   15. 44·1 gm.
16. 5·79 in.   17. 226 sq. in. ; 339 sq. in.
18. 1361 tons.   19. 67,500 galls.
20. 366·6 sq. ft., 1,001 cu. ft.   21. 46·8 cu. ft.
22. 8·15 ft. per sec.   23. 15·8 (5) lb.   24. 17·1 cwt.
25. 0·316 cm.   26. 2·91 ft.
27. 60 sq. in., 363·6 cu. in.   28. 1,976 lb.
29. 0·869 oz.   30. 5·17 cm.
31. 1$\frac{3}{4}$ in., 4·71 in., 13·7 cu. in.   32. 63·23 sq. in.
33. ——.   34. 113 sq. in.

EXERCISE XL (Page 230.)

2. 0·262.
3. 1·745.
4. 45° 50'.
5. 87° 5'.
6. 0·749 rad.
8. 0·314 rad.

9. $\frac{2}{3}, \frac{3}{4}, \frac{4}{5}$.
10. $\frac{\pi n}{30}$ rad.
12. $\frac{\pi}{3}$.

13. $\frac{v}{a}$.
14. 81° 51'. 1·429.

EXERCISE XLI (Page 238.)

1. 0·64, 1·29, 1·93, 2·57 in.
2. 1·67 in.
3. 0·0698, 0·7314, 0·9781.
4. 546 yd.
5. 1·39 cm., 26·2 cm. per sec.
6. 4·54 in.
7. 16·9 in.
8. 4·59 in.
9. 11·47 lb.-wt. in.
10. 0·9796, 0·281, 0·6674.
11. 0·256, 0·9878, 0·8541.
12. 7·775 in.
13. 53·3 yd.
14. (a) 28° 16' ; (b) 45° 38'.
15. (a) 84° 42' ; (b) 9° 37'.
16. 34° 14'.
17. 27° 49'.
18. 10° 29' ; 90·9 yd.
19. 1·67 in., 80° 27'.
20. $\bar{1}$·5999, $\bar{1}$·9965, $\bar{1}$·8359.
21. $\bar{2}$·9842, $\bar{1}$·9498, $\bar{1}$·5174.
22. (a) 15° 27' ; (b) 69° 14'.
23. (a) 72° 12' ; (b) 30° 34'.
24. 41·3 ft.
25. 31° 54'.
26. 1,014 yd.
27. 9·006 in.
28. 42° 30'.

EXERCISE XLII (Page 243.)

1. 0·83, 1·66, 2·49, 3·32 in.
2. 1·590 in.
3. $\frac{AB}{AC}, <1$.
4. 0·5793, 0·9383, 0·1829.
5. 0·1036, 0·9880, 0·9673.
6. 5·31 ft.
7. 6·82 ml.
8. (a) 24° 36' ; (b) 79° 6'.
9. (a) 74° 47' ; (b) 44° 47'.
10. 70° 32'.
11. $\bar{1}$·8169, $\bar{1}$·9759, $\bar{1}$·4833.
12. (a) 49° 48' ; (b) 31° 57'.
13. 15° 36'.
14. 78° 16'.
15. (a) 2·237 in. ; (b) 1·251 in.
17. (a) 0·8776 ; (b) 0·3624.
18. 70·71, 50
19. 0·927, 1·445.

EXERCISE XLIII (Page 247.)

1. $\frac{12}{13}, \frac{5}{13}$.
2. $\frac{8}{\sqrt{89}}, \frac{5}{\sqrt{89}}$.
3. $\frac{2\sqrt{6}}{7}, \frac{5}{7}$.

4. $\frac{2}{5}, \frac{\sqrt{21}}{5}$.
5. $\frac{4}{\sqrt{97}}, \frac{9}{\sqrt{97}}$.
6. $\frac{\sqrt{39}}{8}, \frac{5}{8}$.

7. 36°.
8. 69°.
9. 46° 46'.

10. 70° 7'.   **11.** $(45+x)$°.   **12.** 60°.
13. 0·7986, 0·6637.   **14.** 45°.
15. 6·88, 9·83, 5·64, 3·95, 8·05 in.   **16.** 2,300 ft.
17. (a) 2·92 in. ; (b) 20·80 in.   **18.** 12° 1'.
19. 11·57 in., 6·89 in.   **20.** 460 yd.
21. 4·60, 3·86, 3·16, 2·21 in.   **22.** 47° 10'.
23. 8·240, 13·715 in.   **24.** 10·2 in., 85° 40'.
25. 721 yd., 63° 13', 119° 32', 96° 54', 53° 34'.
26. 8·63 in., 1 ft. 3·80 in.   **27.** (a) 1·97 ; (b) 1¾.
28. 10·76 amp., 2·79.

EXERCISE XLIV (Page 250.)

1. 1·09, 1·73, 2·52, 3·58, 5·20, 8·24 in.   **2.** 36° 52'.
3. 75 ft.   **4.** 56° 19'.   **5.** 28·56 ft.
6. 6·528 ft.   **7.** 0·8647, 0·2177, 3·7815.
8. (a) 64° 34' ; (b) 10° 42'.
9. 1·5190, 0·3186, 0·5124.   **10.** 0·2679, 15° 33'.
11. 0·13 in.   **12.** 10·39 in., 226 cu. in.
13. 143·3 ft., 1,210,000 cu. ft.
14. 3·575 in., 10·73 sq. in.
15. 0·605 in., 6·05 in.   **16.** 37° 24'.   **17.** 38° 40', 51° 20'.
18. 23° 1'.   **19.** 46° 51'.   **20.** 2° 29'.
21. 36° 52'.   **22.** 56° 19'.   **23.** 85° 27'.
24. 75° 4'.   **25.** 16° 42'.

EXERCISE XLV (Page 254.)

1. $\dfrac{LK}{LM}$, $\dfrac{CA}{CB}$, $\dfrac{QR}{QP}$, $\dfrac{ZY}{ZX}$, $\dfrac{KA}{KR}$, $\dfrac{PN}{PO}$.

2. Cos a, tan θ, sin ϕ, sin a, tan θ, cos ϕ.
3. 53° 8', 59° 2', 45° 13', 56° 15'.
4. (i) 46° 34' ; (ii) 29° 45' ; (iii) 32°, 13° ; (iv) 9·233 ft. ; (v) 6·674 in.;
     (vi) 6·787 in., 7·563 in.
5. 68° 12', 2·242 in., 3·312 in.
6. 13·16 in., 14·90 in., 35·67 sq. in.
7. 71°.   **8.** 9·534 in.   **9.** 73° 44'.
10. 52° 52'.   **11.** 67° 7', 43° 14'.   **12.** 13·56 cu. ft.
13. 2·724 in., 6·810 in.   **14.** 5·226 in.   **15.** 0·281 in.
16. 5·980 in.   **17.** 343·2, 542·5, 254·1, 796·6 yd., 53° 29'.
18. 0·212.

EXERCISE XLVI (Page 266.)

1. 12·21 lb.-wt., 55°.   **2.** 4·55 tons wt., 33·3°.
3. 36 m.p.h., 47·9°.   **4.** 14·66 ft. per sec., 60·2°.
5. 10·28 lb.-wt., 50°.   **6.** 8·66, 5 lb.-wt.
7. 10·24.   **8.** 8 knots.
9. 2·93, 2·07 tons wt.   **10.** 1·847, 2·364 in.

11. 43·3 lb.-wt.
12. 2·828 ml.
13. 8·66, 5 in.
14. 10·91, 5·685.
15. 6·13 knots, 4·9 min.
16. 7·70, 10·21 in.
17. 1·879, 0·684 cwt.
18. 16·38 units.
19. 0·0868, 0·492 ton wt.
20. 20·6 knots, N. 14° 2′ W.
21. 18·03 units at 56° 19′ with smaller vector.
22. 50 lb. wt. at 53° 8′ with smaller force.
23. $T \cos 40°$, $T \sin 40°$ lb.-wt., 326·3 lb.-wt.
24. 1·732, 1 cwt.
25. 6·928, 4 cwt.
26. (a) 32° 37′ with horizontal, 59·37 ft. per sec. ; (b) 52° with horizontal, 81·22 ft. per sec.
27. From OX, 1·942, 5·961 in. ; from OY, 5·060, 4·021 in. ; 4·151 in. ; 4·391 in.

EXERCISE XLVII (Page 273.)

1. $\dfrac{\sqrt{3}}{2}, \dfrac{1}{\sqrt{2}}, 0.$
2. $1, \dfrac{1}{\sqrt{3}}, 1.$
3. $4\sqrt{3}$, 4 in.
4. 11 ft., 25° 17′.
5. $8\sqrt{3}$ lb. wt.
6. 20, $5\sqrt{3}$ ft.
7. Sin 60°, cos 30°.
8. $2\sqrt{3}$ in.
9. 45°, $\dfrac{1}{\sqrt{2}}, 1.$
10. 0, 60, $60\sqrt{2}$, $60\sqrt{3}$, 120.
11. 30°, 45°, 60°, 90°, $\frac{1}{2}$, $\dfrac{\sqrt{3}}{2}$; $\dfrac{1}{\sqrt{2}}, \dfrac{1}{\sqrt{2}}$; $\dfrac{\sqrt{3}}{2}, \frac{1}{2}$; 1, 0.
12. 0·766.
15. 38° 10′.
16. 3·464, 7·211, 3·780, 7·626 in.

EXERCISE XLVIII (Page 274.)

1. (i) 21° 15′ ; (ii) 46° 11′.
3. (i) 30° ; (ii) 26° 34′, 4·472 ft.
4. 0·6253, 16° 22′.
5. 0·4337.
6. 13·91.
7. 180·4, 131·1, 68·92, 0 ; 0·00245.
8. Tan θ ; tan $\theta >$ sin θ for 0° $< \theta <$ 90°.
9. Tan θ.
10. Sin θ increases as θ increases from 0° to 90°.
11. 36° 17′.
12. $4\sqrt{3}$, $\dfrac{10\sqrt{3}}{3}$ in.
13. 3·728 ft., 3·502 ft.
14. 12·77, 2·56, 13·86 ft.
15. $3\frac{1}{4}$ in., 134° 46′.
16. 40°, 48° 35′.
17. 3·021 mm.
18. 2·74 cm.
19. 14° 29′, 14° 2′.
20. 15·82 ml.
21. 15·82 ml.
22. 29° 45′, 36° 16′, 66° 1′, 107° 28′.
23. $r\dfrac{\sqrt{3}}{2}, \dfrac{r}{2}$ lb. wt., $\dfrac{2000\sqrt{3}}{3}$, $\dfrac{1000\sqrt{3}}{3}$.
24. 2·475, 2·475, 7·525, 7·92 ft., 18° 12′.

25. 99·44 mm., 25·16 mm.   **26.** 2, 7·746 in., 28° 58′.
27. 3·127 in.
28. 8·457 in., 50·74 sq. in., 0·265 lb. per cu. in.
29. (a) 3·846 cm. ; (b) 10·788 cm.

EXERCISE XLIX (Page 291.)

1. 0·94, −0·71, −0·87.   **2.** 30°, 20°.
3. 0·5000, −0·8660, −0·5774 ; −0·3420, 0·9397, −0·3640.
4. −0·5000, −0·8660, 0·5774 ; −0·7660, 0·6428, −1·1918.
5. (a) 1 ; (b) −1 ; (c) 0.   **6.** Cos θ.
7. 0·9303.   **8.** −0·5769.
9. −0·4470.   **10.** 0·6437.
11. −0·4104.   **12.** 0·7959.
13. −0·3584.   **14.** −0·7880.
15. −2·5172.   **16.** 25° 4′, 154° 56′.
17. 58° 52′, 301° 8′.   **18.** 48° 48′, 228° 48′.
19. 210°, 330°.   **20.** 136° 1′, 223° 59′.
21. 116° 34′, 296° 34′.   **22.** 66° 33′, 113° 27′.
23. 156° 33′, 203° 27′.   **24.** 66° 2′, 246° 2′.
25. −0·85, −0·77, 203·6°, 336·4°.   **28.** 26·6°, 153·4°, 200·0°, 355·4°.
29. 120°.   **30.** 360°, 72°, 720°, 2°.
31. (a) $\frac{1}{2}$; (b) 3 ; (c) 1440 ; (d) 0·072.
32. A, 0·9659, −0·2588, −3·7321.   B, 0·6428, 0·7660, 0·8391.
          C, 0·5736, 0·8192, 0·7002.
33. 0·466, 126° 52′.   **36.** 2, 3.
38. 1·41, 135°, 114·3°.   **39.** 0·9092.
40. −0·3234.   **41.** 1·7777.
42. 0·5402.   **43.** 0·7470.
44. −0·6314.   **45.** 0·8660.
46. −0·7071.   **47.** −1·7321.
48. −0·5.   **49.** 0·5.
50. −0·9659.   **51.** 3·665, 5·760.
52. 0·6435, 5·640.   **53.** 2·191, 5·333.
54. 1·939, 4·344.   **55.** 0·6435, 2·498.
56. 1·030, 4·172.   **57.** $\frac{7\pi}{6}$, $\frac{11\pi}{6}$.
58. 0·91.   **59.** 85·67, 157·83, 205·04 ; 0·0013, 0·0065.
63. $\frac{20}{\pi}$.   **65.** Sin 100πt, 20 sin 100πt.
66. (a) 10 ; (b) $\frac{2}{\pi}$; (c) $\frac{1}{6\pi}$.   **67.** 1640.

EXERCISE L (Page 296.)

1. Cos θ   **2.** Cos θ sin θ.   **3.** Sin² A.
4. 1.   **5.** Sin² α.   **6.** Sin φ.
7. 1 + cos B.   **8.** Cos² θ.   **9.** 1 + sin θ.
10. Tan A.

INDEX

Abscissa, 101
Algebra
— history of, 28
Algebraic processes, 56, 128
Amplitude, 288
Angles, 151, 159
Arc, 170
Areas, 185
— approximation to, 214
Arithmetic
— history of, 1
Averages, 8
Axes, 77

Brackets, 42, 49

Characteristic, 114
Chord, 170
Circle, 149
— constructions, 209
— mensuration of, 220
— theorems, 199, 205
Circumcircle, 211
Cone, 149
— mensuration of, 224
Congruence, 169, 171
Constructions, 177, 187, 209
Contracted methods, 9
Converse, 181
Co-ordinates, 101
— polar, 259
— rectangular, 259
Corollary, 164
Cosine of angle, 241
Cube, 149
Cursor, 127
Cylinder, 149
— mensuration of, 223

Decagon, 164
Decimals, 3
Degree, 153
Diagonal, 163
Directed numbers, 43

Enunciation, 166
Equations
— simple, 37, 59
— simultaneous, 68
— with two roots, 133

Factors
— algebraic, 130
— prime, 13
Formulæ, 29, 129
— transformation of, 64
Fractions, 15, 57, 133

Geometry
— history of, 146
Graphs
— maxima and minima, 100
— of equations, 89, 103
— of sin θ and cos θ, 271, 283
— of a sin θ, 287, 289
— of a sin $p\theta$ and a cos $p\theta$, 288
— of statistics, 74
— solution of equations, 99
— straight line, 84, 101
— with directed numbers, 95

H.C.F., 14, 57
Heptagon, 164
Hexagon, 164

Identities, 295
Incircle, 211
Indices, 108

L.C.M., 14, 57
Lines, 148, 155
— parallel, 158
Locus, 195
Logarithms, 112
— negative characteristics, 122
— of cosines, 242
— of sines, 237

Mantissa, 114
Maxima and minima, 100
Metric system, 2
Mid-ordinate rule, 214
Minute, 153

Net, 150
Nonagon, 164

Octagon, 164
Ordinate, 101
Origin, 78
Oscillations, 289

Parallel lines, 158
Parallelogram, 176
— area of, 185
— theorem, 182
Pentagon, 164
Percentage, 24
Period, 288
Plane, 148, 155
Point, 148
Polygon, 164
— theorems, 167
Prism, 222
— mensuration of, 222
Proportion, 21, 137
Protractor, 154
Pyramid, 149
— mensuration of, 223
Pythagoras' theorem, 188
— converse, 189

Quadrilateral, 163

Radian, 230
Radius, 170
Ratio, 21, 137
Reciprocal, 17
Rectangle, 176
Rhombus, 176

Scale, 77
Secant, 204
Second, 154

Sector, 170
— area of, 221
Segment, 170
Significant figures, 4
Similarity, 169, 174
Simpson's rule, 216
Sine of angle, 231
Slide rule, 125
Solid, 148
Sphere, 149
— mensuration of, 222
Square, 176
— table of, 119
Square root, 19
Surface, 148
Symbols, 29
Symmetry, 160

Tangent, 204
— construction, 210
    of an angle, 249
— theorems, 205
Terms
— like and unlike, 35, 52
Tetrahedron, 149
Theorem, 164
Transversal, 159
Trapezium, 176
— area of, 186
Trapezoidal rule, 215
Triangle, 149, 163
— ambiguous case, 173
— area of, 186
— constructions, 170, 187
— similar, 174
— theorems, 165, 181
Trigonometry
— history of, 228
Trigonometrical ratios
— of acute angles, 231
— of angles of 30°, 45°, 60°, 270
— of angles of any magnitude, 279

Variation, 139
Vector, 261
Vertex, 149

LOGARITHMS

	0	1	2	3	4	5	6	7	8	9	Differences 1	2	3	4	5	6	7	8	9
10	0000	0043	0086	0128	0170	0212	0253	0294	0334	0374	4	8	12	17	21	25	29	33	37
11	0414	0453	0492	0531	0569	0607	0645	0682	0719	0755	4	8	11	15	19	23	26	30	34
12	0792	0828	0864	0899	0934	0969	1004	1038	1072	1106	3	7	10	14	17	21	24	28	31
13	1139	1173	1206	1239	1271	1303	1335	1367	1399	1430	3	6	10	13	16	19	23	26	29
14	1461	1492	1523	1553	1584	1614	1644	1673	1703	1732	3	6	9	12	15	18	21	24	27
15	1761	1790	1818	1847	1875	1903	1931	1959	1987	2014	3	6	8	11	14	17	20	22	25
16	2041	2068	2095	2122	2148	2175	2201	2227	2253	2279	3	5	8	11	13	16	18	21	24
17	2304	2330	2355	2380	2405	2430	2455	2480	2504	2529	2	5	7	10	12	15	17	20	22
18	2553	2577	2601	2625	2648	2672	2695	2718	2742	2765	2	5	7	9	12	14	16	19	21
19	2788	2810	2833	2856	2878	2900	2923	2945	2967	2989	2	4	7	9	11	13	16	18	20
20	3010	3032	3054	3075	3096	3118	3139	3160	3181	3201	2	4	6	8	11	13	15	17	19
21	3222	3243	3263	3284	3304	3324	3345	3365	3385	3404	2	4	6	8	10	12	14	16	18
22	3424	3444	3464	3483	3502	3522	3541	3560	3579	3598	2	4	6	8	10	12	14	15	17
23	3617	3636	3655	3674	3692	3711	3729	3747	3766	3784	2	4	6	7	9	11	13	15	17
24	3802	3820	3838	3856	3874	3892	3909	3927	3945	3962	2	4	5	7	9	11	12	14	16
25	3979	3997	4014	4031	4048	4065	4082	4099	4116	4133	2	3	5	7	9	10	12	14	15
26	4150	4166	4183	4200	4216	4232	4249	4265	4281	4298	2	3	5	7	8	10	11	13	15
27	4314	4330	4346	4362	4378	4393	4409	4425	4440	4456	2	3	5	6	8	9	11	13	14
28	4472	4487	4502	4518	4533	4548	4564	4579	4594	4609	2	3	5	6	8	9	11	12	14
29	4624	4639	4654	4669	4683	4698	4713	4728	4742	4757	1	3	4	6	7	9	10	12	13
30	4771	4786	4800	4814	4829	4843	4857	4871	4886	4900	1	3	4	6	7	9	10	11	13
31	4914	4928	4942	4955	4969	4983	4997	5011	5024	5038	1	3	4	6	7	8	10	11	12
32	5051	5065	5079	5092	5105	5119	5132	5145	5159	5172	1	3	4	5	7	8	9	11	12
33	5185	5198	5211	5224	5237	5250	5263	5276	5289	5302	1	3	4	5	6	8	9	10	12
34	5315	5328	5340	5353	5366	5378	5391	5403	5416	5428	1	3	4	5	6	8	9	10	11
35	5441	5453	5465	5478	5490	5502	5514	5527	5539	5551	1	2	4	5	6	7	9	10	11
36	5563	5575	5587	5599	5611	5623	5635	5647	5658	5670	1	2	4	5	6	7	8	10	11
37	5682	5694	5705	5717	5729	5740	5752	5763	5775	5786	1	2	3	5	6	7	8	9	10
38	5798	5809	5821	5832	5843	5855	5866	5877	5888	5899	1	2	3	5	6	7	8	9	10
39	5911	5922	5933	5944	5955	5966	5977	5988	5999	6010	1	2	3	4	5	7	8	9	10
40	6021	6031	6042	6053	6064	6075	6085	6096	6107	6117	1	2	3	4	5	6	8	9	10
41	6128	6138	6149	6160	6170	6180	6191	6201	6212	6222	1	2	3	4	5	6	7	8	9
42	6232	6243	6253	6263	6274	6284	6294	6304	6314	6325	1	2	3	4	5	6	7	8	9
43	6335	6345	6355	6365	6375	6385	6395	6405	6415	6425	1	2	3	4	5	6	7	8	9
44	6435	6444	6454	6464	6474	6484	6493	6503	6513	6522	1	2	3	4	5	6	7	8	9
45	6532	6542	6551	6561	6571	6580	6590	6599	6609	6618	1	2	3	4	5	6	7	8	9
46	6628	6637	6646	6656	6665	6675	6684	6693	6702	6712	1	2	3	4	5	6	7	7	8
47	6721	6730	6739	6749	6758	6767	6776	6785	6794	6803	1	2	3	4	5	5	6	7	8
48	6812	6821	6830	6839	6848	6857	6866	6875	6884	6893	1	2	3	4	4	5	6	7	8
49	6902	6911	6920	6928	6937	6946	6955	6964	6972	6981	1	2	3	4	4	5	6	7	8
50	6990	6998	7007	7016	7024	7033	7042	7050	7059	7067	1	2	3	3	4	5	6	7	8
51	7076	7084	7093	7101	7110	7118	7126	7135	7143	7152	1	2	3	3	4	5	6	7	8
52	7160	7168	7177	7185	7193	7202	7210	7218	7226	7235	1	2	2	3	4	5	6	7	7
53	7243	7251	7259	7267	7275	7284	7292	7300	7308	7316	1	2	2	3	4	5	6	6	7
54	7324	7332	7340	7348	7356	7364	7372	7380	7388	7396	1	2	2	3	4	5	6	6	7

LOGARITHMS

	0	1	2	3	4	5	6	7	8	9	1	2	3	4	5	6	7	8	9
											differences								

Differences header spans columns 1–9.

	0	**1**	**2**	**3**	**4**	**5**	**6**	**7**	**8**	**9**	**1**	**2**	**3**	**4**	**5**	**6**	**7**	**8**	**9**
55	7404	7412	7419	7427	7435	7443	7451	7459	7466	7474	1	2	2	3	4	5	5	6	7
56	7482	7490	7497	7505	7513	7520	7528	7536	7543	7551	1	2	2	3	4	5	5	6	7
57	7559	7566	7574	7582	7589	7597	7604	7612	7619	7627	1	2	2	3	4	5	5	6	7
58	7634	7642	7649	7657	7664	7672	7679	7686	7694	7701	1	1	2	3	4	4	5	6	7
59	7709	7716	7723	7731	7738	7745	7752	7760	7767	7774	1	1	2	3	4	4	5	6	7
60	7782	7789	7796	7803	7810	7818	7825	7832	7839	7846	1	1	2	3	4	4	5	6	6
61	7853	7860	7868	7875	7882	7889	7896	7903	7910	7917	1	1	2	3	4	4	5	6	6
62	7924	7931	7938	7945	7952	7959	7966	7973	7980	7987	1	1	2	3	4	4	5	6	6
63	7993	8000	8007	8014	8021	8028	8035	8041	8048	8055	1	1	2	3	3	4	5	5	6
64	8062	8069	8075	8082	8089	8096	8102	8109	8116	8122	1	1	2	3	3	4	5	5	6
65	8129	8136	8142	8149	8156	8162	8169	8176	8182	8189	1	1	2	3	3	4	5	5	6
66	8195	8202	8209	8215	8222	8228	8235	8241	8248	8254	1	1	2	3	3	4	5	5	6
67	8261	8267	8274	8280	8287	8293	8299	8306	8312	8319	1	1	2	3	3	4	5	5	6
68	8325	8331	8338	8344	8351	8357	8363	8370	8376	8382	1	1	2	3	3	4	4	5	6
69	8388	8395	8401	8407	8414	8420	8426	8432	8439	8445	1	1	2	2	3	4	4	5	6
70	8451	8457	8463	8470	8476	8482	8488	8494	8500	8506	1	1	2	2	3	4	4	5	6
71	8513	8519	8525	8531	8537	8543	8549	8555	8561	8567	1	1	2	2	3	4	4	5	5
72	8573	8579	8585	8591	8597	8603	8609	8615	8621	8627	1	1	2	2	3	4	4	5	5
73	8633	8639	8645	8651	8657	8663	8669	8675	8681	8686	1	1	2	2	3	4	4	5	5
74	8692	8698	8704	8710	8716	8722	8727	8733	8739	8745	1	1	2	2	3	4	4	5	5
75	8751	8756	8762	8768	8774	8779	8785	8791	8797	8802	1	1	2	2	3	3	4	5	5
76	8808	8814	8820	8825	8831	8837	8842	8848	8854	8859	1	1	2	2	3	3	4	5	5
77	8865	8871	8876	8882	8887	8893	8899	8904	8910	8915	1	1	2	2	3	3	4	4	5
78	8921	8927	8932	8938	8943	8949	8954	8960	8965	8971	1	1	2	2	3	3	4	4	5
79	8976	8982	8987	8993	8998	9004	9009	9015	9020	9025	1	1	2	2	3	3	4	4	5
80	9031	9036	9042	9047	9053	9058	9063	9069	9074	9079	1	1	2	2	3	3	4	4	5
81	9085	9090	9096	9101	9106	9112	9117	9122	9128	9133	1	1	2	2	3	3	4	4	5
82	9138	9143	9149	9154	9159	9165	9170	9175	9180	9186	1	1	2	2	3	3	4	4	5
83	9191	9196	9201	9206	9212	9217	9222	9227	9232	9238	1	1	2	2	3	3	4	4	5
84	9243	9248	9253	9258	9263	9269	9274	9279	9284	9289	1	1	2	2	3	3	4	4	5
85	9294	9299	9304	9309	9315	9320	9325	9330	9335	9340	1	1	2	2	3	3	4	4	5
86	9345	9350	9355	9360	9365	9370	9375	9380	9385	9390	1	1	2	2	3	3	4	4	5
87	9395	9400	9405	9410	9415	9420	9425	9430	9435	9440	0	1	1	2	2	3	3	4	4
88	9445	9450	9455	9460	9465	9469	9474	9479	9484	9489	0	1	1	2	2	3	3	4	4
89	9494	9499	9504	9509	9513	9518	9523	9528	9533	9538	0	1	1	2	2	3	3	4	4
90	9542	9547	9552	9557	9562	9566	9571	9576	9581	9586	0	1	1	2	2	3	3	4	4
91	9590	9595	9600	9605	9609	9614	9619	9624	9628	9633	0	1	1	2	2	3	3	4	4
92	9638	9643	9647	9652	9657	9661	9666	9671	9675	9680	0	1	1	2	2	3	3	4	4
93	9685	9689	9694	9699	9703	9708	9713	9717	9722	9727	0	1	1	2	2	3	3	4	4
94	9731	9736	9741	9745	9750	9754	9759	9763	9768	9773	0	1	1	2	2	3	3	4	4
95	9777	9782	9786	9791	9795	9800	9805	9809	9814	9818	0	1	1	2	2	3	3	4	4
96	9823	9827	9832	9836	9841	9845	9850	9854	9859	9863	0	1	1	2	2	3	3	4	4
97	9868	9872	9877	9881	9886	9890	9894	9899	9903	9908	0	1	1	2	2	3	3	4	4
98	9912	9917	9921	9926	9930	9934	9939	9943	9948	9952	0	1	1	2	2	3	3	4	4
99	9956	9961	9965	9969	9974	9978	9983	9987	9991	9996	0	1	1	2	2	3	3	3	4

ANTI-LOGARITHMS

	0	1	2	3	4	5	6	7	8	9	Differences								
											1	2	3	4	5	6	7	8	9
·00	1000	1002	1005	1007	1009	1012	1014	1016	1019	1021	0	0	1	1	1	1	2	2	2
·01	1023	1026	1028	1030	1033	1035	1038	1040	1042	1045	0	0	1	1	1	1	2	2	2
·02	1047	1050	1052	1054	1057	1059	1062	1064	1067	1069	0	0	1	1	1	1	2	2	2
·03	1072	1074	1076	1079	1081	1084	1086	1089	1091	1094	0	0	1	1	1	1	2	2	2
·04	1096	1099	1102	1104	1107	1109	1112	1114	1117	1119	0	1	1	1	1	2	2	2	2
·05	1122	1125	1127	1130	1132	1135	1138	1140	1143	1146	0	1	1	1	1	2	2	2	2
·06	1148	1151	1153	1156	1159	1161	1164	1167	1169	1172	0	1	1	1	1	2	2	2	2
·07	1175	1178	1180	1183	1186	1189	1191	1194	1197	1199	0	1	1	1	1	2	2	2	2
·08	1202	1205	1208	1211	1213	1216	1219	1222	1225	1227	0	1	1	1	1	2	2	2	3
·09	1230	1233	1236	1239	1242	1245	1247	1250	1253	1256	0	1	1	1	1	2	2	2	3
·10	1259	1262	1265	1268	1271	1274	1276	1279	1282	1285	0	1	1	1	1	2	2	2	3
·11	1288	1291	1294	1297	1300	1303	1306	1309	1312	1315	0	1	1	1	2	2	2	2	3
·12	1318	1321	1324	1327	1330	1334	1337	1340	1343	1346	0	1	1	1	2	2	2	3	3
·13	1349	1352	1355	1358	1361	1365	1368	1371	1374	1377	0	1	1	1	2	2	2	3	3
·14	1380	1384	1387	1390	1393	1396	1400	1403	1406	1409	0	1	1	1	2	2	2	3	3
·15	1413	1416	1419	1422	1426	1429	1432	1435	1439	1442	0	1	1	1	2	2	2	3	3
·16	1445	1449	1452	1455	1459	1462	1466	1469	1472	1476	0	1	1	1	2	2	2	3	3
·17	1479	1483	1486	1489	1493	1496	1500	1503	1507	1510	0	1	1	1	2	2	2	3	3
·18	1514	1517	1521	1524	1528	1531	1535	1538	1542	1545	0	1	1	1	2	2	2	3	3
·19	1549	1552	1556	1560	1563	1567	1570	1574	1578	1581	0	1	1	1	2	2	3	3	3
·20	1585	1589	1592	1596	1600	1603	1607	1611	1614	1618	0	1	1	1	2	2	3	3	3
·21	1622	1626	1629	1633	1637	1641	1644	1648	1652	1656	0	1	1	2	2	2	3	3	3
·22	1660	1663	1667	1671	1675	1679	1683	1687	1690	1694	0	1	1	2	2	2	3	3	3
·23	1698	1702	1706	1710	1714	1718	1722	1726	1730	1734	0	1	1	2	2	2	3	3	4
·24	1738	1742	1746	1750	1754	1758	1762	1766	1770	1774	0	1	1	2	2	2	3	3	4
·25	1778	1782	1786	1791	1795	1799	1803	1807	1811	1816	0	1	1	2	2	2	3	3	4
·26	1820	1824	1828	1832	1837	1841	1845	1849	1854	1858	0	1	1	2	2	3	3	3	4
·27	1862	1866	1871	1875	1879	1884	1888	1892	1897	1901	0	1	1	2	2	3	3	4	4
·28	1905	1910	1914	1919	1923	1928	1932	1936	1941	1945	0	1	1	2	2	3	3	4	4
·29	1950	1954	1959	1963	1968	1972	1977	1982	1986	1991	0	1	1	2	2	3	3	4	4
·30	1995	2000	2004	2009	2014	2018	2023	2028	2032	2037	0	1	1	2	2	3	3	4	4
·31	2042	2046	2051	2056	2061	2065	2070	2075	2080	2084	0	1	1	2	2	3	3	4	4
·32	2089	2094	2099	2104	2109	2113	2118	2123	2128	2133	0	1	1	2	2	3	3	4	4
·33	2138	2143	2148	2153	2158	2163	2168	2173	2178	2183	0	1	1	2	2	3	3	4	4
·34	2188	2193	2198	2203	2208	2213	2218	2223	2228	2234	1	1	2	2	3	3	4	4	5
·35	2239	2244	2249	2254	2259	2265	2270	2275	2280	2286	1	1	2	2	3	3	4	4	5
·36	2291	2296	2301	2307	2312	2317	2323	2328	2333	2339	1	1	2	2	3	3	4	4	5
·37	2344	2350	2355	2360	2366	2371	2377	2382	2388	2393	1	1	2	2	3	3	4	4	5
·38	2399	2404	2410	2415	2421	2427	2432	2438	2443	2449	1	1	2	2	3	3	4	4	5
·39	2455	2460	2466	2472	2477	2483	2489	2495	2500	2506	1	1	2	2	3	3	4	5	5
·40	2512	2518	2523	2529	2535	2541	2547	2553	2559	2564	1	1	2	2	3	4	4	5	5
·41	2570	2576	2582	2588	2594	2600	2606	2612	2618	2624	1	1	2	2	3	4	4	5	5
·42	2630	2636	2642	2649	2655	2661	2667	2673	2679	2685	1	1	2	2	3	4	4	5	6
·43	2692	2698	2704	2710	2716	2723	2729	2735	2742	2748	1	1	2	3	3	4	4	5	6
·44	2754	2761	2767	2773	2780	2786	2793	2799	2805	2812	1	1	2	3	3	4	4	5	6
·45	2818	2825	2831	2838	2844	2851	2858	2864	2871	2877	1	1	2	3	3	4	5	5	6
·46	2884	2891	2897	2904	2911	2917	2924	2931	2938	2944	1	1	2	3	3	4	5	5	6
·47	2951	2958	2965	2972	2979	2985	2992	2999	3006	3013	1	1	2	3	3	4	5	5	6
·48	3020	3027	3034	3041	3048	3055	3062	3069	3076	3083	1	1	2	3	4	4	5	6	6
·49	3090	3097	3105	3112	3119	3126	3133	3141	3148	3155	1	1	2	3	4	4	5	6	6

ANTI-LOGARITHMS

	0	1	2	3	4	5	6	7	8	9	Differences								
											1	2	3	4	5	6	7	8	9
·50	3162	3170	3177	3184	3192	3199	3206	3214	3221	3228	1	1	2	3	4	4	5	6	7
·51	3236	3243	3251	3258	3266	3273	3281	3289	3296	3304	1	2	2	3	4	5	5	6	7
·52	3311	3319	3327	3334	3342	3350	3357	3365	3373	3381	1	2	2	3	4	5	5	6	7
·53	3388	3396	3404	3412	3420	3428	3436	3443	3451	3459	1	2	2	3	4	5	6	6	7
·54	3467	3475	3483	3491	3499	3508	3516	3524	3532	3540	1	2	2	3	4	5	6	6	7
·55	3548	3556	3565	3573	3581	3589	3597	3606	3614	3622	1	2	2	3	4	5	6	7	7
·56	3631	3639	3648	3656	3664	3673	3681	3690	3698	3707	1	2	3	3	4	5	6	7	8
·57	3715	3724	3733	3741	3750	3758	3767	3776	3784	3793	1	2	3	3	4	5	6	7	8
·58	3802	3811	3819	3828	3837	3846	3855	3864	3873	3882	1	2	3	4	4	5	6	7	8
·59	3890	3899	3908	3917	3926	3936	3945	3954	3963	3972	1	2	3	4	5	5	6	7	8
·60	3981	3990	3999	4009	4018	4027	4036	4046	4055	4064	1	2	3	4	5	6	6	7	8
·61	4074	4083	4093	4102	4111	4121	4130	4140	4150	4159	1	2	3	4	5	6	7	8	9
·62	4169	4178	4188	4198	4207	4217	4227	4236	4246	4256	1	2	3	4	5	6	7	8	9
·63	4266	4276	4285	4295	4305	4315	4325	4335	4345	4355	1	2	3	4	5	6	7	8	9
·64	4365	4375	4385	4395	4406	4416	4426	4436	4446	4457	1	2	3	4	5	6	7	8	9
·65	4467	4477	4487	4498	4508	4519	4529	4539	4550	4560	1	2	3	4	5	6	7	8	9
·66	4571	4581	4592	4603	4613	4624	4634	4645	4656	4667	1	2	3	4	5	6	7	9	10
·67	4677	4688	4699	4710	4721	4732	4742	4753	4764	4775	1	2	3	4	5	7	8	9	10
·68	4786	4797	4808	4819	4831	4842	4853	4864	4875	4887	1	2	3	4	6	7	8	9	10
·69	4898	4909	4920	4932	4943	4955	4966	4977	4989	5000	1	2	3	4	6	7	8	9	10
·70	5012	5023	5035	5047	5058	5070	5082	5093	5105	5117	1	2	4	5	6	7	8	9	11
·71	5129	5140	5152	5164	5176	5188	5200	5212	5224	5236	1	2	4	5	6	7	8	10	11
·72	5248	5260	5272	5284	5297	5309	5321	5333	5346	5358	1	2	4	5	6	7	9	10	11
·73	5370	5383	5395	5408	5420	5433	5445	5458	5470	5483	1	3	4	5	6	8	9	10	11
·74	5495	5508	5521	5534	5546	5559	5572	5585	5598	5610	1	3	4	5	6	8	9	10	12
·75	5623	5636	5649	5662	5675	5689	5702	5715	5728	5741	1	3	4	5	7	8	9	10	12
·76	5754	5768	5781	5794	5808	5821	5834	5848	5861	5875	1	3	4	5	7	8	9	11	12
·77	5888	5902	5916	5929	5943	5957	5970	5984	5998	6012	1	3	4	5	7	8	10	11	12
·78	6026	6039	6053	6067	6081	6095	6109	6124	6138	6152	1	3	4	6	7	8	10	11	13
·79	6166	6180	6194	6209	6223	6237	6252	6266	6281	6295	1	3	4	6	7	9	10	11	13
·80	6310	6324	6339	6353	6368	6383	6397	6412	6427	6442	1	3	4	6	7	9	10	12	13
·81	6457	6471	6486	6501	6516	6531	6546	6561	6577	6592	2	3	5	6	8	9	11	12	14
·82	6607	6622	6637	6653	6668	6683	6699	6714	6730	6745	2	3	5	6	8	9	11	12	14
·83	6761	6776	6792	6808	6823	6839	6855	6871	6887	6902	2	3	5	6	8	9	11	13	14
·84	6918	6934	6950	6966	6982	6998	7015	7031	7047	7063	2	3	5	6	8	10	11	13	15
·85	7079	7096	7112	7129	7145	7161	7178	7194	7211	7228	2	3	5	7	8	10	12	13	15
·86	7244	7261	7278	7295	7311	7328	7345	7362	7379	7396	2	3	5	7	8	10	12	13	15
·87	7413	7430	7447	7464	7482	7499	7516	7534	7551	7568	2	3	5	7	9	10	12	14	16
·88	7586	7603	7621	7638	7656	7674	7691	7709	7727	7745	2	4	5	7	9	11	12	14	16
·89	7762	7780	7798	7816	7834	7852	7870	7889	7907	7925	2	4	5	7	9	11	13	14	16
·90	7943	7962	7980	7998	8017	8035	8054	8072	8091	8110	2	4	6	7	9	11	13	15	17
·91	8128	8147	8166	8185	8204	8222	8241	8260	8279	8299	2	4	6	8	9	11	13	15	17
·92	8318	8337	8356	8375	8395	8414	8433	8453	8472	8492	2	4	6	8	10	12	14	15	17
·93	8511	8531	8551	8570	8590	8610	8630	8650	8670	8690	2	4	6	8	10	12	14	16	18
·94	8710	8730	8750	8770	8790	8810	8831	8851	8872	8892	2	4	6	8	10	12	14	16	18
·95	8913	8933	8954	8974	8995	9016	9036	9057	9078	9099	2	4	6	8	10	12	15	17	19
·96	9120	9141	9162	9183	9204	9226	9247	9268	9290	9311	2	4	6	8	11	13	15	17	19
·97	9333	9354	9376	9397	9419	9441	9462	9484	9506	9528	2	4	7	9	11	13	15	17	20
·98	9550	9572	9594	9616	9638	9661	9683	9705	9727	9750	2	4	7	9	11	13	16	18	20
·99	9772	9795	9817	9840	9863	9886	9908	9931	9954	9977	2	5	7	9	11	14	16	18	20

NATURAL SINES

	0′	6′	12′	18′	24′	30′	36′	42′	48′	54′	Differences				
											1′	2′	3′	4′	5′
0	·0000	0017	0035	0052	0070	0087	0105	0122	0140	0157	3	6	9	12	15
1	·0175	0192	0209	0227	0244	0262	0279	0297	0314	0332	3	6	9	12	15
2	·0349	0366	0384	0401	0419	0436	0454	0471	0488	0506	3	6	9	12	15
3	·0523	0541	0558	0576	0593	0610	0628	0645	0663	0680	3	6	9	12	15
4	·0698	0715	0732	0750	0767	0785	0802	0819	0837	0854	3	6	9	12	14
5	·0872	0889	0906	0924	0941	0958	0976	0993	1011	1028	3	6	9	12	14
6	·1045	1063	1080	1097	1115	1132	1149	1167	1184	1201	3	6	9	12	14
7	·1219	1236	1253	1271	1288	1305	1323	1340	1357	1374	3	6	9	12	14
8	·1392	1409	1426	1444	1461	1478	1495	1513	1530	1547	3	6	9	12	14
9	·1564	1582	1599	1616	1633	1650	1668	1685	1702	1719	3	6	9	12	14
10	·1736	1754	1771	1788	1805	1822	1840	1857	1874	1891	3	6	9	11	14
11	·1908	1925	1942	1959	1977	1994	2011	2028	2045	2062	3	6	9	11	14
12	·2079	2096	2113	2130	2147	2164	2181	2198	2215	2233	3	6	9	11	14
13	·2250	2267	2284	2300	2317	2334	2351	2368	2385	2402	3	6	8	11	14
14	·2419	2436	2453	2470	2487	2504	2521	2538	2554	2571	3	6	8	11	14
15	·2588	2605	2622	2639	2656	2672	2689	2706	2723	2740	3	6	8	11	14
16	·2756	2773	2790	2807	2823	2840	2857	2874	2890	2907	3	6	8	11	14
17	·2924	2940	2957	2974	2990	3007	3024	3040	3057	3074	3	6	8	11	14
18	·3090	3107	3123	3140	3156	3173	3190	3206	3223	3239	3	6	8	11	14
19	·3256	3272	3289	3305	3322	3338	3355	3371	3387	3404	3	5	8	11	14
20	·3420	3437	3453	3469	3486	3502	3518	3535	3551	3567	3	5	8	11	14
21	·3584	3600	3616	3633	3649	3665	3681	3697	3714	3730	3	5	8	11	14
22	·3746	3762	3778	3795	3811	3827	3843	3859	3875	3891	3	5	8	11	14
23	·3907	3923	3939	3955	3971	3987	4003	4019	4035	4051	3	5	8	11	14
24	·4067	4083	4099	4115	4131	4147	4163	4179	4195	4210	3	5	8	11	13
25	·4226	4242	4258	4274	4289	4305	4321	4337	4352	4368	3	5	8	11	13
26	·4384	4399	4415	4431	4446	4462	4478	4493	4509	4524	3	5	8	10	13
27	·4540	4555	4571	4586	4602	4617	4633	4648	4664	4679	3	5	8	10	13
28	·4695	4710	4726	4741	4756	4772	4787	4802	4818	4833	3	5	8	10	13
29	·4848	4863	4879	4894	4909	4924	4939	4955	4970	4985	3	5	8	10	13
30	·5000	5015	5030	5045	5060	5075	5090	5105	5120	5135	3	5	8	10	13
31	·5150	5165	5180	5195	5210	5225	5240	5255	5270	5284	2	5	7	10	12
32	·5299	5314	5329	5344	5358	5373	5388	5402	5417	5432	2	5	7	10	12
33	·5446	5461	5476	5490	5505	5519	5534	5548	5563	5577	2	5	7	10	12
34	·5592	5606	5621	5635	5650	5664	5678	5693	5707	5721	2	5	7	10	12
35	·5736	5750	5764	5779	5793	5807	5821	5835	5850	5864	2	5	7	9	12
36	·5878	5892	5906	5920	5934	5948	5962	5976	5990	6004	2	5	7	9	12
37	·6018	6032	6046	6060	6074	6088	6101	6115	6129	6143	2	5	7	9	12
38	·6157	6170	6184	6198	6211	6225	6239	6252	6266	6280	2	5	7	9	11
39	·6293	6307	6320	6334	6347	6361	6374	6388	6401	6414	2	4	7	9	11
40	·6428	6441	6455	6468	6481	6494	6508	6521	6534	6547	2	4	7	9	11
41	·6561	6574	6587	6600	6613	6626	6639	6652	6665	6678	2	4	7	9	11
42	·6691	6704	6717	6730	6743	6756	6769	6782	6794	6807	2	4	6	9	11
43	·6820	6833	6845	6858	6871	6884	6896	6909	6921	6934	2	4	6	8	11
44	·6947	6959	6972	6984	6997	7009	7022	7034	7046	7059	2	4	6	8	10

NATURAL SINES

°	0′	6′	12′	18′	24′	30′	36′	42′	48′	54′	1′	2′	3′	4′	5′
45	·7071	7083	7096	7108	7120	7133	7145	7157	7169	7181	2	4	6	8	10
46	·7193	7206	7218	7230	7242	7254	7266	7278	7290	7302	2	4	6	8	10
47	7314	7325	7337	7349	7361	7373	7385	7396	7408	7420	2	4	6	8	10
48	·7431	7443	7455	7466	7478	7490	7501	7513	7524	7536	2	4	6	8	10
49	·7547	7559	7570	7581	7593	7604	7615	7627	7638	7649	2	4	6	8	9
50	·7660	7672	7683	7694	7705	7716	7727	7738	7749	7760	2	4	6	7	9
51	·7771	7782	7793	7804	7815	7826	7837	7848	7859	7869	2	4	5	7	9
52	·7880	7891	7902	7912	7923	7934	7944	7955	7965	7976	2	4	5	7	9
53	·7986	7997	8007	8018	8028	8039	8049	8059	8070	8080	2	3	5	7	9
54	·8090	8100	8111	8121	8131	8141	8151	8161	8171	8181	2	3	5	7	8
55	·8192	8202	8211	8221	8231	8241	8251	8261	8271	8281	2	3	5	7	8
56	·8290	8300	8310	8320	8329	8339	8348	8358	8368	8377	2	3	5	6	8
57	·8387	8396	8406	8415	8425	8434	8443	8453	8462	8471	2	3	5	6	8
58	·8480	8490	8499	8508	8517	8526	8536	8545	8554	8563	2	3	5	6	8
59	·8572	8581	8590	8599	8607	8616	8625	8634	8643	8652	1	3	4	6	7
60	·8660	8669	8678	8686	8695	8704	8712	8721	8729	8738	1	3	4	6	7
61	·8746	8755	8763	8771	8780	8788	8796	8805	8813	8821	1	3	4	6	7
62	·8829	8838	8846	8854	8862	8870	8878	8886	8894	8902	1	3	4	5	7
63	·8910	8918	8926	8934	8942	8949	8957	8965	8973	8980	1	3	4	5	6
64	·8988	8996	9003	9011	9018	9026	9033	9041	9048	9056	1	3	4	5	6
65	·9063	9070	9078	9085	9092	9100	9107	9114	9121	9128	1	2	4	5	6
66	·9135	9143	9150	9157	9164	9171	9178	9184	9191	9198	1	2	3	5	6
67	·9205	9212	9219	9225	9232	9239	9245	9252	9259	9265	1	2	3	4	6
68	·9272	9278	9285	9291	9298	9304	9311	9317	9323	9330	1	2	3	4	5
69	·9336	9342	9348	9354	9361	9367	9373	9379	9385	9391	1	2	3	4	5
70	·9397	9403	9409	9415	9421	9426	9432	9438	9444	9449	1	2	3	4	5
71	·9455	9461	9466	9472	9478	9483	9489	9494	9500	9505	1	2	3	4	5
72	·9511	9516	9521	9527	9532	9537	9542	9548	9553	9558	1	2	3	3	4
73	·9563	9568	9573	9578	9583	9588	9593	9598	9603	9608	1	2	2	3	4
74	·9613	9617	9622	9627	9632	9636	9641	9646	9650	9655	1	2	2	3	4
75	·9659	9664	9668	9673	9677	9681	9686	9690	9694	9699	1	1	2	3	4
76	·9703	9707	9711	9715	9720	9724	9728	9732	9736	9740	1	1	2	3	3
77	·9744	9748	9751	9755	9759	9763	9767	9770	9774	9778	1	1	2	3	3
78	·9781	9785	9789	9792	9796	9799	9803	9806	9810	9813	1	1	2	2	3
79	·9816	9820	9823	9826	9829	9833	9836	9839	9842	9845	1	1	2	2	3
80	·9848	9851	9854	9857	9860	9863	9866	9869	9871	9874	0	1	1	2	2
81	·9877	9880	9882	9885	9888	9890	9893	9895	9898	9900	0	1	1	2	2
82	·9903	9905	9907	9910	9912	9914	9917	9919	9921	9923	0	1	1	2	2
83	·9925	9928	9930	9932	9934	9936	9938	9940	9942	9943	0	1	1	1	2
84	·9945	9947	9949	9951	9952	9954	9956	9957	9959	9960	0	1	1	1	1
85	·9962	9963	9965	9966	9968	9969	9971	9972	9973	9974	0	0	1	1	1
86	·9976	9977	9978	9979	9980	9981	9982	9983	9984	9985	0	0	1	1	
87	·9986	9987	9988	9989	9990	9990	9991	9992	9993	9993					
88	·9994	9995	9995	9996	9996	9997	9997	9997	9998	9998					
89	·9998	9999	9999	9999	9999	1·000	1·000	1·000	1·000	1·000					

NATURAL COSINES

	0′	6′	12′	18′	24′	30′	36′	42′	48′	54′	Subtract Differences				
											1′	2′	3′	4′	5′
0	1·000	1·000	1·000	1·000	1·000	1·000	9999	9999	9999	9999					
1	·9998	9998	9998	9997	9997	9997	9996	9996	9995	9995					
2	·9994	9993	9993	9992	9991	9990	9990	9989	9988	9987					
3	·9986	9985	9984	9983	9982	9981	9980	9979	9978	9977	0	0	1	1	1
4	·9976	9974	9973	9972	9971	9969	9968	9966	9965	9963	0	0	1	1	1
5	·9962	9960	9959	9957	9956	9954	9952	9951	9949	9947	0	1	1	1	1
6	·9945	9943	9942	9940	9938	9936	9934	9932	9930	9928	0	1	1	1	2
7	·9925	9923	9921	9919	9917	9914	9912	9910	9907	9905	0	1	1	2	2
8	·9903	9900	9898	9895	9893	9890	9888	9885	9882	9880	0	1	1	2	2
9	·9877	9874	9871	9869	9866	9863	9860	9857	9854	9851	0	1	1	2	2
10	·9848	9845	9842	9839	9836	9833	9829	9826	9823	9820	1	1	2	2	3
11	·9816	9813	9810	9806	9803	9799	9796	9792	9789	9785	1	1	2	2	3
12	·9781	9778	9774	9770	9767	9763	9759	9755	9751	9748	1	1	2	3	3
13	·9744	9740	9736	9732	9728	9724	9720	9715	9711	9707	1	1	2	3	3
14	·9703	9699	9694	9690	9686	9681	9677	9673	9668	9664	1	1	2	3	4
15	·9659	9655	9650	9646	9641	9636	9632	9627	9622	9617	1	2	2	3	4
16	·9613	9608	9603	9598	9593	9588	9583	9578	9573	9568	1	2	2	3	4
17	·9563	9558	9553	9548	9542	9537	9532	9527	9521	9516	1	2	3	4	4
18	·9511	9505	9500	9494	9489	9483	9478	9472	9466	9461	1	2	3	4	5
19	·9455	9449	9444	9438	9432	9426	9421	9415	9409	9403	1	2	3	4	5
20	·9397	9391	9385	9379	9373	9367	9361	9354	9348	9342	1	2	3	4	5
21	·9336	9330	9323	9317	9311	9304	9298	9291	9285	9278	1	2	3	4	5
22	·9272	9265	9259	9252	9245	9239	9232	9225	9219	9212	1	2	3	4	6
23	·9205	9198	9191	9184	9178	9171	9164	9157	9150	9143	1	2	3	5	6
24	·9135	9128	9121	9114	9107	9100	9092	9085	9078	9070	1	2	4	5	6
25	·9063	9056	9048	9041	9033	9026	9018	9011	9003	8996	1	3	4	5	6
26	·8988	8980	8973	8965	8957	8949	8942	8934	8926	8918	1	3	4	5	6
27	·8910	8902	8894	8886	8878	8870	8862	8854	8846	8838	1	3	4	5	7
28	·8829	8821	8813	8805	8796	8788	8780	8771	8763	8755	1	3	4	6	7
29	·8746	8738	8729	8721	8712	8704	8695	8686	8678	8669	1	3	4	6	7
30	·8660	8652	8643	8634	8625	8616	8607	8599	8590	8581	1	3	4	6	7
31	·8572	8563	8554	8545	8536	8526	8517	8508	8499	8490	2	3	5	6	8
32	·8480	8471	8462	8453	8443	8434	8425	8415	8406	8396	2	3	5	6	8
33	·8387	8377	8368	8358	8348	8339	8329	8320	8310	8300	2	3	5	6	8
34	·8290	8281	8271	8261	8251	8241	8231	8221	8211	8202	2	3	5	7	8
35	·8192	8181	8171	8161	8151	8141	8131	8121	8111	8100	2	3	5	7	8
36	·8090	8080	8070	8059	8049	8039	8028	8018	8007	7997	2	3	5	7	9
37	·7986	7976	7965	7955	7944	7934	7923	7912	7902	7891	2	4	5	7	9
38	·7880	7869	7859	7848	7837	7826	7815	7804	7793	7782	2	4	5	7	9
39	·7771	7760	7749	7738	7727	7716	7705	7694	7683	7672	2	4	6	7	9
40	·7660	7649	7638	7627	7615	7604	7593	7581	7570	7559	2	4	6	8	9
41	·7547	7536	7524	7513	7501	7490	7478	7466	7455	7443	2	4	6	8	10
42	·7431	7420	7408	7396	7385	7373	7361	7349	7337	7325	2	4	6	8	10
43	·7314	7302	7290	7278	7266	7254	7242	7230	7218	7206	2	4	6	8	10
44	·7193	7181	7169	7157	7145	7133	7120	7108	7096	7083	2	4	6	8	10

NATURAL COSINES

°	0'	6'	12'	18'	24'	30'	36'	42'	48'	54'	Subtract Differences				
---	----	----	-----	-----	-----	-----	-----	-----	-----	-----	1'	2'	3'	4'	5'
45	·7071	7059	7046	7034	7022	7009	6997	6984	6972	6959	2	4	6	8	10
46	·6947	6934	6921	6909	6896	6884	6871	6858	6845	6833	2	4	6	8	11
47	·6820	6807	6794	6782	6769	6756	6743	6730	6717	6704	2	4	6	9	11
48	·6691	6678	6665	6652	6639	6626	6613	6600	6587	6574	2	4	7	9	11
49	·6561	6547	6534	6521	6508	6494	6481	6468	6455	6441	2	4	7	9	11
50	·6428	6414	6401	6388	6374	6361	6347	6334	6320	6307	2	4	7	9	11
51	·6293	6280	6266	6252	6239	6225	6211	6198	6184	6170	2	5	7	9	11
52	·6157	6143	6129	6115	6101	6088	6074	6060	6046	6032	2	5	7	9	12
53	·6018	6004	5990	5976	5962	5948	5934	5920	5906	5892	2	5	7	9	12
54	·5878	5864	5850	5835	5821	5807	5793	5779	5764	5750	2	5	7	9	12
55	·5736	5721	5707	5693	5678	5664	5650	5635	5621	5606	2	5	7	10	12
56	·5592	5577	5563	5548	5534	5519	5505	5490	5476	5461	2	5	7	10	12
57	·5446	5432	5417	5402	5388	5373	5358	5344	5329	5314	2	5	7	10	12
58	·5299	5284	5270	5255	5240	5225	5210	5195	5180	5165	2	5	7	10	12
59	·5150	5135	5120	5105	5090	5075	5060	5045	5030	5015	3	5	8	10	13
60	·5000	4985	4970	4955	4939	4924	4909	4894	4879	4863	3	5	8	10	13
61	·4848	4833	4818	4802	4787	4772	4756	4741	4726	4710	3	5	8	10	13
62	·4695	4679	4664	4648	4633	4617	4602	4586	4571	4555	3	5	8	10	13
63	·4540	4524	4509	4493	4478	4462	4446	4431	4415	4399	3	5	8	10	13
64	·4384	4368	4352	4337	4321	4305	4289	4274	4258	4242	3	5	8	11	13
65	·4226	4210	4195	4179	4163	4147	4131	4115	4099	4083	3	5	8	11	13
66	·4067	4051	4035	4019	4003	3987	3971	3955	3939	3923	3	5	8	11	13
67	·3907	3891	3875	3859	3843	3827	3811	3795	3778	3762	3	5	8	11	13
68	·3746	3730	3714	3697	3681	3665	3649	3633	3616	3600	3	5	8	11	14
69	·3584	3567	3551	3535	3518	3502	3486	3469	3453	3437	3	5	8	11	14
70	·3420	3404	3387	3371	3355	3338	3322	3305	3289	3272	3	5	8	11	14
71	·3256	3239	3223	3206	3190	3173	3156	3140	3123	3107	3	6	8	11	14
72	·3090	3074	3057	3040	3024	3007	2990	2974	2957	2940	3	6	8	11	14
73	·2924	2907	2890	2874	2857	2840	2823	2807	2790	2773	3	6	8	11	14
74	·2756	2740	2723	2706	2689	2672	2656	2639	2622	2605	3	6	8	11	14
75	·2588	2571	2554	2538	2521	2504	2487	2470	2453	2436	3	6	8	11	14
76	·2419	2402	2385	2368	2351	2334	2317	2300	2284	2267	3	6	8	11	14
77	·2250	2233	2215	2198	2181	2164	2147	2130	2113	2096	3	6	9	11	14
78	·2079	2062	2045	2028	2011	1994	1977	1959	1942	1925	3	6	9	11	14
79	·1908	1891	1874	1857	1840	1822	1805	1788	1771	1754	3	6	9	11	14
80	·1736	1719	1702	1685	1668	1650	1633	1616	1599	1582	3	6	9	11	14
81	·1564	1547	1530	1513	1495	1478	1461	1444	1426	1409	3	6	9	12	14
82	·1392	1374	1357	1340	1323	1305	1288	1271	1253	1236	3	6	9	12	14
83	·1219	1201	1184	1167	1149	1132	1115	1097	1080	1063	3	6	9	12	14
84	·1045	1028	1011	0993	0976	0958	0941	0924	0906	0889	3	6	9	12	14
85	·0872	0854	0837	0819	0802	0785	0767	0750	0732	0715	3	6	9	12	14
86	·0698	0680	0663	0645	0628	0610	0593	0576	0558	0541	3	6	9	12	15
87	·0523	0506	0488	0471	0454	0436	0419	0401	0384	0366	3	6	9	12	15
88	·0349	0332	0314	0297	0279	0262	0244	0227	0209	0192	3	6	9	12	15
89	·0175	0157	0140	0122	0105	0087	0070	0052	0035	0017	3	6	9	12	15

11*

NATURAL TANGENTS

	0′	6′	12′	18′	24′	30′	36′	42′	48′	54′	Differences				
											1′	2′	3′	4′	5′
0	·0000	0017	0035	0052	0070	0087	0105	0122	0140	0157	3	6	9	12	15
1	·0175	0192	0209	0227	0244	0262	0279	0297	0314	0332	3	6	9	12	15
2	·0349	0367	0384	0402	0419	0437	0454	0472	0489	0507	3	6	9	12	15
3	·0524	0542	0559	0577	0594	0612	0629	0647	0664	0682	3	6	9	12	15
4	·0699	0717	0734	0752	0769	0787	0805	0822	0840	0857	3	6	9	12	15
5	·0875	0892	0910	0928	0945	0963	0981	0998	1016	1033	3	6	9	12	15
6	·1051	1069	1086	1104	1122	1139	1157	1175	1192	1210	3	6	9	12	15
7	·1228	1246	1263	1281	1299	1317	1334	1352	1370	1388	3	6	9	12	15
8	·1405	1423	1441	1459	1477	1495	1512	1530	1548	1566	3	6	9	12	15
9	·1584	1602	1620	1638	1655	1673	1691	1709	1727	1745	3	6	9	12	15
10	·1763	1781	1799	1817	1835	1853	1871	1890	1908	1926	3	6	9	12	15
11	·1944	1962	1980	1998	2016	2035	2053	2071	2089	2107	3	6	9	12	15
12	·2126	2144	2162	2180	2199	2217	2235	2254	2272	2290	3	6	9	12	15
13	·2309	2327	2345	2364	2382	2401	2419	2438	2456	2475	3	6	9	12	15
14	·2493	2512	2530	2549	2568	2586	2605	2623	2642	2661	3	6	9	12	16
15	·2679	2698	2717	2736	2754	2773	2792	2811	2830	2849	3	6	9	13	16
16	·2867	2886	2905	2924	2943	2962	2981	3000	3019	3038	3	6	9	13	16
17	·3057	3076	3096	3115	3134	3153	3172	3191	3211	3230	3	6	10	13	16
18	·3249	3269	3288	3307	3327	3346	3365	3385	3404	3424	3	6	10	13	16
19	·3443	3463	3482	3502	3522	3541	3561	3581	3600	3620	3	7	10	13	16
20	·3640	3659	3679	3699	3719	3739	3759	3779	3799	3819	3	7	10	13	17
21	·3839	3859	3879	3899	3919	3939	3959	3979	4000	4020	3	7	10	13	17
22	·4040	4061	4081	4101	4122	4142	4163	4183	4204	4224	3	7	10	14	17
23	·4245	4265	4286	4307	4327	4348	4369	4390	4411	4431	3	7	10	14	17
24	·4452	4473	4494	4515	4536	4557	4578	4599	4621	4642	4	7	11	14	18
25	·4663	4684	4706	4727	4748	4770	4791	4813	4834	4856	4	7	11	14	18
26	·4877	4899	4921	4942	4964	4986	5008	5029	5051	5073	4	7	11	15	18
27	·5095	5117	5139	5161	5184	5206	5228	5250	5272	5295	4	7	11	15	18
28	·5317	5340	5362	5384	5407	5430	5452	5475	5498	5520	4	8	11	15	19
29	·5543	5566	5589	5612	5635	5658	5681	5704	5727	5750	4	8	12	15	19
30	·5774	5797	5820	5844	5867	5890	5914	5938	5961	5985	4	8	12	16	20
31	·6009	6032	6056	6080	6104	6128	6152	6176	6200	6224	4	8	12	16	20
32	·6249	6273	6297	6322	6346	6371	6395	6420	6445	6469	4	8	12	16	20
33	·6494	6519	6544	6569	6594	6619	6644	6669	6694	6720	4	8	13	17	21
34	·6745	6771	6796	6822	6847	6873	6899	6924	6950	6976	4	9	13	17	21
35	·7002	7028	7054	7080	7107	7133	7159	7186	7212	7239	4	9	13	18	22
36	·7265	7292	7319	7346	7373	7400	7427	7454	7481	7508	5	9	14	18	23
37	·7536	7563	7590	7618	7646	7673	7701	7729	7757	7785	5	9	14	18	23
38	·7813	7841	7869	7898	7926	7954	7983	8012	8040	8069	5	9	14	19	24
39	·8098	8127	8156	8185	8214	8243	8273	8302	8332	8361	5	10	15	20	24
40	·8391	8421	8451	8481	8511	8541	8571	8601	8632	8662	5	10	15	20	25
41	·8693	8724	8754	8785	8816	8847	8878	8910	8941	8972	5	10	16	21	26
42	·9004	9036	9067	9099	9131	9163	9195	9228	9260	9293	5	11	16	21	27
43	·9325	9358	9391	9424	9457	9490	9523	9556	9590	9623	6	11	17	22	28
44	·9657	9691	9725	9759	9793	9827	9861	9896	9930	9965	6	11	17	23	29

NATURAL TANGENTS

°	0'	6'	12'	18'	24'	30'	36'	42'	48'	54'	Differences				
											1'	2'	3'	4'	5'
45	1·0000	0035	0070	0105	0141	0176	0212	0247	0283	0319	6	12	18	24	30
46	1·0355	0392	0428	0464	0501	0538	0575	0612	0649	0686	6	12	18	25	31
47	1·0724	0761	0799	0837	0875	0913	0951	0990	1028	1067	6	13	19	25	32
48	1·1106	1145	1184	1224	1263	1303	1343	1383	1423	1463	7	13	20	26	33
49	1·1504	1544	1585	1626	1667	1708	1750	1792	1833	1875	7	14	21	28	34
50	1·1918	1960	2002	2045	2088	2131	2174	2218	2261	2305	7	14	22	29	36
51	1·2349	2393	2437	2482	2527	2572	2617	2662	2708	2753	8	15	23	30	38
52	1·2799	2846	2892	2938	2985	3032	3079	3127	3175	3222	8	16	24	31	39
53	1·3270	3319	3367	3416	3465	3514	3564	3613	3663	3713	8	16	25	33	41
54	1·3764	3814	3865	3916	3968	4019	4071	4124	4176	4229	9	17	26	34	43
55	1·4281	4335	4388	4442	4496	4550	4605	4659	4715	4770	9	18	27	36	45
56	1·4826	4882	4938	4994	5051	5108	5166	5224	5282	5340	10	19	29	38	48
57	1·5399	5458	5517	5577	5637	5697	5757	5818	5880	5941	10	20	30	40	50
58	1·6003	6066	6128	6191	6255	6319	6383	6447	6512	6577	11	21	32	43	53
59	1·6643	6709	6775	6842	6909	6977	7045	7113	7180	7251	11	23	34	45	56
60	1·7321	7391	7461	7532	7603	7675	7747	7820	7893	7966	12	24	36	48	60
61	1·8040	8115	8190	8265	8341	8418	8495	8572	8650	8728	13	26	38	51	64
62	1·8807	8887	8967	9047	9128	9210	9292	9375	9458	9542	14	27	41	55	68
63	1·9626	9711	9797	9883	9970	0057	0145	0233	0323	0413	15	29	44	58	73
64	2·0503	0594	0686	0778	0872	0965	1060	1155	1251	1348	16	31	47	63	78
65	2·1445	1543	1642	1742	1842	1943	2045	2148	2251	2355	17	34	51	68	85
66	2·2460	2566	2673	2781	2889	2998	3109	3220	3332	3445	18	37	55	73	91
67	2·3559	3673	3789	3906	4023	4142	4262	4383	4504	4627	20	40	60	79	99
68	2·4751	4876	5002	5129	5257	5386	5517	5649	5782	5916	22	43	65	87	108
69	2·6051	6187	6325	6464	6605	6746	6889	7034	7179	7326	24	47	71	95	119
70	2·7475	7625	7776	7929	8083	8239	8397	8556	8716	8878	26	52	78	104	131
71	2·9042	9208	9375	9544	9714	9887	0061	0237	0415	0595	29	58	87	116	145
72	3·0777	0961	1146	1334	1524	1716	1910	2106	2305	2506	32	64	96	129	161
73	3·2709	2914	3122	3332	3544	3759	3977	4197	4420	4646	36	72	108	144	180
74	3·4874	5105	5339	5576	5816	6059	6305	6554	6806	7062	41	81	122	163	204
75	3·7321	7583	7848	8118	8391	8667	8947	9232	9520	9812	46	93	139	186	232
76	4·0108	0408	0713	1022	1335	1653	1976	2303	2635	2972					
77	4·3315	3662	4015	4373	4737	5107	5483	5864	6252	6646					
78	4·7046	7453	7867	8288	8716	9152	9594	0045	0504	0970					
79	5·1446	1929	2422	2924	3435	3955	4486	5026	5578	6140					
80	5·6713	7297	7894	8502	9124	9758	0405	1066	1742	2432					
81	6·3138	3859	4596	5350	6122	6912	7720	8548	9395	0264					
82	7·1154	2066	3002	3962	4947	5958	6996	8062	9158	0285					
83	8·1443	2636	3863	5126	6427	7769	9152	0579	2052	3572					
84	9·514	9·677	9·845	10·02	10·20	10·39	10·58	10·78	10·99	11·20					
85	11·43	11·66	11·91	12·16	12·43	12·71	13·00	13·30	13·62	13·95					
86	14·30	14·67	15·06	15·46	15·89	16·35	16·83	17·34	17·89	18·46					
87	19·08	19·74	20·45	21·20	22·02	22·90	23·86	24·90	26·03	27·27					
88	28·64	30·14	31·82	33·69	35·80	38·19	40·92	44·07	47·74	52·08					
89	57·29	63·66	71·62	81·85	95·49	114·6	143·2	191·0	286·5	573·0					

	0′	6′	12′	18′	24′	30′	36′	42′	48′	54′	1′	2′	3′	4′	5′
0	−∞	$\bar{3}$·242	$\bar{3}$·543	$\bar{3}$·719	$\bar{3}$·844	$\bar{3}$·941	$\bar{2}$·020	$\bar{2}$·087	$\bar{2}$·145	$\bar{2}$·196					
1	$\bar{2}$·2419	2832	3210	3558	3880	4179	4459	4723	4971	5206					
2	$\bar{2}$·5428	5640	5842	6035	6220	6397	6567	6731	6889	7041					
3	$\bar{2}$·7188	7330	7468	7602	7731	7857	7979	8098	8213	8326					
4	$\bar{2}$·8436	8543	8647	8749	8849	8946	9042	9135	9226	9315					
5	$\bar{2}$·9403	9489	9573	9655	9736	9816	9894	9970	0046	0120	13	26	39	52	66
6	$\bar{1}$·0192	0264	0334	0403	0472	0539	0605	0670	0734	0797	11	22	33	44	55
7	$\bar{1}$·0859	0920	0981	1040	1099	1157	1214	1271	1326	1381	10	19	29	38	48
8	$\bar{1}$·1436	1489	1542	1594	1646	1697	1747	1797	1847	1895	8	17	25	34	42
9	$\bar{1}$·1943	1991	2038	2085	2131	2176	2221	2266	2310	2353	8	15	23	30	38
10	$\bar{1}$·2397	2439	2482	2524	2565	2606	2647	2687	2727	2767	7	14	20	27	34
11	$\bar{1}$·2806	2845	2883	2921	2959	2997	3034	3070	3107	3143	6	12	19	25	31
12	$\bar{1}$·3179	3214	3250	3284	3319	3353	3387	3421	3455	3488	6	11	17	23	28
13	$\bar{1}$·3521	3554	3586	3618	3650	3682	3713	3745	3775	3806	5	11	16	21	26
14	$\bar{1}$·3837	3867	3897	3927	3957	3986	4015	4044	4073	4102	5	10	15	20	24
15	$\bar{1}$·4130	4158	4186	4214	4242	4269	4296	4323	4350	4377	5	9	14	18	23
16	$\bar{1}$·4403	4430	4456	4482	4508	4533	4559	4584	4609	4634	4	9	13	17	21
17	$\bar{1}$·4659	4684	4709	4733	4757	4781	4805	4829	4853	4876	4	8	12	16	20
18	$\bar{1}$·4900	4923	4946	4969	4992	5015	5037	5060	5082	5104	4	8	11	15	19
19	$\bar{1}$·5126	5148	5170	5192	5213	5235	5256	5278	5299	5320	4	7	11	14	18
20	$\bar{1}$·5341	5361	5382	5402	5423	5443	5463	5484	5504	5523	3	7	10	14	17
21	$\bar{1}$·5543	5563	5583	5602	5621	5641	5660	5679	5698	5717	3	6	10	13	16
22	$\bar{1}$·5736	5754	5773	5792	5810	5828	5847	5865	5883	5901	3	6	9	12	15
23	$\bar{1}$·5919	5937	5954	5972	5990	6007	6024	6042	6059	6076	3	6	9	12	15
24	$\bar{1}$·6093	6110	6127	6144	6161	6177	6194	6210	6227	6243	3	6	8	11	14
25	$\bar{1}$·6259	6276	6292	6308	6324	6340	6356	6371	6387	6403	3	5	8	11	13
26	$\bar{1}$·6418	6434	6449	6465	6480	6495	6510	6526	6541	6556	3	5	8	10	13
27	$\bar{1}$·6570	6585	6600	6615	6629	6644	6659	6673	6687	6702	2	5	7	10	12
28	$\bar{1}$·6716	6730	6744	6759	6773	6787	6801	6814	6828	6842	2	5	7	9	12
29	$\bar{1}$·6856	6869	6883	6896	6910	6923	6937	6950	6963	6977	2	4	7	9	11
30	$\bar{1}$·6990	7003	7016	7029	7042	7055	7068	7080	7093	7106	2	4	6	9	11
31	$\bar{1}$·7118	7131	7144	7156	7168	7181	7193	7205	7218	7230	2	4	6	8	10
32	$\bar{1}$·7242	7254	7266	7278	7290	7302	7314	7326	7338	7349	2	4	6	8	10
33	$\bar{1}$·7361	7373	7384	7396	7407	7419	7430	7442	7453	7464	2	4	6	8	10
34	$\bar{1}$·7476	7487	7498	7509	7520	7531	7542	7553	7564	7575	2	4	6	7	9
35	$\bar{1}$·7586	7597	7607	7618	7629	7640	7650	7661	7671	7682	2	4	5	7	9
36	$\bar{1}$·7692	7703	7713	7723	7734	7744	7754	7764	7774	7785	2	3	5	7	9
37	$\bar{1}$·7795	7805	7815	7825	7835	7844	7854	7864	7874	7884	2	3	5	7	8
38	$\bar{1}$·7893	7903	7913	7922	7932	7941	7951	7960	7970	7979	2	3	5	6	8
39	$\bar{1}$·7989	7998	8007	8017	8026	8035	8044	8053	8063	8072	2	3	5	6	8
40	$\bar{1}$·8081	8090	8099	8108	8117	8125	8134	8143	8152	8161	1	3	4	6	7
41	$\bar{1}$·8169	8178	8187	8195	8204	8213	8221	8230	8238	8247	1	3	4	6	7
42	$\bar{1}$·8255	8264	8272	8280	8289	8297	8305	8313	8322	8330	1	3	4	6	7
43	$\bar{1}$·8338	8346	8354	8362	8370	8378	8386	8394	8402	8410	1	3	4	5	7
44	$\bar{1}$·8418	8426	8433	8441	8449	8457	8464	8472	8480	8487	1	3	4	5	6

LOG. SINES

	0'	6'	12'	18'	24'	30'	36'	42'	48'	54'	1'	2'	3'	4'	5'
45	1̄·8495	8502	8510	8517	8525	8532	8540	8547	8555	8562	1	2	4	5	6
46	1̄·8569	8577	8584	8591	8598	8606	8613	8620	8627	8634	1	2	4	5	6
47	1̄·8641	8648	8655	8662	8669	8676	8683	8690	8697	8704	1	2	3	5	6
48	1̄·8711	8718	8724	8731	8738	8745	8751	8758	8765	8771	1	2	3	4	6
49	1̄·8778	8784	8791	8797	8804	8810	8817	8823	8830	8836	1	2	3	4	5
50	1̄·8843	8849	8855	8862	8868	8874	8880	8887	8893	8899	1	2	3	4	5
51	1̄·8905	8911	8917	8923	8929	8935	8941	8947	8953	8959	1	2	3	4	5
52	1̄·8965	8971	8977	8983	8989	8995	9000	9006	9012	9018	1	2	3	4	5
53	1̄·9023	9029	9035	9041	9046	9052	9057	9063	9069	9074	1	2	3	4	5
54	1̄·9080	9085	9091	9096	9101	9107	9112	9118	9123	9128	1	2	3	4	5
55	1̄·9134	9139	9144	9149	9155	9160	9165	9170	9175	9181	1	2	3	3	4
56	1̄·9186	9191	9196	9201	9206	9211	9216	9221	9226	9231	1	2	3	3	4
57	1̄·9236	9241	9246	9251	9255	9260	9265	9270	9275	9279	1	2	2	3	4
58	1̄·9284	9289	9294	9298	9303	9308	9312	9317	9322	9326	1	2	2	3	4
59	1̄·9331	9335	9340	9344	9349	9353	9358	9362	9367	9371	1	1	2	3	4
60	1̄·9373	9380	9384	9388	9393	9397	9401	9406	9410	9414	1	1	2	3	4
61	1̄·9418	9422	9427	9431	9435	9439	9443	9447	9451	9455	1	1	2	3	3
62	1̄·9459	9463	9467	9471	9475	9479	9483	9487	9491	9495	1	1	2	3	3
63	1̄·9499	9503	9506	9510	9514	9518	9522	9525	9529	9533	1	1	2	3	3
64	1̄·9537	9540	9544	9548	9551	9555	9558	9562	9566	9569	1	1	2	2	3
65	1̄·9573	9576	9580	9583	9587	9590	9594	9597	9601	9604	1	1	2	2	3
66	1̄·9607	9611	9614	9617	9621	9624	9627	9631	9634	9637	1	1	2	2	3
67	1̄·9640	9643	9647	9650	9653	9656	9659	9662	9666	9669	1	1	2	2	3
68	1̄·9672	9675	9678	9681	9684	9687	9690	9693	9696	9699	0	1	1	2	2
69	1̄·9702	9704	9707	9710	9713	9716	9719	9722	9724	9727	0	1	1	2	2
70	1̄·9730	9733	9735	9738	9741	9743	9746	9749	9751	9754	0	1	1	2	2
71	1̄·9757	9759	9762	9764	9767	9770	9772	9775	9777	9780	0	1	1	2	2
72	1̄·9782	9785	9787	9789	9792	9794	9797	9799	9801	9804	0	1	1	2	2
73	1̄·9806	9808	9811	9813	9815	9817	9820	9822	9824	9826	0	1	1	1	2
74	1̄·9828	9831	9833	9835	9837	9839	9841	9843	9845	9847	0	1	1	1	2
75	1̄·9849	9851	9853	9855	9857	9859	9861	9863	9865	9867	0	1	1	1	2
76	1̄·9869	9871	9873	9875	9876	9878	9880	9882	9884	9885	0	1	1	1	2
77	1̄·9887	9889	9891	9892	9894	9896	9897	9899	9901	9902	0	1	1	1	1
78	1̄·9904	9906	9907	9909	9910	9912	9913	9915	9916	9918	0	1	1	1	1
79	1̄·9919	9921	9922	9924	9925	9927	9928	9929	9931	9932	0	0	1	1	1
80	1̄·9934	9935	9936	9937	9939	9940	9941	9943	9944	9945	0	0	1	1	1
81	1̄·9946	9947	9949	9950	9951	9952	9953	9954	9955	9956	0	0	1	1	1
82	1̄·9958	9959	9960	9961	9962	9963	9964	9965	9966	9967	0	0	0	1	1
83	1̄·9968	9968	9969	9970	9971	9972	9973	9974	9975	9975					
84	1̄·9976	9977	9978	9978	9979	9980	9981	9981	9982	9983					
85	1̄·9983	9984	9985	9985	9986	9987	9987	9988	9988	9989					
86	1̄·9989	9990	9990	9991	9991	9992	9992	9993	9993	9994					
87	1̄·9994	9994	9995	9995	9996	9996	9996	9996	9997	9997					
88	1̄·9997	9998	9998	9998	9998	9999	9999	9999	9999	9999					
89	1̄·9999	9999	0̄000	0̄000	0̄000	0̄000	0̄000	0̄000	0̄000	0̄000					

LOG. COSINES

	0'	6'	12'	18'	24'	30'	36'	42'	48'	54'	1'	2'	3'	4'	5'
											Subtract Differences				
0	0·0000	0000	0000	0000	0000	0000	0000	0000	0000	9̄999					
1	1̄·9999	9999	9999	9999	9999	9999	9998	9998	9998	9998					
2	1̄·9997	9997	9997	9996	9996	9996	9996	9995	9995	9994					
3	1̄·9994	9994	9993	9993	9992	9992	9991	9991	9990	9990					
4	1̄·9989	9989	9988	9988	9987	9987	9986	9985	9985	9984					
5	1̄·9983	9983	9982	9981	9981	9980	9979	9978	9978	9977					
6	1̄·9976	9975	9975	9974	9973	9972	9971	9970	9969	9968					
7	1̄·9968	9967	9966	9965	9964	9963	9962	9961	9960	9959	0	0	0	1	1
8	1̄·9958	9956	9955	9954	9953	9952	9951	9950	9949	9947	0	0	1	1	1
9	1̄·9946	9945	9944	9943	9941	9940	9939	9937	9936	9935	0	0	1	1	1
10	1̄·9934	9932	9931	9929	9928	9927	9925	9924	9922	9921	0	0	1	1	1
11	1̄·9919	9918	9916	9915	9913	9912	9910	9909	9907	9906	0	1	1	1	1
12	1̄·9904	9902	9901	9899	9897	9896	9894	9892	9891	9889	0	1	1	1	1
13	1̄·9887	9885	9884	9882	9880	9878	9876	9875	9873	9871	0	1	1	1	2
14	1̄·9869	9867	9865	9863	9861	9859	9857	9855	9853	9851	0	1	1	1	2
15	1̄·9849	9847	9845	9843	9841	9839	9837	9835	9833	9831	0	1	1	1	2
16	1̄·9828	9826	9824	9822	9820	9817	9815	9813	9811	9808	0	1	1	1	2
17	1̄·9806	9804	9801	9799	9797	9794	9792	9789	9787	9785	0	1	1	2	2
18	1̄·9782	9780	9777	9775	9772	9770	9767	9764	9762	9759	0	1	1	2	2
19	1̄·9757	9754	9751	9749	9746	9743	9741	9738	9735	9733	0	1	1	2	2
20	1̄·9730	9727	9724	9722	9719	9716	9713	9710	9707	9704	0	1	1	2	2
21	1̄·9702	9699	9696	9693	9690	9687	9684	9681	9678	9675	0	1	1	2	2
22	1̄·9672	9669	9666	9662	9659	9656	9653	9650	9647	9643	1	1	2	2	3
23	1̄·9640	9637	9634	9631	9627	9624	9621	9617	9614	9611	1	1	2	2	3
24	1̄·9607	9604	9601	9597	9594	9590	9587	9583	9580	9576	1	1	2	2	3
25	1̄·9573	9569	9566	9562	9558	9555	9551	9548	9544	9540	1	1	2	2	3
26	1̄·9537	9533	9529	9525	9522	9518	9514	9510	9506	9503	1	1	2	3	3
27	1̄·9499	9495	9491	9487	9483	9479	9475	9471	9467	9463	1	1	2	3	3
28	1̄·9459	9455	9451	9447	9443	9439	9435	9431	9427	9422	1	1	2	3	3
29	1̄·9418	9414	9410	9406	9401	9397	9393	9388	9384	9380	1	1	2	3	4
30	1̄·9375	9371	9367	9362	9358	9353	9349	9344	9340	9335	1	1	2	3	4
31	1̄·9331	9326	9322	9317	9312	9308	9303	9298	9294	9289	1	2	2	3	4
32	1̄·9284	9279	9275	9270	9265	9260	9255	9251	9246	9241	1	2	2	3	4
33	1̄·9236	9231	9226	9221	9216	9211	9206	9201	9196	9191	1	2	3	3	4
34	1̄·9186	9181	9175	9170	9165	9160	9155	9149	9144	9139	1	2	3	3	4
35	1̄·9134	9128	9123	9118	9112	9107	9101	9096	9091	9085	1	2	3	4	5
36	1̄·9080	9074	9069	9063	9057	9052	9046	9041	9035	9029	1	2	3	4	5
37	1̄·9023	9018	9012	9006	9000	8995	8989	8983	8977	8971	1	2	3	4	5
38	1̄·8965	8959	8953	8947	8941	8935	8929	8923	8917	8911	1	2	3	4	5
39	1̄·8905	8899	8893	8887	8880	8874	8868	8862	8855	8849	1	2	3	4	5
40	1̄·8843	8836	8830	8823	8817	8810	8804	8797	8791	8784	1	2	3	4	5
41	1̄·8778	8771	8765	8758	8751	8745	8738	8731	8724	8718	1	2	3	5	6
42	1̄·8711	8704	8697	8690	8683	8676	8669	8662	8655	8648	1	2	3	5	6
43	1̄·8641	8634	8627	8620	8613	8606	8598	8591	8584	8577	1	2	4	5	6
44	1̄·8569	8562	8555	8547	8540	8532	8525	8517	8510	8502	1	2	4	5	6

LOG. COSINES

°	0′	6′	12′	18′	24′	30′	36′	42′	48′	54′	1′	2′	3′	4′	5′
45	$\bar{1}$·8495	8487	8480	8472	8464	8457	8449	8441	8433	8426	1	3	4	5	6
46	$\bar{1}$·8418	8410	8402	8394	8386	8378	8370	8362	8354	8346	1	3	4	5	7
47	$\bar{1}$·8338	8330	8322	8313	8305	8297	8289	8280	8272	8264	1	3	4	6	7
48	$\bar{1}$·8255	8247	8238	8230	8221	8213	8204	8195	8187	8178	1	3	4	6	7
49	$\bar{1}$·8169	8161	8152	8143	8134	8125	8117	8108	8099	8090	1	3	4	6	7
50	$\bar{1}$·8081	8072	8063	8053	8044	8035	8026	8017	8007	7998	2	3	5	6	8
51	$\bar{1}$·7989	7979	7970	7960	7951	7941	7932	7922	7913	7903	2	3	5	6	8
52	$\bar{1}$·7893	7884	7874	7864	7854	7844	7835	7825	7815	7805	2	3	5	7	8
53	$\bar{1}$·7795	7785	7774	7764	7754	7744	7734	7723	7713	7703	2	3	5	7	9
54	$\bar{1}$·7692	7682	7671	7661	7650	7640	7629	7618	7607	7597	2	4	5	7	9
55	$\bar{1}$·7586	7575	7564	7553	7542	7531	7520	7509	7498	7487	2	4	6	7	9
56	$\bar{1}$·7476	7464	7453	7442	7430	7419	7407	7396	7384	7373	2	4	6	8	10
57	$\bar{1}$·7361	7349	7338	7326	7314	7302	7290	7278	7266	7254	2	4	6	8	10
58	$\bar{1}$·7242	7230	7218	7205	7193	7181	7168	7156	7144	7131	2	4	6	8	10
59	$\bar{1}$·7118	7106	7093	7080	7068	7055	7042	7029	7016	7003	2	4	6	9	11
60	$\bar{1}$·6990	6977	6963	6950	6937	6923	6910	6896	6883	6869	2	4	7	9	11
61	$\bar{1}$·6856	6842	6828	6814	6801	6787	6773	6759	6744	6730	2	5	7	9	12
62	$\bar{1}$·6716	6702	6687	6673	6659	6644	6629	6615	6600	6585	2	5	7	10	12
63	$\bar{1}$·6570	6556	6541	6526	6510	6495	6480	6465	6449	6434	3	5	8	10	13
64	$\bar{1}$·6418	6403	6387	6371	6356	6340	6324	6308	6292	6276	3	5	8	11	13
65	$\bar{1}$·6259	6243	6227	6210	6194	6177	6161	6144	6127	6110	3	6	8	11	14
66	$\bar{1}$·6093	6076	6059	6042	6024	6007	5990	5972	5954	5937	3	6	9	12	15
67	$\bar{1}$·5919	5901	5883	5865	5847	5828	5810	5792	5773	5754	3	6	9	12	15
68	$\bar{1}$·5736	5717	5698	5679	5660	5641	5621	5602	5583	5563	3	6	10	13	16
69	$\bar{1}$·5543	5523	5504	5484	5463	5443	5423	5402	5382	5361	3	7	10	14	17
70	$\bar{1}$·5341	5320	5299	5278	5256	5235	5213	5192	5170	5148	4	7	11	14	18
71	$\bar{1}$·5126	5104	5082	5060	5037	5015	4992	4969	4946	4923	4	8	11	15	19
72	$\bar{1}$·4900	4876	4853	4829	4805	4781	4757	4733	4709	4684	4	8	12	16	20
73	$\bar{1}$·4659	4634	4609	4584	4559	4533	4508	4482	4456	4430	4	9	13	17	21
74	$\bar{1}$·4403	4377	4350	4323	4296	4269	4242	4214	4186	4158	5	9	14	18	23
75	$\bar{1}$·4130	4102	4073	4044	4015	3986	3957	3927	3897	3867	5	10	15	20	24
76	$\bar{1}$·3837	3806	3775	3745	3713	3682	3650	3618	3586	3554	5	11	16	21	26
77	$\bar{1}$·3521	3488	3455	3421	3387	3353	3319	3284	3250	3214	6	11	17	23	28
78	$\bar{1}$·3179	3143	3107	3070	3034	2997	2959	2921	2883	2845	6	12	19	25	31
79	$\bar{1}$·2806	2767	2727	2687	2647	2606	2565	2524	2482	2439	7	14	20	27	34
80	$\bar{1}$·2397	2353	2310	2266	2221	2176	2131	2085	2038	1991	8	15	23	30	38
81	$\bar{1}$·1943	1895	1847	1797	1747	1697	1646	1594	1542	1489	8	17	25	34	42
82	$\bar{1}$·1436	1381	1326	1271	1214	1157	1099	1040	0981	0920	10	19	29	38	48
83	$\bar{1}$·0859	0797	0734	0670	0605	0539	0472	0403	0334	0264	11	22	33	44	55
84	$\bar{1}$·0192	0120	0046	$\bar{9}$970	$\bar{9}$894	$\bar{9}$816	$\bar{9}$736	$\bar{9}$655	$\bar{9}$573	$\bar{9}$489	13	26	39	52	66
85	$\bar{2}$·9403	9315	9226	9135	9042	8946	8849	8749	8647	8543					
86	$\bar{2}$·8436	8326	8213	8098	7979	7857	7731	7602	7468	7330					
87	$\bar{2}$·7188	7041	6889	6731	6567	6397	6220	6035	5842	5640					
88	$\bar{2}$·5428	5206	4971	4723	4459	4179	3880	3558	3210	2832					
89	$\bar{2}$·242	$\bar{2}$·196	$\bar{2}$·145	$\bar{2}$·087	$\bar{2}$·020	$\bar{3}$·941	$\bar{3}$·844	$\bar{3}$·719	$\bar{3}$·543	$\bar{3}$·242					

LOG. TANGENTS

	0'	6'	12'	18'	24'	30'	36'	42'	48'	54'	1'	2'	3'	4'	5'
											Differences				
0	— ∞	$\bar{3}$·242	$\bar{3}$·543	$\bar{3}$·719	$\bar{3}$·844	$\bar{3}$·941	$\bar{2}$·020	$\bar{2}$·087	$\bar{2}$·145	$\bar{2}$·196					
1	$\bar{2}$·2419	2833	3211	3559	3881	4181	4461	4725	4973	5208					
2	$\bar{2}$·5431	5643	5845	6038	6223	6401	6571	6736	6894	7046					
3	$\bar{2}$·7194	7337	7475	7609	7739	7865	7988	8107	8223	8336					
4	$\bar{2}$·8446	8554	8659	8762	8862	8960	9056	9150	9241	9331					
5	$\bar{2}$·9420	9506	9591	9674	9756	9836	9915	9992	$\bar{0}$068	$\bar{0}$143	13	26	40	53	66
6	$\bar{1}$·0216	0289	$\bar{0}$360	0430	0499	0567	0633	0699	0764	0828	11	22	34	45	56
7	$\bar{1}$·0891	0954	1015	1076	1135	1194	1252	1310	1367	1423	10	20	29	39	49
8	$\bar{1}$·1478	1533	1587	1640	1693	1745	1797	1848	1898	1948	9	17	26	35	43
9	$\bar{1}$·1997	2046	2094	2142	2189	2236	2282	2328	2374	2419	8	16	23	31	39
10	$\bar{1}$·2463	2507	2551	2594	2637	2680	2722	2764	2805	2846	7	14	21	28	35
11	$\bar{1}$·2887	2927	2967	3006	3046	3085	3123	3162	3200	3237	6	13	19	26	32
12	$\bar{1}$·3275	3312	3349	3385	3422	3458	3493	3529	3564	3599	6	12	18	24	30
13	$\bar{1}$·3634	3668	3702	3736	3770	3804	3837	3870	3903	3935	6	11	17	22	28
14	$\bar{1}$·3968	4000	4032	4064	4095	4127	4158	4189	4220	4250	5	10	16	21	26
15	$\bar{1}$·4281	4311	4341	4371	4400	4430	4459	4488	4517	4546	5	10	15	20	25
16	$\bar{1}$·4575	4603	4632	4660	4688	4716	4744	4771	4799	4826	5	9	14	19	23
17	$\bar{1}$·4853	4880	4907	4934	4961	4987	5014	5040	5066	5092	4	9	13	18	22
18	$\bar{1}$·5118	5143	5169	5195	5220	5245	5270	5295	5320	5345	4	8	13	17	21
19	$\bar{1}$·5370	5394	5419	5443	5467	5491	5516	5539	5563	5587	4	8	12	16	20
20	$\bar{1}$·5611	5634	5658	5681	5704	5727	5750	5773	5796	5819	4	8	12	15	19
21	$\bar{1}$·5842	5864	5887	5909	5932	5954	5976	5998	6020	6042	4	7	11	15	19
22	$\bar{1}$·6064	6086	6108	6129	6151	6172	6194	6215	6236	6257	4	7	11	14	18
23	$\bar{1}$·6279	6300	6321	6341	6362	6383	6404	6424	6445	6465	3	7	10	14	17
24	$\bar{1}$·6486	6506	6527	6547	6567	6587	6607	6627	6647	6667	3	7	10	13	17
25	$\bar{1}$·6687	6706	6726	6746	6765	6785	6804	6824	6843	6863	3	7	10	13	16
26	$\bar{1}$·6882	6901	6920	6939	6958	6977	6996	7015	7034	7053	3	6	9	13	16
27	$\bar{1}$·7072	7090	7109	7128	7146	7165	7183	7202	7220	7238	3	6	9	12	15
28	$\bar{1}$·7257	7275	7293	7311	7330	7348	7366	7384	7402	7420	3	6	9	12	15
29	$\bar{1}$·7438	7455	7473	7491	7509	7526	7544	7562	7579	7597	3	6	9	12	15
30	$\bar{1}$·7614	7632	7649	7667	7684	7701	7719	7736	7753	7771	3	6	9	12	14
31	$\bar{1}$·7788	7805	7822	7839	7856	7873	7890	7907	7924	7941	3	6	9	11	14
32	$\bar{1}$·7958	7975	7992	8008	8025	8042	8059	8075	8092	8109	3	6	8	11	14
33	$\bar{1}$·8125	8142	8158	8175	8191	8208	8224	8241	8257	8274	3	5	8	11	14
34	$\bar{1}$·8290	8306	8323	8339	8355	8371	8388	8404	8420	8436	3	5	8	11	14
35	$\bar{1}$·8452	8468	8484	8501	8517	8533	8549	8565	8581	8597	3	5	8	11	13
36	$\bar{1}$·8613	8629	8644	8660	8676	8692	8708	8724	8740	8755	3	5	8	11	13
37	$\bar{1}$·8771	8787	8803	8818	8834	8850	8865	8881	8897	8912	3	5	8	10	13
38	$\bar{1}$·8928	8944	8959	8975	8990	9006	9022	9037	9053	9068	3	5	8	10	13
39	$\bar{1}$·9084	9099	9115	9130	9146	9161	9176	9192	9207	9223	3	5	8	10	13
40	$\bar{1}$·9238	9254	9269	9284	9300	9315	9330	9346	9361	9376	3	5	8	10	13
41	$\bar{1}$·9392	9407	9422	9438	9453	9468	9483	9499	9514	9529	3	5	8	10	13
42	$\bar{1}$·9544	9560	9575	9590	9605	9621	9636	9651	9666	9681	3	5	8	10	13
43	$\bar{1}$·9697	9712	9727	9742	9757	9772	9788	9803	9818	9833	3	5	8	10	13
44	$\bar{1}$·9848	9864	9879	9894	9909	9924	9939	9955	9970	9985	3	5	8	10	13

LOG. TANGENTS

°	0′	6′	12′	18′	24′	30′	36′	42′	48′	54′	1′	2′	3′	4′	5′
45	·0000	0015	0030	0045	0061	0076	0091	0106	0121	0136	3	5	8	10	13
46	·0152	0167	0182	0197	0212	0228	0243	0258	0273	0288	3	5	8	10	13
47	·0303	0319	0334	0349	0364	0379	0395	0410	0425	0440	3	5	8	10	13
48	·0456	0471	0486	0501	0517	0532	0547	0562	0578	0593	3	5	8	10	13
49	·0608	0624	0639	0654	0670	0685	0700	0716	0731	0746	3	5	8	10	13
50	·0762	0777	0793	0808	0824	0839	0854	0870	0885	0901	3	5	8	10	13
51	·0916	0932	0947	0963	0978	0994	1010	1025	1041	1056	3	5	8	10	13
52	·1072	1088	1103	1119	1135	1150	1166	1182	1197	1213	3	5	8	10	13
53	·1229	1245	1260	1276	1292	1308	1324	1340	1356	1371	3	5	8	11	13
54	·1387	1403	1419	1435	1451	1467	1483	1499	1516	1532	3	5	8	11	13
55	·1548	1564	1580	1596	1612	1629	1645	1661	1677	1694	3	5	8	11	14
56	·1710	1726	1743	1759	1776	1792	1809	1825	1842	1858	3	5	8	11	14
57	·1875	1891	1908	1925	1941	1958	1975	1992	2008	2025	3	6	8	11	14
58	·2042	2059	2076	2093	2110	2127	2144	2161	2178	2195	3	6	9	11	14
59	·2212	2229	2247	2264	2281	2299	2316	2333	2351	2368	3	6	9	12	14
60	·2386	2403	2421	2438	2456	2474	2491	2509	2527	2545	3	6	9	12	15
61	·2562	2580	2598	2616	2634	2652	2670	2689	2707	2725	3	6	9	12	15
62	·2743	2762	2780	2798	2817	2835	2854	2872	2891	2910	3	6	9	12	15
63	·2928	2947	2966	2985	3004	3023	3042	3061	3080	3099	3	6	9	13	16
64	·3118	3137	3157	3176	3196	3215	3235	3254	3274	3294	3	7	10	13	16
65	·3313	3333	3353	3373	3393	3413	3433	3453	3473	3494	3	7	10	13	17
66	·3514	3535	3555	3576	3596	3617	3638	3659	3679	3700	3	7	10	14	17
67	·3721	3743	3764	3785	3806	3828	3849	3871	3892	3914	4	7	11	14	18
68	·3936	3958	3980	4002	4024	4046	4068	4091	4113	4136	4	7	11	15	19
69	·4158	4181	4204	4227	4250	4273	4296	4319	4342	4366	4	8	12	15	19
70	·4389	4413	4437	4461	4484	4509	4533	4557	4581	4606	4	8	12	16	20
71	·4630	4655	4680	4705	4730	4755	4780	4805	4831	4857	4	8	13	17	21
72	·4882	4908	4934	4960	4986	5013	5039	5066	5093	5120	4	9	13	18	22
73	·5147	5174	5201	5229	5256	5284	5312	5340	5368	5397	5	9	14	19	23
74	·5425	5454	5483	5512	5541	5570	5600	5629	5659	5689	5	10	15	20	25
75	·5719	5750	5780	5811	5842	5873	5905	5936	5968	6000	5	10	16	21	26
76	·6032	6065	6097	6130	6163	6196	6230	6264	6298	6332	6	11	17	22	28
77	·6366	6401	6436	6471	6507	6542	6578	6615	6651	6688	6	12	18	24	30
78	·6725	6763	6800	6838	6877	6915	6954	6994	7033	7073	6	13	19	26	32
79	·7113	7154	7195	7236	7278	7320	7363	7406	7449	7493	7	14	21	28	35
80	·7537	7581	7626	7672	7718	7764	7811	7858	7906	7954	8	16	23	31	39
81	·8003	8052	8102	8152	8203	8255	8307	8360	8413	8467	9	17	26	35	43
82	·8522	8577	8633	8690	8748	8806	8865	8924	8985	9046	10	20	29	39	49
83	·9109	9172	9236	9301	9367	9433	9501	9570	9640	9711	11	22	34	45	56
84	·9784	9857	9932	0̄008	0̄085	0̄164	0̄244	0̄326	0̄409	0̄494	13	26	40	53	66
85	1·0580	0669	0759	0850	0944	1040	1138	1238	1341	1446					
86	1·1554	1664	1777	1893	2012	2135	2261	2391	2525	2663					
87	1·2806	2954	3106	3264	3429	3599	3777	3962	4155	4357					
88	1·4569	4792	5027	5275	5539	5819	6119	6441	6789	7167					
89	1·7581	8038	8550	9130	9800	0̄591	1̄561	2̄810	4̄571	7̄581					

SQUARES

| | 0 | 1 | 2 | 3 | 4 | 5 | 6 | 7 | 8 | 9 | \
Differences | | | | | | | | |
|---|---|---|---|---|---|---|---|---|---|---|---|---|---|---|---|---|---|---|---|
| | | | | | | | | | | | 1 | 2 | 3 | 4 | 5 | 6 | 7 | 8 | 9 |
| 10 | 1000 | 1020 | 1040 | 1061 | 1082 | 1103 | 1124 | 1145 | 1166 | 1188 | 2 | 4 | 6 | 8 | 11 | 13 | 15 | 17 | 19 |
| 11 | 1210 | 1232 | 1254 | 1277 | 1300 | 1323 | 1346 | 1369 | 1392 | 1416 | 2 | 5 | 7 | 9 | 12 | 14 | 16 | 18 | 21 |
| 12 | 1440 | 1464 | 1488 | 1513 | 1538 | 1563 | 1588 | 1613 | 1638 | 1664 | 3 | 5 | 8 | 10 | 13 | 15 | 18 | 20 | 23 |
| 13 | 1690 | 1716 | 1742 | 1769 | 1796 | 1823 | 1850 | 1877 | 1904 | 1932 | 3 | 5 | 8 | 11 | 14 | 16 | 19 | 22 | 24 |
| 14 | 1960 | 1988 | 2016 | 2045 | 2074 | 2103 | 2132 | 2161 | 2190 | 2220 | 3 | 6 | 9 | 12 | 15 | 17 | 20 | 23 | 26 |
| 15 | 2250 | 2280 | 2310 | 2341 | 2372 | 2403 | 2434 | 2465 | 2496 | 2528 | 3 | 6 | 9 | 12 | 16 | 19 | 22 | 25 | 28 |
| 16 | 2560 | 2592 | 2624 | 2657 | 2690 | 2723 | 2756 | 2789 | 2822 | 2856 | 3 | 7 | 10 | 13 | 17 | 20 | 23 | 26 | 30 |
| 17 | 2890 | 2924 | 2958 | 2993 | 3028 | 3063 | 3098 | 3133 | 3168 | 3204 | 4 | 7 | 11 | 14 | 18 | 21 | 25 | 28 | 32 |
| 18 | 3240 | 3276 | 3312 | 3349 | 3386 | 3423 | 3460 | 3497 | 3534 | 3572 | 4 | 7 | 11 | 15 | 19 | 22 | 26 | 30 | 33 |
| 19 | 3610 | 3648 | 3686 | 3725 | 3764 | 3803 | 3842 | 3881 | 3920 | 3960 | 4 | 8 | 12 | 16 | 20 | 23 | 27 | 31 | 35 |
| 20 | 4000 | 4040 | 4080 | 4121 | 4162 | 4203 | 4244 | 4285 | 4326 | 4368 | 4 | 8 | 12 | 16 | 21 | 25 | 29 | 33 | 37 |
| 21 | 4410 | 4452 | 4494 | 4537 | 4580 | 4623 | 4666 | 4709 | 4752 | 4796 | 4 | 9 | 13 | 17 | 22 | 26 | 30 | 34 | 39 |
| 22 | 4840 | 4884 | 4928 | 4973 | 5018 | 5063 | 5108 | 5153 | 5198 | 5244 | 5 | 9 | 14 | 18 | 23 | 27 | 32 | 36 | 41 |
| 23 | 5290 | 5336 | 5382 | 5429 | 5476 | 5523 | 5570 | 5617 | 5664 | 5712 | 5 | 9 | 14 | 19 | 24 | 28 | 33 | 38 | 42 |
| 24 | 5760 | 5808 | 5856 | 5905 | 5954 | 6003 | 6052 | 6101 | 6150 | 6200 | 5 | 10 | 15 | 20 | 25 | 29 | 34 | 39 | 44 |
| 25 | 6250 | 6300 | 6350 | 6401 | 6452 | 6503 | 6554 | 6605 | 6656 | 6708 | 5 | 10 | 15 | 20 | 26 | 31 | 36 | 41 | 46 |
| 26 | 6760 | 6812 | 6864 | 6917 | 6970 | 7023 | 7076 | 7129 | 7182 | 7236 | 5 | 11 | 16 | 21 | 27 | 32 | 37 | 42 | 48 |
| 27 | 7290 | 7344 | 7398 | 7453 | 7508 | 7563 | 7618 | 7673 | 7728 | 7784 | 6 | 11 | 17 | 22 | 28 | 33 | 39 | 44 | 50 |
| 28 | 7840 | 7896 | 7952 | 8009 | 8066 | 8123 | 8180 | 8237 | 8294 | 8352 | 6 | 11 | 17 | 23 | 29 | 34 | 40 | 46 | 51 |
| 29 | 8410 | 8468 | 8526 | 8585 | 8644 | 8703 | 8762 | 8821 | 8880 | 8940 | 6 | 12 | 18 | 24 | 30 | 35 | 41 | 47 | 53 |
| 30 | 9000 | 9060 | 9120 | 9181 | 9242 | 9303 | 9364 | 9425 | 9486 | 9548 | 6 | 12 | 18 | 24 | 31 | 37 | 43 | 49 | 55 |
| 31 | 9610 | 9672 | 9734 | 9797 | 9860 | 9923 | 9986 | | | | 6 | 13 | 19 | 25 | 32 | 38 | 44 | 50 | 57 |
| 31 | | | | | | | | 1005 | 1011 | 1018 | 1 | 1 | 2 | 3 | 3 | 4 | 4 | 5 | 6 |
| 32 | 1024 | 1030 | 1037 | 1043 | 1050 | 1056 | 1063 | 1069 | 1076 | 1082 | 1 | 1 | 2 | 3 | 3 | 4 | 5 | 5 | 6 |
| 33 | 1089 | 1096 | 1102 | 1109 | 1116 | 1122 | 1129 | 1136 | 1142 | 1149 | 1 | 1 | 2 | 3 | 3 | 4 | 5 | 5 | 6 |
| 34 | 1156 | 1163 | 1170 | 1176 | 1183 | 1190 | 1197 | 1204 | 1211 | 1218 | 1 | 1 | 2 | 3 | 3 | 4 | 5 | 6 | 6 |
| 35 | 1225 | 1232 | 1239 | 1246 | 1253 | 1260 | 1267 | 1274 | 1282 | 1289 | 1 | 1 | 2 | 3 | 4 | 4 | 5 | 6 | 6 |
| 36 | 1296 | 1303 | 1310 | 1318 | 1325 | 1332 | 1340 | 1347 | 1354 | 1362 | 1 | 1 | 2 | 3 | 4 | 4 | 5 | 6 | 7 |
| 37 | 1369 | 1376 | 1384 | 1391 | 1399 | 1406 | 1414 | 1421 | 1429 | 1436 | 1 | 2 | 2 | 3 | 4 | 5 | 5 | 6 | 7 |
| 38 | 1444 | 1452 | 1459 | 1467 | 1475 | 1482 | 1490 | 1498 | 1505 | 1513 | 1 | 2 | 2 | 3 | 4 | 5 | 5 | 6 | 7 |
| 39 | 1521 | 1529 | 1537 | 1544 | 1552 | 1560 | 1568 | 1576 | 1584 | 1592 | 1 | 2 | 2 | 3 | 4 | 5 | 6 | 6 | 7 |
| 40 | 1600 | 1608 | 1616 | 1624 | 1632 | 1640 | 1648 | 1656 | 1665 | 1673 | 1 | 2 | 2 | 3 | 4 | 5 | 6 | 6 | 7 |
| 41 | 1681 | 1689 | 1697 | 1706 | 1714 | 1722 | 1731 | 1739 | 1747 | 1756 | 1 | 2 | 2 | 3 | 4 | 5 | 6 | 7 | 7 |
| 42 | 1764 | 1772 | 1781 | 1789 | 1798 | 1806 | 1815 | 1823 | 1832 | 1840 | 1 | 2 | 3 | 3 | 4 | 5 | 6 | 7 | 8 |
| 43 | 1849 | 1858 | 1866 | 1875 | 1884 | 1892 | 1901 | 1910 | 1918 | 1927 | 1 | 2 | 3 | 4 | 4 | 5 | 6 | 7 | 8 |
| 44 | 1936 | 1945 | 1954 | 1962 | 1971 | 1980 | 1989 | 1998 | 2007 | 2016 | 1 | 2 | 3 | 4 | 5 | 5 | 6 | 7 | 8 |
| 45 | 2025 | 2034 | 2043 | 2052 | 2061 | 2070 | 2079 | 2088 | 2098 | 2107 | 1 | 2 | 3 | 4 | 5 | 5 | 6 | 7 | 8 |
| 46 | 2116 | 2125 | 2134 | 2144 | 2153 | 2162 | 2172 | 2181 | 2190 | 2200 | 1 | 2 | 3 | 4 | 5 | 6 | 7 | 7 | 8 |
| 47 | 2209 | 2218 | 2228 | 2237 | 2247 | 2256 | 2266 | 2275 | 2285 | 2294 | 1 | 2 | 3 | 4 | 5 | 6 | 7 | 8 | 9 |
| 48 | 2304 | 2314 | 2323 | 2333 | 2343 | 2352 | 2362 | 2372 | 2381 | 2391 | 1 | 2 | 3 | 4 | 5 | 6 | 7 | 8 | 9 |
| 49 | 2401 | 2411 | 2421 | 2430 | 2440 | 2450 | 2460 | 2470 | 2480 | 2490 | 1 | 2 | 3 | 4 | 5 | 6 | 7 | 8 | 9 |
| 50 | 2500 | 2510 | 2520 | 2530 | 2540 | 2550 | 2560 | 2570 | 2581 | 2591 | 1 | 2 | 3 | 4 | 5 | 6 | 7 | 8 | 9 |
| 51 | 2601 | 2611 | 2621 | 2632 | 2642 | 2652 | 2663 | 2673 | 2683 | 2694 | 1 | 2 | 3 | 4 | 5 | 6 | 7 | 8 | 9 |
| 52 | 2704 | 2714 | 2725 | 2735 | 2746 | 2756 | 2767 | 2777 | 2788 | 2798 | 1 | 2 | 3 | 4 | 5 | 6 | 7 | 8 | 9 |
| 53 | 2809 | 2820 | 2830 | 2841 | 2852 | 2862 | 2873 | 2884 | 2894 | 2905 | 1 | 2 | 3 | 4 | 5 | 6 | 7 | 9 | 10 |
| 54 | 2916 | 2927 | 2938 | 2948 | 2959 | 2970 | 2981 | 2992 | 3003 | 3014 | 1 | 2 | 3 | 4 | 6 | 7 | 8 | 9 | 10 |

SQUARES

	0	1	2	3	4	5	6	7	8	9	Differences 1	2	3	4	5	6	7	8	9
55	3025	3036	3047	3058	3069	3080	3091	3102	3114	3125	1	2	3	4	6	7	8	9	10
56	3136	3147	3158	3170	3181	3192	3204	3215	3226	3238	1	2	3	5	6	7	8	9	10
57	3249	3260	3272	3283	3295	3306	3318	3329	3341	3352	1	2	3	5	6	7	8	9	10
58	3364	3376	3387	3399	3411	3422	3434	3446	3457	3469	1	2	4	5	6	7	8	9	11
59	3481	3493	3505	3516	3528	3540	3552	3564	3576	3588	1	2	4	5	6	7	8	10	11
60	3600	3612	3624	3636	3648	3660	3672	3684	3697	3709	1	2	4	5	6	7	8	10	11
61	3721	3733	3745	3758	3770	3782	3795	3807	3819	3832	1	2	4	5	6	7	9	10	11
62	3844	3856	3869	3881	3894	3906	3919	3931	3944	3956	1	3	4	5	6	8	9	10	11
63	3969	3982	3994	4007	4020	4032	4045	4058	4070	4083	1	3	4	5	6	8	9	10	11
64	4096	4109	4122	4134	4147	4160	4173	4186	4199	4212	1	3	4	5	6	8	9	10	12
65	4225	4238	4251	4264	4277	4290	4303	4316	4330	4343	1	3	4	5	7	8	9	10	12
66	4356	4369	4382	4396	4409	4422	4436	4449	4462	4476	1	3	4	5	7	8	9	11	12
67	4489	4502	4516	4529	4543	4556	4570	4583	4597	4610	1	3	4	5	7	8	9	11	12
68	4624	4638	4651	4665	4679	4692	4706	4720	4733	4747	1	3	4	5	7	8	10	11	12
69	4761	4775	4789	4802	4816	4830	4844	4858	4872	4886	1	3	4	6	7	8	10	11	13
70	4900	4914	4928	4942	4956	4970	4984	4998	5013	5027	1	3	4	6	7	8	10	11	13
71	5041	5055	5069	5084	5098	5112	5127	5141	5155	5170	1	3	4	6	7	9	10	11	13
72	5184	5198	5213	5227	5242	5256	5271	5285	5300	5314	1	3	4	6	7	9	10	12	13
73	5329	5344	5358	5373	5388	5402	5417	5432	5446	5461	1	3	4	6	7	9	10	12	13
74	5476	5491	5506	5520	5535	5550	5565	5580	5595	5610	1	3	4	6	7	9	10	12	13
75	5625	5640	5655	5670	5685	5700	5715	5730	5746	5761	2	3	5	6	8	9	11	12	14
76	5776	5791	5806	5822	5837	5852	5868	5883	5898	5914	2	3	5	6	8	9	11	12	14
77	5929	5944	5960	5975	5991	6006	6022	6037	6053	6068	2	3	5	6	8	9	11	12	14
78	6084	6100	6115	6131	6147	6162	6178	6194	6209	6225	2	3	5	6	8	9	11	13	14
79	6241	6257	6273	6288	6304	6320	6336	6352	6368	6384	2	3	5	6	8	10	11	13	14
80	6400	6416	6432	6448	6464	6480	6496	6512	6529	6545	2	3	5	6	8	10	11	13	14
81	6561	6577	6593	6610	6626	6642	6659	6675	6691	6708	2	3	5	7	8	10	11	13	15
82	6724	6740	6757	6773	6790	6806	6823	6839	6856	6872	2	3	5	7	8	10	12	13	15
83	6889	6906	6922	6939	6956	6972	6989	7006	7022	7039	2	3	5	7	8	10	12	13	15
84	7056	7073	7090	7106	7123	7140	7157	7174	7191	7208	2	3	5	7	8	10	12	14	15
85	7225	7242	7259	7276	7293	7310	7327	7344	7362	7379	2	3	5	7	9	10	12	14	15
86	7396	7413	7430	7448	7465	7482	7500	7517	7534	7552	2	3	5	7	9	10	12	14	16
87	7569	7586	7604	7621	7639	7656	7674	7691	7709	7726	2	4	5	7	9	11	12	14	16
88	7744	7762	7779	7797	7815	7832	7850	7868	7885	7903	2	4	5	7	9	11	12	14	16
89	7921	7939	7957	7974	7992	8010	8028	8046	8064	8082	2	4	5	7	9	11	13	14	16
90	8100	8118	8136	8154	8172	8190	8208	8226	8245	8263	2	4	5	7	9	11	13	14	16
91	8281	8299	8317	8336	8354	8372	8391	8409	8427	8446	2	4	5	7	9	11	13	15	16
92	8464	8482	8501	8519	8538	8556	8575	8593	8612	8630	2	4	6	7	9	11	13	15	17
93	8649	8668	8686	8705	8724	8742	8761	8780	8798	8817	2	4	6	7	9	11	13	15	17
94	8836	8855	8874	8892	8911	8930	8949	8968	8987	9006	2	4	6	8	9	11	13	15	17
95	9025	9044	9063	9082	9101	9120	9139	9158	9178	9197	2	4	6	8	10	11	13	15	17
96	9216	9235	9254	9274	9293	9312	9332	9351	9370	9390	2	4	6	8	10	12	14	15	17
97	9409	9428	9448	9467	9487	9506	9526	9545	9565	9584	2	4	6	8	10	12	14	16	18
98	9604	9624	9643	9663	9683	9702	9722	9742	9761	9781	2	4	6	8	10	12	14	16	18
99	9801	9821	9841	9860	9880	9900	9920	9940	9960	9980	2	4	6	8	10	12	14	16	18

RECIPROCALS

	0	1	2	3	4	5	6	7	8	9	Subtract Differences								
											1	2	3	4	5	6	7	8	9
1·0	1·0000	9901	9804	9709	9615	9524	9434	9346	9259	9174	9	18	27	36	45	55	64	73	82
1·1	·9091	9009	8929	8850	8772	8696	8621	8547	8475	8403	8	15	23	30	38	45	53	61	68
1·2	·8333	8264	8197	8130	8065	8000	7937	7874	7813	7752	6	13	19	26	32	38	45	51	58
1·3	·7692	7634	7576	7519	7463	7407	7353	7299	7246	7194	5	11	16	22	27	33	38	44	49
1·4	·7143	7092	7042	6993	6944	6897	6849	6803	6757	6711	5	10	14	19	24	29	33	38	43
1·5	·6667	6623	6579	6536	6494	6452	6410	6369	6329	6289	4	8	13	17	21	25	29	33	38
1·6	·6250	6211	6173	6135	6098	6061	6024	5988	5952	5917	4	7	11	15	18	22	26	29	33
1·7	·5882	5848	5814	5780	5747	5714	5682	5650	5618	5587	3	6	10	13	16	20	23	26	29
1·8	·5556	5525	5495	5464	5435	5405	5376	5348	5319	5291	3	6	9	12	15	18	20	23	26
1·9	·5263	5236	5208	5181	5155	5128	5102	5076	5051	5025	3	5	8	11	13	16	18	21	24
2·0	·5000	4975	4950	4926	4902	4878	4854	4831	4808	4785	2	5	7	10	12	14	17	19	21
2·1	·4762	4739	4717	4695	4673	4651	4630	4608	4587	4566	2	4	7	9	11	13	15	17	20
2·2	·4545	4525	4505	4484	4464	4444	4425	4405	4386	4367	2	4	6	8	10	12	14	16	18
2·3	·4348	4329	4310	4292	4274	4255	4237	4219	4202	4184	2	4	5	7	9	11	13	14	16
2·4	·4167	4149	4132	4115	4098	4082	4065	4049	4032	4016	2	3	5	7	8	10	12	13	15
2·5	·4000	3984	3968	3953	3937	3922	3906	3891	3876	3861	2	3	5	6	8	9	11	12	14
2·6	·3846	3831	3817	3802	3788	3774	3759	3745	3731	3717	1	3	4	6	7	9	10	11	13
2·7	·3704	3690	3676	3663	3650	3636	3623	3610	3597	3584	1	3	4	5	7	8	9	11	12
2·8	·3571	3559	3546	3534	3521	3509	3497	3484	3472	3460	1	2	4	5	6	7	9	10	11
2·9	·3448	3436	3425	3413	3401	3390	3378	3367	3356	3344	1	2	3	5	6	7	8	9	10
3·0	·3333	3322	3311	3300	3289	3279	3268	3257	3247	3236	1	2	3	4	5	6	7	9	10
3·1	·3226	3215	3205	3195	3185	3175	3165	3155	3145	3135	1	2	3	4	5	6	7	8	9
3·2	·3125	3115	3106	3096	3086	3077	3067	3058	3049	3040	1	2	3	4	5	6	7	8	9
3·3	·3030	3021	3012	3003	2994	2985	2976	2967	2959	2950	1	2	3	4	4	5	6	7	8
3·4	·2941	2933	2924	2915	2907	2899	2890	2882	2874	2865	1	2	3	3	4	5	6	7	8
3·5	·2857	2849	2841	2833	2825	2817	2809	2801	2793	2786	1	2	2	3	4	5	6	6	7
3·6	·2778	2770	2762	2755	2747	2740	2732	2725	2717	2710	1	2	2	3	4	5	5	6	7
3·7	·2703	2695	2688	2681	2674	2667	2660	2653	2646	2639	1	1	2	3	4	4	5	6	6
3·8	·2632	2625	2618	2611	2604	2597	2591	2584	2577	2571	1	1	2	3	3	4	5	5	6
3·9	·2564	2558	2551	2545	2538	2532	2525	2519	2513	2506	1	1	2	3	3	4	4	5	6
4·0	·2500	2494	2488	2481	2475	2469	2463	2457	2451	2445	1	1	2	2	3	4	4	5	5
4·1	·2439	2433	2427	2421	2415	2410	2404	2398	2392	2387	1	1	2	2	3	3	4	5	5
4·2	·2381	2375	2370	2364	2358	2353	2347	2342	2336	2331	1	1	2	2	3	3	4	5	5
4·3	·2326	2320	2315	2309	2304	2299	2294	2288	2283	2278	1	1	2	2	3	3	4	4	5
4·4	·2273	2268	2262	2257	2252	2247	2242	2237	2232	2227	1	1	2	2	3	3	4	4	5
4·5	·2222	2217	2212	2208	2203	2198	2193	2188	2183	2179	0	1	1	2	2	3	3	4	4
4·6	·2174	2169	2165	2160	2155	2151	2146	2141	2137	2132	0	1	1	2	2	3	3	4	4
4·7	·2128	2123	2119	2114	2110	2105	2101	2096	2092	2088	0	1	1	2	2	3	3	4	4
4·8	·2083	2079	2075	2070	2066	2062	2058	2053	2049	2045	0	1	1	2	2	2	3	3	4
4·9	·2041	2037	2033	2028	2024	2020	2016	2012	2008	2004	0	1	1	2	2	2	3	3	4
5·0	·2000	1996	1992	1988	1984	1980	1976	1972	1969	1965	0	1	1	2	2	2	3	3	4
5·1	·1961	1957	1953	1949	1946	1942	1938	1934	1931	1927	0	1	1	2	2	2	3	3	3
5·2	·1923	1919	1916	1912	1908	1905	1901	1898	1894	1890	0	1	1	1	2	2	3	3	3
5·3	·1887	1883	1880	1876	1873	1869	1866	1862	1859	1855	0	1	1	1	2	2	2	3	3
5·4	·1852	1848	1845	1842	1838	1835	1832	1828	1825	1821	0	1	1	1	2	2	2	3	3

RECIPROCALS

	0	1	2	3	4	5	6	7	8	9	Subtract Differences								
											1	2	3	4	5	6	7	8	9
5·5	·1818	1815	1812	1808	1805	1802	1799	1795	1792	1789	0	1	1	1	2	2	2	3	3
5·6	·1786	1783	1779	1776	1773	1770	1767	1764	1761	1757	0	1	1	1	2	2	2	3	3
5·7	·1754	1751	1748	1745	1742	1739	1736	1733	1730	1727	0	1	1	1	2	2	2	2	3
5·8	·1724	1721	1718	1715	1712	1709	1706	1704	1701	1698	0	1	1	1	1	2	2	2	3
5·9	·1695	1692	1689	1686	1684	1681	1678	1675	1672	1669	0	1	1	1	1	2	2	2	3
6·0	·1667	1664	1661	1658	1656	1653	1650	1647	1645	1642	0	1	1	1	1	2	2	2	2
6·1	·1639	1637	1634	1631	1629	1626	1623	1621	1618	1616	0	1	1	1	1	2	2	2	2
6·2	·1613	1610	1608	1605	1603	1600	1597	1595	1592	1590	0	1	1	1	1	1	2	2	2
6·3	·1587	1585	1582	1580	1577	1575	1572	1570	1567	1565	0	0	1	1	1	1	2	2	2
6·4	·1563	1560	1558	1555	1553	1550	1548	1546	1543	1541	0	0	1	1	1	1	2	2	2
6·5	·1538	1536	1534	1531	1529	1527	1524	1522	1520	1517	0	0	1	1	1	1	2	2	2
6·6	·1515	1513	1511	1508	1506	1504	1502	1499	1497	1495	0	0	1	1	1	1	2	2	2
6·7	·1493	1490	1488	1486	1484	1481	1479	1477	1475	1473	0	0	1	1	1	1	2	2	2
6·8	·1471	1468	1466	1464	1462	1460	1458	1456	1453	1451	0	0	1	1	1	1	2	2	2
6·9	·1449	1447	1445	1443	1441	1439	1437	1435	1433	1431	0	0	1	1	1	1	1	2	2
7·0	·1429	1427	1425	1422	1420	1418	1416	1414	1412	1410	0	0	1	1	1	1	1	2	2
7·1	·1408	1406	1404	1403	1401	1399	1397	1395	1393	1391	0	0	1	1	1	1	1	2	2
7·2	·1389	1387	1385	1383	1381	1379	1377	1376	1374	1372	0	0	1	1	1	1	1	2	2
7·3	·1370	1368	1366	1364	1362	1361	1359	1357	1355	1353	0	0	1	1	1	1	1	2	2
7·4	·1351	1350	1348	1346	1344	1342	1340	1339	1337	1335	0	0	1	1	1	1	1	2	2
7·5	·1333	1332	1330	1328	1326	1325	1323	1321	1319	1318	0	0	1	1	1	1	1	1	2
7·6	·1316	1314	1312	1311	1309	1307	1305	1304	1302	1300	0	0	1	1	1	1	1	1	2
7·7	·1299	1297	1295	1294	1292	1290	1289	1287	1285	1284	0	0	0	1	1	1	1	1	1
7·8	·1282	1280	1279	1277	1276	1274	1272	1271	1269	1267	0	0	0	1	1	1	1	1	1
7·9	·1266	1264	1263	1261	1259	1258	1256	1255	1253	1252	0	0	0	1	1	1	1	1	1
8·0	·1250	1248	1247	1245	1244	1242	1241	1239	1238	1236	0	0	0	1	1	1	1	1	1
8·1	·1235	1233	1232	1230	1229	1227	1225	1224	1222	1221	0	0	0	1	1	1	1	1	1
8·2	·1220	1218	1217	1215	1214	1212	1211	1209	1208	1206	0	0	0	1	1	1	1	1	1
8·3	·1205	1203	1202	1200	1199	1198	1196	1195	1193	1192	0	0	0	1	1	1	1	1	1
8·4	·1190	1189	1188	1186	1185	1183	1182	1181	1179	1178	0	0	0	1	1	1	1	1	1
8·5	·1176	1175	1174	1172	1171	1170	1168	1167	1166	1164	0	0	0	1	1	1	1	1	1
8·6	·1163	1161	1160	1159	1157	1156	1155	1153	1152	1151	0	0	0	1	1	1	1	1	1
8·7	·1149	1148	1147	1145	1144	1143	1142	1140	1139	1138	0	0	0	1	1	1	1	1	1
8·8	·1136	1135	1134	1133	1131	1130	1129	1127	1126	1125	0	0	0	1	1	1	1	1	1
8·9	·1124	1122	1121	1120	1119	1117	1116	1115	1114	1112	0	0	0	1	1	1	1	1	1
9·0	·1111	1110	1109	1107	1106	1105	1104	1103	1101	1100	0	0	0	1	1	1	1	1	1
9·1	·1099	1098	1096	1095	1094	1093	1092	1091	1089	1088	0	0	0	1	1	1	1	1	1
9·2	·1087	1086	1085	1083	1082	1081	1080	1079	1078	1076	0	0	0	0	1	1	1	1	1
9·3	·1075	1074	1073	1072	1071	1070	1068	1067	1066	1065	0	0	0	0	1	1	1	1	1
9·4	·1064	1063	1062	1060	1059	1058	1057	1056	1055	1054	0	0	0	0	1	1	1	1	1
9·5	·1053	1052	1050	1049	1048	1047	1046	1045	1044	1043	0	0	0	0	1	1	1	1	1
9·6	·1042	1041	1040	1038	1037	1036	1035	1034	1033	1032	0	0	0	0	1	1	1	1	1
9·7	·1031	1030	1029	1028	1027	1026	1025	1024	1022	1021	0	0	0	0	1	1	1	1	1
9·8	·1020	1019	1018	1017	1016	1015	1014	1013	1012	1011	0	0	0	0	0	1	1	1	1
9·9	·1010	1009	1008	1007	1006	1005	1004	1003	1002	1001	0	0	0	0	0	1	1	1	1

DEGREES TO RADIANS

Differences—	1' 3	2' 6	3' 9	4' 12	5' 15

	Radians	6'	12'	18'	24'	30'	36'	42'	48'	54'
0	·0000	0017	0035	0052	0070	0087	0105	0122	0140	0157
1	·0175	0192	0209	0227	0244	0262	0279	0297	0314	0332
2	·0349	0367	0384	0401	0419	0436	0454	0471	0489	0506
3	·0524	0541	0559	0576	0593	0611	0628	0646	0663	0681
4	·0698	0716	0733	0750	0768	0785	0803	0820	0838	0855
5	·0873	0890	0908	0925	0942	0960	0977	0995	1012	1030
6	·1047	1065	1082	1100	1117	1134	1152	1169	1187	1204
7	·1222	1239	1257	1274	1292	1309	1326	1344	1361	1379
8	·1396	1414	1431	1449	1466	1484	1501	1518	1536	1553
9	·1571	1588	1606	1623	1641	1658	1676	1693	1710	1728
10	·1745	1763	1780	1798	1815	1833	1850	1868	1885	1902
11	·1920	1937	1955	1972	1990	2007	2025	2042	2059	2077
12	·2094	2112	2129	2147	2164	2182	2199	2217	2234	2251
13	·2269	2286	2304	2321	2339	2356	2374	2391	2409	2426
14	·2443	2461	2478	2496	2513	2531	2548	2566	2583	2601
15	·2618	2635	2653	2670	2688	2705	2723	2740	2758	2775
16	·2793	2810	2827	2845	2862	2880	2897	2915	2932	2950
17	·2967	2985	3002	3019	3037	3054	3072	3089	3107	3124
18	·3142	3159	3176	3194	3211	3229	3246	3264	3281	3299
19	·3316	3334	3351	3368	3386	3403	3421	3438	3456	3473
20	·3491	3508	3526	3543	3560	3578	3595	3613	3630	3648
21	·3665	3683	3700	3718	3735	3752	3770	3787	3805	3822
22	·3840	3857	3875	3892	3910	3927	3944	3962	3979	3997
23	·4014	4032	4049	4067	4084	4102	4119	4136	4154	4171
24	·4189	4206	4224	4241	4259	4276	4294	4311	4328	4346
25	·4363	4381	4398	4416	4433	4451	4468	4485	4503	4520
26	·4538	4555	4573	4590	4608	4625	4643	4660	4677	4695
27	·4712	4730	4747	4765	4782	4800	4817	4835	4852	4869
28	·4887	4904	4921	4939	4957	4974	4992	5009	5027	5044
29	·5061	5079	5096	5114	5131	5149	5166	5184	5201	5219
30	·5236	5253	5271	5288	5306	5323	5341	5358	5376	5393
31	·5411	5428	5445	5463	5480	5498	5515	5533	5550	5568
32	·5585	5603	5620	5637	5655	5672	5690	5707	5725	5742
33	·5760	5777	5794	5812	5829	5847	5864	5882	5899	5917
34	·5934	5952	5969	5986	6004	6021	6039	6056	6074	6091
35	·6109	6126	6144	6161	6178	6196	6213	6231	6248	6266
36	·6283	6301	6318	6336	6353	6370	6388	6405	6423	6440
37	·6458	6475	6493	6510	6528	6545	6562	6580	6597	6615
38	·6632	6650	6667	6685	6702	6720	6737	6754	6772	6789
39	·6807	6824	6842	6859	6877	6894	6912	6929	6946	6964
40	·6981	6999	7016	7034	7051	7069	7086	7103	7121	7138
41	·7156	7173	7191	7208	7226	7243	7261	7278	7295	7313
42	·7330	7348	7365	7383	7400	7418	7435	7453	7470	7487
43	·7505	7522	7540	7557	7575	7592	7610	7627	7645	7662
44	·7679	7697	7714	7732	7749	7767	7784	7802	7819	7837

DEGREES TO RADIANS

Differences—	1' 3	2' 6	3' 9	4' 12	5' 15

°	Radians	6'	12'	18'	24'	30'	36'	42'	48'	54'
45	·7854	7871	7889	7906	7924	7941	7959	7976	7994	8011
46	·8029	8046	8063	8081	8098	8116	8133	8151	8168	8186
47	·8203	8221	8238	8255	8273	8290	8308	8325	8343	8360
48	·8378	8395	8412	8430	8447	8465	8482	8500	8517	8535
49	·8552	8570	8587	8604	8622	8639	8657	8674	8692	8709
50	·8727	8744	8762	8779	8796	8814	8831	8849	8866	8884
51	·8901	8919	8936	8954	8971	8988	9006	9023	9041	9058
52	·9076	9093	9111	9128	9146	9163	9180	9198	9215	9233
53	·9250	9268	9285	9303	9320	9338	9355	9372	9390	9407
54	·9425	9442	9460	9477	9495	9512	9529	9547	9564	9582
55	·9599	9617	9634	9652	9669	9687	9704	9721	9739	9756
56	·9774	9791	9809	9826	9844	9861	9879	9896	9913	9931
57	·9948	9966	9983	0001	0018	0036	0053	0071	0088	0105
58	1·0123	0140	0158	0175	0193	0210	0228	0245	0263	0280
59	1·0297	0315	0332	0350	0367	0385	0402	0420	0437	0455
60	1·0472	0489	0507	0524	0542	0559	0577	0594	0612	0629
61	1·0647	0664	0681	0699	0716	0734	0751	0769	0786	0804
62	1·0821	0838	0856	0873	0891	0908	0926	0943	0961	0978
63	1·0996	1013	1030	1048	1065	1083	1100	1118	1135	1153
64	1·1170	1188	1205	1222	1240	1257	1275	1292	1310	1327
65	1·1345	1362	1380	1397	1414	1432	1449	1467	1484	1502
66	1·1519	1537	1554	1572	1589	1606	1624	1641	1659	1676
67	1·1694	1711	1729	1746	1764	1781	1798	1816	1833	1851
68	1·1868	1886	1903	1921	1938	1956	1973	1990	2008	2025
69	1·2043	2060	2078	2095	2113	2130	2147	2165	2182	2200
70	1·2217	2235	2252	2270	2287	2305	2322	2339	2357	2374
71	1·2392	2409	2427	2444	2462	2479	2497	2514	2531	2549
72	1·2566	2584	2601	2619	2636	2654	2671	2689	2706	2723
73	1·2741	2758	2776	2793	2811	2828	2846	2863	2881	2898
74	1·2915	2933	2950	2968	2985	3003	3020	3038	3055	3073
75	1·3090	3107	3125	3142	3160	3177	3195	3212	3230	3247
76	1·3265	3282	3299	3317	3334	3352	3369	3387	3404	3422
77	1·3439	3456	3474	3491	3509	3526	3544	3561	3579	3596
78	1·3614	3631	3648	3666	3683	3701	3718	3736	3753	3771
79	1·3788	3806	3823	3840	3858	3875	3893	3910	3928	3945
80	1·3963	3980	3998	4015	4032	4050	4067	4085	4102	4120
81	1·4137	4155	4172	4190	4207	4224	4242	4259	4277	4294
82	1·4312	4329	4347	4364	4382	4399	4416	4434	4451	4469
83	1·4486	4504	4521	4539	4556	4573	4591	4608	4626	4643
84	1·4661	4678	4696	4713	4731	4748	4765	4783	4800	4818
85	1·4835	4853	4870	4888	4905	4923	4940	4957	4975	4992
86	1·5010	5027	5045	5062	5080	5097	5115	5132	5149	5167
87	1·5184	5202	5219	5237	5254	5272	5289	5307	5324	5341
88	1·5359	5376	5394	5411	5429	5446	5464	5481	5499	5516
89	1·5533	5551	5568	5586	5603	5621	5638	5656	5673	5691